Inside Earth

PRENTICE HALL Science Explorer

PEARSON
Prentice Hall

Boston, Massachusetts
Upper Saddle River, New Jersey

ISBN 0-13-190278-4   8 9 10   11 10 09 08

Everything you need

For Students...

STUDY WORKSHEETS

Section Summaries
• Supports less-proficient readers and English-language learners with easily accessible content summaries

Guided Reading and Study
• Promotes active reading and enhances study skills for all students as they follow along with the text

Review and Reinforce
• Motivates students to build vocabulary, review main ideas, and interpret diagrams, charts, and graphs

Enrich
• Encourages students to apply core concepts in a new context

LABS AND ACTIVITIES

Chapter Project
• Guides students in open-ended inquiry with scoring rubrics and teacher notes

Student Edition Labs
• Provides blackline masters of the Student Edition Labs in an easy-to-grade format

Laboratory Investigations
• Applies and extends key concepts for each chapter using in-depth labs with full support for hands-on inquiry

ASSESSMENT

Performance Assessments
• Assesses problem-solving and process skills with scoring rubrics and suggested outcomes

Chapter and Book Tests
• Monitors student mastery of standards-driven content and skills

For You...

Look for the RED BAR

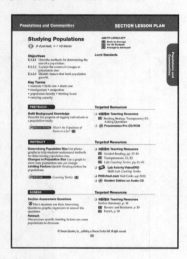

Section Lesson Plans
• Provides section-by-section planning tools that emphasize the National Science Education Standards

Teacher Notes
• Includes point-of-use support for Chapter Projects, Laboratory Investigations, and Performance Assessment

Answer Keys
• Complete answers for all worksheets

Look for the COLOR TRANSPARENCY PLANNER

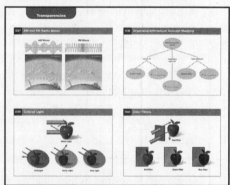

Transparency Thumbnails
• Enables full-color review of all the transparencies that support the chapters

Contents

Inside Earth

Science Explorer ▪ *Target Reading Skills Handbook*

🜂 Target Reading Skills

Identifying Main Ideas

Identifying the main idea helps you understand what you are reading. Sometimes the main idea can be easy to find. For example, suppose that you are reading just one paragraph. Very often you will find the main idea in the first sentence, the topic sentence. The other sentences in the paragraph provide supporting details or support the ideas in the topic sentence.

Sometimes, however, the first sentence is not the topic sentence. Sometimes you may have to look further. In those cases, it might help to read the paragraph and summarize what you have read. Your summary can give you the main idea.

A textbook has many paragraphs, each one with its own main idea. However, just as a paragraph has a main idea and supporting details, so does the text under each heading in your textbook. Sometimes the main idea is the heading itself. Other times it is more difficult to find. You may have to infer a main idea by combining information from several paragraphs.

To practice this skill, you can use a graphic organizer that looks like this one.

Main Idea		
Detail	**Detail**	**Detail**
a.	**b.**	**c.**

Outlining

Outlining shows you how supporting details relate to main ideas. You can make an outline as you read. Using this skill can make you a more careful reader.

Your outline can be made up of sentences, simple phrases, or single words. What matters is that you follow a formal structure. To outline while you read, use a plan like this one.

I. Section Title
  A. Main Heading
    1. Subheading
      a. Detail
      b. Detail
      c. Detail

The main ideas or topics are labeled as Roman numerals. The supporting details or subtopics are labeled A, B, C, and so on. Other levels of supporting information can be added under heads. When you outline in this way, you are deciding just how important a piece of information is.

Science Explorer • *Target Reading Skills Handbook*

Comparing and Contrasting

You can use comparing and contrasting to better understand similarities and differences between two or more concepts. Look for clue words as you read. When concepts or topics are similar, you will probably see words such as *also, just as, like, likewise,* or *in the same way.* When concepts or topics are different, you will see *but, however, although, whereas, on the other hand,* or *unlike.*

To use this skill, it sometimes helps to make a Venn diagram. In this type of graphic organizer, the similarities are in the middle, where the two circles overlap.

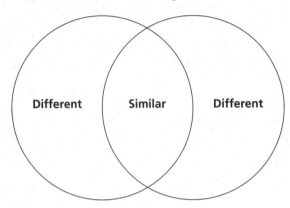

Relating Cause and Effect

Identifying causes and effects can help you understand the relationships among events. A cause is what makes something happen. An effect is what happens. In science, many actions cause other actions to occur.

Sometimes you have to look hard to see a cause-and-effect relationship in reading. You can watch for clue words to help you identify causes and effects. Look for *because, so, since, therefore, results, cause,* or *lead to.*

Sometimes a cause-and-effect relationship occurs in a chain. For example, an effect can have more than one cause, or a cause can have several effects. Seeing and understanding the relationships helps you understand science processes. You can use a graphic organizer like this one.

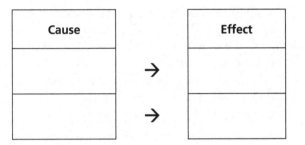

Asking Questions

Your textbook is organized using headings and subheadings. You can read the material under those headings by turning each heading into a question. For example, you might change the heading "Protecting Yourself During an Earthquake" to "How can you protect yourself during an earthquake?" Asking questions in this way will help you look for answers while reading. You can use a graphic organizer like this one to ask questions.

Question	Answer

Science Explorer • *Target Reading Skills Handbook*

Sequencing

Sequencing is the order in which a series of events occurs. As you read, look for clue words that tell you the sequence or the order in which things happen. You see words such as *first, next, then,* or *finally.* When a process is being described, watch for numbered steps. Sometimes there are clues provided for you. Using the sequencing reading skill will help you understand and visualize the steps in a process. You can also use it to list events in the order of their occurrence.

You can use a graphic organizer to show the sequence of events or steps. The one most commonly used is a flowchart like this one.

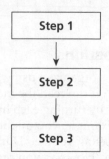

Sometimes, though, a cycle diagram works better.

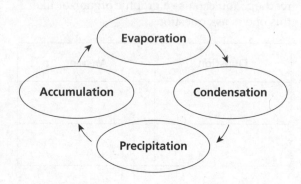

Using Prior Knowledge

Use prior knowledge to relate what you are reading to something that you already know. It is easier to learn when you can link new ideas to something that is already familiar to you. For example, if you know that fish are actually breathing oxygen that is dissolved in water, you wil be able to understand how or why gills work.

Using prior knowledge can help you make logical assumptions or draw conclusions about what you are reading. But be careful. Your prior knowledge might sometimes be wrong. As you read, you can confirm or correct your prior knowledge.

Use a graphic organizer like this one to link your prior knowledge to what you are learning as you read.

What You Know
1.
2.
3.

What You Learned
1.
2.
3.

Science Explorer ▪ *Target Reading Skills Handbook*

Previewing Visuals

Looking at visuals before you read can help you better understand a topic. Preview the visuals by reading labels and captions. For example, if you preview the visuals in a chapter about volcanoes, you will see more than just photographs of erupting volcanoes. You will see maps, diagrams, and photographs of rocks. These might tell you that you will learn where volcanoes are found, how they form, and what sort of rock is created when volcanoes erupt. Previewing visuals helps you understand and enjoy what you read.

One way to apply this strategy is to choose a few photographs, diagrams, or other visuals to preview. Then write questions about what you see. Answer the questions as you read.

Identifying Supporting Evidence

In science, you will read about hypotheses. A hypothesis is a possible explanation for scientific observations made by scientists or an answer to a scientific question. A hypothesis is tested over and over again. The tests may produce evidence that supports the hypothesis. When enough supporting evidence is collected, a hypothesis may become a theory.

Identifying supporting evidence in your reading can help you understand a hypothesis or theory. Evidence is made up of facts. Facts are information that can be confirmed by testing or observation.

When you are identifying supporting evidence, a graphic organizer like this one can be helpful.

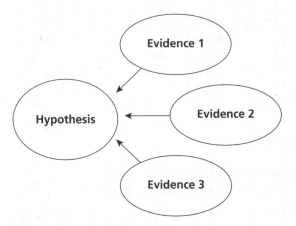

Building Vocabulary

To understand what someone is saying, you have to know the language that person is speaking. To understand science, you need to know what the words mean.

There are many ways to build your vocabulary. You can look up the meaning of a new word in a dictionary or glossary. Then you can write its definition in your own words. You can use the new word in a sentence. To figure out the meaning of a new word, you can use context clues or surrounding words. Look for prefixes and suffixes in the new word to help you break it down. Building vocabulary will get easier with practice.

Guidelines for Laboratory Safety

This section on laboratory safety is included as a resource for the teacher. Rather than providing definitive rules and regulations, the information is intended to be the basis for the establishment of safe laboratory practice. Pearson Prentice Hall and its consultants make no claims as to the completeness of this material. Not all the precautions necessitated by the use, storage, and disposal of materials are covered here. Additional steps and safeguards may be required.

Responsibilities of the Teacher and the School

Laboratory safety is a shared responsibility. Both the school and the teacher need to be sure that all educational activities protect and promote the health and safety of students and the environment. To accomplish this goal, teachers need to understand the hazards, precautions, and emergency procedures associated with laboratory activities. When schools or teachers fail to live up to this responsibility, their behavior may be considered negligent. As a result, they may be liable for resulting injuries.

The best way to avoid being considered negligent is to ask yourself four simple questions:

1. What are the hazards?
2. What are the worst things that could happen?
3. What do I need to do if they do happen?
4. What are the prudent practices, protective facilities, and protective equipment needed to minimize the risk?

Be sure that you can answer all four of these questions before starting any science activity or demonstration. Then you can reduce the risks to an acceptable level—a level where the educational benefits of the activity outweigh the risks.

General Safety Strategies

Teachers should promote a "safety first" philosophy through personal example and by the careful planning and implementation of safety strategies.

The following strategies will help create an enjoyable, instructional, and safe environment.

1. Set up a safety committee made up of both teachers and administrators. Arrange to meet regularly to set safety policies for the school, discuss any safety problems that might arise, and organize periodic inspections of classrooms and laboratory equipment.

2. Establish a safety and health reference shelf in a resource center.

3. Develop detailed plans explaining what to do in case of emergency, including spills, cuts, burns, electric shock, poisoning, and fire. Review the procedures periodically throughout the school year.

4. Inform students of these emergency plans and carry out unannounced drills.

5. Explain to students how to use the intercom or other available means of communication to get help during an emergency.

6. Keep up to date in first aid and CPR (cardiopulmonary resuscitation) training.

7. Post emergency phone numbers for ambulance, fire, police, hospital, and the poison control center next to the telephone.

8. Perform laboratory investigations before assigning them to students. Take note of any potential hazards; devise plans for dealing with any possible mishaps or emergencies.

9. Emphasize safety considerations in pre-lab discussions. Display posters dealing with safety issues in the classroom as reminders.

10. Keep classroom aisles and exits free of obstructions.

11. During an investigation, move about the classroom to keep a constant watch for potentially dangerous situations.

12. Curtail inappropriate behavior immediately. Wild play and practical jokes are forbidden during labs. Once students realize that the practice of safety is a required part of the course, they will accept a serious approach to laboratory work.

13. Never leave students unattended while they are engaged in science activities.

14. Require proper clothing at all times. Insist that long hair, dangling jewelry, and loose clothing be restrained; do not allow students to wear open shoes.

15. Insist that students wear safety goggles when the lab requires it.

16. Encourage students to keep lab work space neat and clear of extraneous objects, such as books and jackets.

17. Make sure that investigations utilizing toxic, fuming, or flammable materials are performed under a fume hood.

18. Keep the fume hood clear of unnecessary chemicals and equipment. Have the fume hood checked periodically to ensure that it is operating safely and efficiently.

19. Demonstrate to students the proper handling of glass materials, such as beakers and graduated cylinders.

20. Only wastepaper should be discarded in wastepaper receptacles. Keep a separate container for broken glass.

21. Substitute plastic containers for glass ones whenever possible, including graduated cylinders and beakers.

22. Consider the use of dispensing containers for liquids. They help prevent spills, skin contact with chemicals, and waste.

23. Use hot plates in place of open flames whenever possible. Never use open flames or hot plates when flammables are present in the room.

24. Use only nonmercury thermometers in investigations that call for the measurement of temperature.

25. Do not permit students to insert glass tubing or thermometers into rubber stoppers. If necessary, do this task yourself. When inserting these items into rubber stoppers, use safety stoppers, which have holes with beveled edges and are easier to use. Use glycerin or water to lubricate the glass.

26. All electrical equipment used in the lab should have GFI (Ground Fault Interrupter) switches.

27. Do not leave equipment that is operating or plugged in unattended.

28. When working with live animals or plants, check ahead of time for students who may have allergies to the specimens.

29. Students should wear disposable nitrile, latex, or food-handling gloves when handling live animals or nonliving specimens.

30. Wearing safety equipment is required of all students.

31. Report in writing unsafe conditions to the department head, maintenance director, and principal.

32. Have clearly defined penalties for violations of safety rules. Have these penalties approved and supported by the principal.

33. Document safety training, rules violations, and penalties in your records.

34. Keep a record of injuries and incidents (close calls), no matter how minor they may seem. Discuss these events at a department meeting to avoid similar occurrences.

Guidelines for Laboratory Safety *(continued)*

35. As a class, review the safety rules and symbols. Make sure students understand the safety rules.

36. Require students to sign the safety contract.

37. Conduct quarterly inspections of the classrooms and storage areas to maintain safe conditions.

Safety Equipment

Any classroom where laboratory investigations are performed should contain at least one each of the following pieces of safety equipment: (1) fire extinguisher, (2) fire blanket, (3) fire alarm, (4) phone or intercom to the office, (5) eyewash station, (6) safety shower, (7) safety hood, and (8) first-aid kit. If any of these basic pieces of safety equipment are not available, you may need to modify your laboratory program until the situation is remedied.

Make sure students know the location and proper use of all safety equipment. Where appropriate and practical, have students handle or operate the equipment so that they become familiar with it. Make sure all safety equipment is in good working order. All malfunctions should be promptly reported in writing to the proper school or district administrator.

Fire equipment At the beginning of the school year, you may wish to give each student the opportunity to actually operate a fire extinguisher, as the sound and action of a CO_2 fire extinguisher can be quite alarming to those who have never used one. You may also want to have students practice smothering imaginary flames on one another with the fire blanket.

Eyewash station The eyewash station should be used if chemicals are splashed onto the face or eyes. The exposed area should be left in the running water for five to ten minutes.

Safety shower The shower is used when chemicals have been spilled on a student's body or clothing. The student should stand under the shower until the chemical is completely diluted. Have a bathrobe or some type of replacement clothing handy in case the student's clothing is so badly contaminated that it must be removed.

You may want to set up one or two spill kits in your laboratory. The contents of a spill kit are used to neutralize chemicals, such as acids and bases, so that they can be cleaned up more easily. Baking soda (sodium bicarbonate) can be used to neutralize acids. Vinegar (acetic acid) can be used to neutralize bases. Commercial spill kits for acids, bases, and a number of other chemicals are available from supply houses.

Safety hood Use a safety hood whenever students are working with volatile or noxious chemicals. Make sure that the room is well ventilated when students are using any kind of chemicals or are working with preserved specimens. Warn students of the flammability and toxicity of various chemicals.

First-aid kit A typical first-aid kit contains an assortment of antiseptics, bandages, gauze pads, and scissors. Most also contain simple instructions for use. Be sure to read the instructions if you are not familiar with basic first-aid procedures. A first-aid kit should be taken on all field trips. For field trips, you may wish to add such items as a bee-sting kit, meat tenderizer, tweezers, and calamine lotion. Do not dispense medication (including aspirin).

Guidelines for the Use and Care of Animals

Animals are an essential part of a science curriculum. The judicious use of live or preserved animals can help students realize that the study of science is relevant, fascinating, and rewarding. It is important to be aware of and sensitive to ethical and practical concerns when studying animals. The purpose of this section is to discuss some realistic guidelines for using animals in the classroom.

1. Whenever possible, live animals should be observed in their natural habitats or in zoos, parks, and aquariums.

2. Check the state and federal codes regarding animal welfare that apply in your area. You may also wish to refer to guidelines published by the National Science Teachers Association, the National Association of Biology Teachers, and the International Science Fair. Make students aware of all safety rules and regulations regarding animals.

3. Before bringing a live animal into the classroom, determine whether a proper habitat can be maintained in the classroom. Such a habitat includes temperature, space, and type of food. Students should have a clear understanding of the appropriate care needed by the live animals brought into the classroom. Do not allow students to tap on animal enclosures or otherwise disturb the animals.

4. No wild vertebrate animals should be brought into the classroom. Purchase animals from a reputable dealer only.

5. Live animals should be nonpoisonous and healthy. Any mammals used in the classroom should be vaccinated against rabies unless the animals were purchased recently from a reliable scientific supply company. Quarantine any animal to make sure it is disease-free before bringing it into the classroom.

6. Make sure that the living quarters of classroom animals are clean, located away from stressful situations, appropriately spacious, and secure enough to confine the animal. You may wish to lock cages to prevent the accidental release of animals; the small padlocks used on luggage are good for this purpose.

7. Remove wastes from animal living quarters daily. Thoroughly clean animal living quarters periodically to ensure that they are odor and germ-free. Provide a daily supply of fresh water and any other needs specific to the particular animal.

8. Provide for the care of animals during weekends and school vacations. Inform the custodial staff of the presence of animals and warn them of any special requirements. For example, turning off the aquarium pump to save electricity or spraying the classroom for insects can be fatal to animals.

9. Students should be instructed how to handle each species brought into the classroom. Make students aware that they can receive painful wounds from the improper handling of some animals.

10. Animals should be handled only if necessary. If an animal is frightened or excited, pregnant, feeding, or with its young, special handling is required.

11. Students should thoroughly clean their hands after handling animals or the quarters containing animals.

12. Animals should be returned to their natural habitat after an observation period of not longer than 14 days. However, laboratory-bred animals or species that are not native to an area should not be released into the environment.

13. If an animal must be euthanized, do not allow students to watch. Contact the local humane society for advice.

© Pearson Education, Inc., publishing as Pearson Prentice Hall. All rights reserved.

Guidelines for the Use and Care of Animals *(continued)*

14. Before performing any experiment involving live animals, check local and state regulations. In some states, certification is required before a teacher is permitted to experiment with animals.

15. No animal studies involving anesthetic drugs, pathogenic organisms, toxicological products, carcinogens, or radiation should be performed.

16. Any experiment requiring live animals should have a clearly defined objective relating to the teaching and learning of some scientific principle.

17. No experimental procedures that will cause pain, discomfort, or harm to animals should be done in the classroom or at home.

18. Surgical procedures should not be performed on live animals.

19. If fertilized bird eggs are opened, the embryo should be destroyed humanely two days before it would have hatched, at the latest.

20. When working with preserved animals, make sure that students maintain a serious and respectful attitude toward the specimens.

Handling Ethical Issues

There is much controversy regarding the use of animals in scientific research. This controversy extends to preserved animals in dissections as well as to live animals in experiments. Although the debate over what uses of animals are appropriate in a science classroom can be emotionally charged, it can also provide an opportunity for students to closely examine a current issue. You may wish to have students read current literature on the subject and contact groups and individuals with varying points of view.

Stress that it is important to make a rational, informed decision before taking a stand on any issue. Point out that it is vital to know and understand the arguments on all sides of an issue. Help students analyze the sources they find in terms of bias and the reliability and objectivity of the author(s). Help them to distinguish between fact and opinion. Encourage them to question what they read and hear. Challenge them to discover the hidden assumptions and implications of different points of view.

If dissections are a part of your curriculum and a student chooses to avoid dissections because of ethical concerns, respect that student's opinion. Point out, however, that no simulation or videotape can completely replace hands-on experience.

Guidelines for Safe Disposal of Laboratory Wastes

Every effort should be made to recover, recycle, and reuse materials used in the laboratory. When disposal is required, however, specific procedures should be followed to ensure that your school complies with local, state, and federal regulations.

1. Discard only dry paper into ordinary wastebaskets.

2. Discard broken glass into a separate container clearly marked "For Broken Glass Only."

3. Acidic or basic solutions need to be neutralized before disposal. Slowly add dilute sodium hydroxide to acids and dilute hydrochloric acid to bases until pH paper shows that they are no longer strongly acidic or basic. Then flush the solutions down the drain with a lot of water.

4. Before each investigation, instruct your students concerning where and how they are to dispose of chemicals that are used or produced during the investigation. Specific teacher notes addressing disposal are provided on each lab as appropriate.

5. Keep each excess or used chemical in a separate container; do not mix them. This allows for possible recycling or reuse. It also eliminates unexpected reactions or the need for expensive separation by a contractor if the wastes must be disposed of professionally.

6. Only nonflammable, neutral, nontoxic, nonreactive, and water-soluble chemicals should be flushed down the drain.

7. When growing bacterial cultures, use only disposable petri dishes. After streaking, the dishes should be sealed and not opened again by students. After the lab, students should return the unopened dishes to you and wash their hands with antibacterial soap.

8. For the safe disposal of bacterial cultures, autoclave the petri dishes and discard them without opening. If no autoclave is available, carefully open the dishes (never have a student do this), pour full-strength bleach into the dishes, and let them stand for a day. Then pour the bleach from the petri dishes down a drain and flush the drain with lots of water. Tape the petri dishes back together and place them in a sealed plastic bag. Wrap the plastic bag with a brown paper bag or newspaper and tape securely. Throw the sealed package in the trash. Thoroughly disinfect the work area with bleach.

9. To grow mold, use a new, sealable plastic bag that is two to three times larger than the material to be placed inside. Seal the bag and tape it shut. After the bag is sealed, students should not open it. To dispose of the bag and mold culture, make a small cut near an edge of the bag and cook the bag in a microwave oven on a high setting for at least one minute. Discard the bag according to local ordinance, usually in the trash.

Laboratory Safety

Name _____ Date _____ Class _____

Science Safety Rules

To prepare yourself to work safely in the laboratory, read the following safety rules. Then read them a second time. Make sure you understand and follow each rule. Ask your teacher to explain any rules you do not understand.

Dress Code

1. To protect yourself from injuring your eyes, wear safety goggles whenever you work with chemicals, flames, glassware, or any substance that might get into your eyes. If you wear contact lenses, notify your teacher.

2. Wear an apron or a lab coat whenever you work with corrosive chemicals or substances that can stain.

3. Tie back long hair to keep it away from any chemicals, flames, or equipment.

4. Remove or tie back any article of clothing or jewelry that can hang down and touch chemicals, flames, or equipment. Roll up or secure long sleeves.

5. Never wear open shoes or sandals.

General Precautions

6. Read all directions for an experiment several times before beginning the activity. Carefully follow all written and oral instructions. If you are in doubt about any part of the experiment, ask your teacher for assistance.

7. Never perform activities that are not assigned or authorized by your teacher. Obtain permission before "experimenting" on your own. Never handle any equipment unless you have specific permission.

8. Never perform lab activities without direct supervision.

9. Never eat or drink in the laboratory.

10. Keep work areas clean and tidy at all times. Bring only notebooks and lab manuals or written lab procedures to the work area. All other items, such as purses and backpacks, should be left in a designated area.

11. Do not engage in horseplay.

First Aid

12. Always report all accidents or injuries to your teacher, no matter how minor. Notify your teacher immediately about any fires.

13. Learn what to do in case of specific accidents, such as getting acid in your eyes or on your skin. (Rinse acids from your body with plenty of water.)

14. Be aware of the location of the first-aid kit, but do not use it unless instructed by your teacher. In case of injury, your teacher should administer first aid. Your teacher may also send you to the school nurse or call a physician.

15. Know the location of the emergency equipment such as the fire extinguisher and fire blanket.

16. Know the location of the nearest telephone and whom to contact in an emergency.

Heating and Fire Safety

17. Never use a heat source, such as a candle, burner, or hot plate, without wearing safety goggles.

18. Never heat anything unless instructed to do so. A chemical that is harmless when cool may be dangerous when heated.

19. Keep all combustible materials away from flames. Never use a flame or spark near a combustible chemical.

20. Never reach across a flame.

21. Before using a laboratory burner, make sure you know proper procedures for lighting and adjusting the burner, as demonstrated by your teacher. Do not touch the burner. It may be hot. Never leave a lighted burner unattended. Turn off the burner when it is not in use.

22. Chemicals can splash or boil out of a heated test tube. When heating a substance in a test tube, make sure that the mouth of the tube is not pointed at you or anyone else.

23. Never heat a liquid in a closed container. The expanding gases produced may shatter the container.

24. Before picking up a container that has been heated, first hold the back of your hand near it. If you can feel heat on the back of your hand, the container is too hot to handle. Use an oven mitt to pick up a container that has been heated.

Laboratory Safety ▪ *Science Safety Rules*

Using Chemicals Safely

25. Never mix chemicals "for the fun of it." You might produce a dangerous, possibly explosive substance.

26. Never put your face near the mouth of a container that holds chemicals. Many chemicals are poisonous. Never touch, taste, or smell a chemical unless you are instructed by your teacher to do so.

27. Use only those chemicals needed in the activity. Read and double-check labels on supply bottles before removing any chemicals. Take only as much as you need. Keep all containers closed when chemicals are not being used.

28. Dispose of all chemicals as instructed by your teacher. To avoid contamination, never return chemicals to their original containers. Never pour untreated chemicals or other substances into the sink or trash containers.

29. Be extra careful when working with acids or bases. Pour all chemicals over the sink or a container, not over your work surface.

30. If you are instructed to test for odors, use a wafting motion to direct the odors to your nose. Do not inhale the fumes directly from the container.

31. When mixing an acid and water, always pour the water into the container first and then add the acid to the water. Never pour water into an acid.

32. Take extreme care not to spill any material in the laboratory. Wash chemical spills and splashes immediately with plenty of water. Immediately begin rinsing with water any acids that get on your skin or clothing, and notify your teacher of any acid spill at the same time.

Using Glassware Safely

33. Never force glass tubing or a thermometer into a rubber stopper or rubber tubing. Have your teacher insert the glass tubing or thermometer if required for an activity.

34. If you are using a laboratory burner, use a wire screen to protect glassware from any flame. Never heat glassware that is not thoroughly dry on the outside.

35. Keep in mind that hot glassware looks cool. Never pick up glassware without first checking to see if it is hot. Use an oven mitt. See rule 24.

36. Never use broken or chipped glassware. If glassware breaks, notify your teacher and dispose of the glassware in the proper broken-glassware container.

37. Never eat or drink from glassware.

38. Thoroughly clean glassware before putting it away.

Using Sharp Instruments

39. Handle scalpels or other sharp instruments with extreme care. Never cut material toward you; cut away from you.

40. Immediately notify your teacher if you cut your skin when working in the laboratory.

Animal and Plant Safety

41. Never perform experiments that cause pain, discomfort, or harm to animals. This rule applies at home as well as in the classroom.

42. Animals should be handled only if absolutely necessary. Your teacher will instruct you how to handle each animal species brought into the classroom.

43. If you know that you are allergic to certain plants, molds, or animals, tell your teacher before doing an activity in which these are used.

44. During field work, protect your skin by wearing long pants, long sleeves, socks, and closed shoes. Know how to recognize the poisonous plants and fungi in your area, as well as plants with thorns, and avoid contact with them. Never eat any part of a plant or fungus.

45. Wash your hands thoroughly after handling animals or a cage containing animals. Wash your hands when you are finished with any activity involving animal parts, plants, or soil.

End-of-Experiment Rules

46. After an experiment has been completed, turn off all burners or hot plates. If you used a gas burner, check that the gas-line valve to the burner is off. Unplug hot plates.

47. Turn off and unplug any other electrical equipment that you used.

48. Clean up your work area and return all equipment to its proper place.

49. Dispose of waste materials as instructed by your teacher.

50. Wash your hands after every experiment.

Laboratory Safety

Laboratory Safety ▪ *Safety Symbols*

Safety Symbols

These symbols appear in laboratory activities. They warn of possible dangers in the laboratory and remind you to work carefully.

Safety Goggles Wear safety goggles to protect your eyes in any activity involving chemicals, flames or heating, or glassware.

Lab Apron Wear a laboratory apron to protect your skin and clothing from damage.

Breakage Handle breakable materials, such as glassware, with care. Do not touch broken glassware.

Heat-Resistant Gloves Use an oven mitt or other hand protection when handling hot materials such as hot plates or hot glassware.

Plastic Gloves Wear disposable plastic gloves when working with harmful chemicals and organisms. Keep your hands away from your face, and dispose of the gloves according to your teacher's instructions.

Heating Use a clamp or tongs to pick up hot glassware. Do not touch hot objects with your bare hands.

Flames Before you work with flames, tie back loose hair and clothing. Follow instructions from your teacher about lighting and extinguishing flames.

No Flames When using flammable materials, make sure there are no flames, sparks, or other exposed heat sources present.

Corrosive Chemical Avoid getting acid or other corrosive chemicals on your skin or clothing or in your eyes. Do not inhale the vapors. Wash your hands after the activity.

Poison Do not let any poisonous chemical come into contact with your skin, and do not inhale its vapors. Wash your hands when you are finished with the activity.

Fumes Work in a ventilated area when harmful vapors may be involved. Avoid inhaling vapors directly. Only test an odor when directed to do so by your teacher, and use a wafting motion to direct the vapor toward your nose.

Sharp Object Scissors, scalpels, knives, needles, pins, and tacks can cut your skin. Always direct a sharp edge or point away from yourself and others.

Animal Safety Treat live or preserved animals or animal parts with care to avoid harming the animals or yourself. Wash your hands when you are finished with the activity.

Plant Safety Handle plants only as directed by your teacher. If you are allergic to certain plants, tell your teacher; do not do an activity involving those plants. Avoid touching harmful plants such as poison ivy. Wash your hands when you are finished with the activity.

Electric Shock To avoid electric shock, never use electrical equipment around water, or when the equipment is wet or your hands are wet. Be sure cords are untangled and cannot trip anyone. Unplug equipment not in use.

Physical Safety When an experiment involves physical activity, avoid injuring yourself or others. Alert your teacher if there is any reason you should not participate.

Disposal Dispose of chemicals and other laboratory materials safely. Follow the instructions from your teacher.

Hand Washing Wash your hands thoroughly when finished with the activity. Use antibacterial soap and warm water. Rinse well.

General Safety Awareness When this symbol appears, follow the instructions provided. When you are asked to develop your own procedure in a lab, have your teacher approve your plan before you go further.

Laboratory Safety Contract

I, _____ ,

(please print full name)

have read the Science Safety Rules and Safety Symbols sections, understand their contents completely, and agree to demonstrate compliance with all safety rules and guidelines that have been established in each of the following categories:

(please check)

❑ Dress Code

❑ General Precautions

❑ First Aid

❑ Heating and Fire Safety

❑ Using Chemicals Safely

❑ Using Glassware Safely

❑ Using Sharp Instruments

❑ Animal and Plant Safety

❑ End-of-Experiment Rules

_____

(signature)

Date _____

Interdisciplinary Exploration · *Pompeii*

Science: Comparing Pompeii With Other Archaeological Sites

Materials

photographs of archaeological sites from books or magazines

Procedure

1. Find a photograph of an archaeological site in a magazine or book. You might look for photos of structures that were made by the Mayans, the Anasazi, or maybe the ancient Egyptians.

2. Compare the structures in your photograph with those at Pompeii. Make note of any similarities or differences.

3. Record your observations in a table like the one below.

Comparison of Pompeii and Your Site		
	Pompeii	**Your Site**
Age of ruins		
Location of ruins		
Types of buildings		
People		
Other		

Analyze and Conclude

1. How are the two sites similar?

2. How are the two sites different?

3. Think about the people who lived at Pompeii and at your site. What do you think life was like for these two different groups of people?

Interdisciplinary Exploration ▪ *Pompeii*

Science: Formation of a Pyroclastic Flow

Remember that a pyroclastic flow is a flow of hot gas, ash, and pumice that moves rapidly down the side of a volcano. Most of the people who died in Pompeii were killed by pyroclastic flows. The steps on this page show how the pyroclastic flows that destroyed Pompeii formed.

Eruption column

During an explosive eruption like the one that destroyed Pompeii, hot gas, ash, and pumice are propelled high into the air. The column of hot gas, ash, and pumice is called an eruption column. The force of the eruption often is strong enough to cause the eruption column to move straight up. Eventually, the ash and pumice fall back to the ground.

Pyroclastic flow

Sometimes the amount of ash and pumice in the lower part of the eruption column is very high. When this occurs, the lower part of the eruption column can become too dense to rise. Hot gas, ash, and pumice flow sideways down the mountain as a pyroclastic flow. At night, hot pyroclastic flows often appear to glow. That is why they sometimes are called glowing avalanches.

Interdisciplinary Exploration ▪ *Pompeii*

Science: Formation of a Pyroclastic Flow *(continued)*

Use the figures on the previous page to help you answer the questions below. Write your answers in the spaces provided.

1. What is an eruption column?

_____

_____

2. Why do eruption columns often shoot straight up into the air?

_____

_____

_____

3. Why might part of an eruption column collapse to form a pyroclastic flow?

_____

_____

_____

4. Why are pyroclastic flows sometimes called *glowing avalanches*?

_____

_____

5. Pyroclastic flows killed about 2,000 people in Pompeii. Why do you think pyroclastic flows are so dangerous?

_____

_____

_____

Science: Volcanic Soils

One benefit of volcanic eruptions is the high-quality soil that develops from the ash and pumice. After an eruption, a blanket of ash and pumice covers the region near the volcano. These materials are made mostly of volcanic glass. At first, this glassy material is not good for growing plants. However, as time passes, the ash and pumice start to become fertile soil. The volcanic glass breaks down to form new materials. Important plant nutrients are released during the process. As plants grow, the surface of the soil becomes dark and rich.

Before the eruption of Vesuvius in A.D. 79, agriculture was important to the city of Pompeii. Mount Vesuvius had erupted many times before, so its slopes were fertile. People grew grapes, olives, and many other fruits and vegetables. They brought the produce to the city. There, it would be eaten or used to produce other food products, such as olive oil.

Today, the region around Mount Vesuvius remains an important agricultural area. Much of the soil in Italy is not good for growing plants. But because of the eruptions of Mount Vesuvius, the region near this volcano has fertile soil. The people who live there grow a variety of fruits and vegetables. If you ever visit this region, you might try a pizza with homemade tomato sauce and fresh vegetables. It seems ironic that the same processes that destroyed Pompeii benefit so many people today.

Answer the following questions on a separate sheet of paper.

1. What benefit of volcanic eruptions is described?

2. What material makes up ash and pumice?

3. How does a layer of pumice and ash change through time?

4. How is soil near Mount Vesuvius unusual in the country of Italy?

5. Why do people live near active volcanoes in spite of the possibility that the volcano might erupt again?

Science: The Plaster Casts of Pompeii

If you visit the excavated ruins of Pompeii, you'll see eerie plaster casts of people or a cast of a dog. These casts provide information about life in Pompeii. The steps below show how the casts are made.

During the eruption of Vesuvius, a dog was buried by a pyroclastic flow. Through time, the dog's body decayed. A hollow opening in the ash layer remained. This void, called a mold, has the shape of the dog's body.

An archaeologist discovered the mold, and plaster was poured into it. The plaster hardened to form a cast of the dog.

The cast is dug out of the ash layer. It looks exactly like the dog that died during the eruption.

Answer the following questions on a separate sheet of paper.

1. How does a mold differ from a cast?

2. What material was used to make the casts at Pompeii?

3. Why does the cast of the dog have exactly the same shape as the dog that was killed during the eruption?

4. Summarize how the casts in Pompeii were made.

5. How do casts of people help scientists understand what life was like in Pompeii about 2,000 years ago?

Interdisciplinary Exploration ▪ *Pompeii*

Mathematics: Roman Numerals

The citizens of the Roman Empire wrote numbers differently from the way that you do today. They used a system in which letters represent numbers. The letters are called Roman numerals. You may have seen a clock that has Roman numerals on its face. Some Roman numerals and their values are shown in the table below. Additional numbers were written by stringing the letter symbols together. For example, the number 121 would be written CXXI.

Roman Numeral	Value of Symbol
M	1,000
D	500
C	100
L	50
X	10
V	5
I	1

Use Roman numerals to write the values listed below.

1. 1,211

2. 250

3. 510

4. 52

5. 2,050

Write the values of the Roman numerals listed below.

6. VIII

7. CLII

8. MMC

9. DCLII

10. MLX

Interdisciplinary Exploration ▪ *Pompeii*

Mathematics: Measuring the Explosiveness of Volcanic Eruptions

Because volcanic eruptions are so dangerous, a way to measure their explosiveness was developed. Volcanic eruptions are given a number from 0 to 8. The higher the number is, the more explosive the eruption. The number is called the VEI, or volcano explosivity index. Each number on the scale represents an eruption that is about 10 times more explosive than the next lower number. The table shows the VEIs for some eruptions.

Explosiveness of Some Volcanic Eruptions		
Volcano	**Year of Eruption**	**VEI**
Toba, Indonesia	about 74,000 years ago	8
Vesuvius, Italy	A.D. 79	5
Tambora, Indonesia	1815	7
Krakatau, Indonesia	1883	6
Mount Pelée, Martinique	1902	4
Mount St. Helens, United States	1980	5

1. Which eruption was most explosive? How do you know?

   _____

2. Which eruption was least explosive?

3. How does the eruption of Vesuvius that destroyed Pompeii compare with the other eruptions?

   _____

   _____

4. About how many times more explosive was the Tambora eruption of 1815 than the Mount St. Helens eruption of 1980? How do you know?

   _____

   _____

5. About how many times more explosive was the Toba eruption that occurred about 74,000 years ago than the Mount St. Helens eruption of 1980? Explain.

   _____

   _____

Social Studies: The Scrolls of the Roman Empire

The people who lived in Pompeii and other Roman cities wrote differently than you do today. Computers didn't exist. Even paper and ball-point pens hadn't been invented yet. Instead, Romans wrote on scrolls that were made from the papyrus plant. A scroll is a roll of writing material.

Papyrus is a reed-like plant that was common along the Nile River. The stems of this plant were collected and cut into strips. The strips then were placed side by side in two layers to make sheets. The sheets were pasted together and rolled into scrolls. Pens that often were made from reeds were used to write on the scrolls.

The Romans used papyrus scrolls to record important information. They often contained government documents or writings about science and history. A library of scrolls existed at Herculaneum. This Roman city was destroyed, along with Pompeii, during the eruption of Mount Vesuvius.

Today, scientists and historians are working together to read the ancient scrolls. The scrolls were badly damaged and buried during the eruption. When they first were dug up, they weren't even recognized as scrolls. They looked like pieces of burned wood. By carefully peeling the burned scrolls apart and using modern technology, people are able to read the scrolls of Herculaneum. Historians are learning more about Roman life, beliefs, and culture.

Answer the following questions on a separate sheet of paper.

1. Why couldn't the citizens of Pompeii write on the same type of paper that you do?

2. What is a scroll?

3. How were scrolls made from the papyrus plant?

4. Which Roman city had a library of scrolls?

5. What can historians learn from the Roman scrolls?

Interdisciplinary Exploration

Name _____ Date _____ Class_____

Social Studies: Vulcan, Blacksmith of the Gods

Ancient Romans believed in many gods. One of them was the god of fire, Vulcan. According to Roman mythology, Vulcan lived and worked on Vulcano, a small volcanic island off the northern coast of Sicily. Working in his blacksmith shop beneath a smoking cinder cone, Vulcan forged thunderbolts and weapons for the gods.

There is more than one story about how the god Vulcan was born. One story says that he was the son of Jupiter and Juno. Jupiter was the king of the gods and Juno was his wife. Another story says that Vulcan was the son of Juno, but that he had no father. In one story Vulcan was hurled down a mountainside by his mother. In another story it was his father who threw him down the mountain. Depending on the story, Vulcan's legs were permanently damaged in the fall or he was born with misshapen legs. All of the myths, however, agree that he was not a handsome man. Even so, he eventually married Venus, the goddess of love and beauty.

In another story about Vulcan, Jupiter had called a council of the gods together on Mount Olympus. When the gods had assembled, Jupiter accused Vulcan of having helped Jupiter's enemies. Vulcan seemed surprised and denied having done so. Vulcan was very good at making weapons in his blacksmith shop. In fact, he made the best spears on Earth. After all, they were being made to be used by the gods themselves. But some of the gods who used Vulcan's weapons had become Jupiter's enemies. So, Jupiter blamed Vulcan for having provided the weapons that were used against him. As punishment, he banished Vulcan from Mount Olympus, the home of the gods. Vulcan went to the island of Sicily and settled there. His blacksmith shop is said to remain beneath Mount Etna, Europe's most active volcano.

Answer the following questions on a separate sheet of paper.

1. Who was king of the gods in Roman mythology?

2. What was Vulcan's occupation?

3. Who was Vulcan's wife?

4. Why was Vulcan banished from Mount Olympus?

5. According to the myth, where did Vulcan go to live after leaving Mount Olympus?

Interdisciplinary Exploration • *Pompeii*

Language Arts: Quotes From Pliny the Elder

In some ways, life in ancient Pompeii may not have been much different from life as we know it today. Many of Pliny the Elder's sayings sound very familiar to us. Below are some quotes from Pliny. In the space provided below each one, rephrase the quote in your own words.

1. In comparing various authors with one another, I have discovered that some of the gravest and latest writers have transcribed, word for word, from former works, without making acknowledgment.
   Natural History, Book I, Dedication, Section. 22

   _____

   _____

2. Indeed, what is there that does not appear marvelous when it comes to our knowledge for the first time? How many things, too, are looked upon as quite impossible until they have been actually affected?
   Natural History, Book VII, Section 8

   _____

   _____

3. With man, most of his misfortunes are occasioned by man.
   Natural History, Book I, Section 5

   _____

   _____

4. The best plan is to profit by the folly of others.
   Natural History, Book XVIII, Section 44

   _____

   _____

5. Explain how reading quotes from Pliny the Elder might give us a better idea of what life was like in ancient Rome. Did people think differently in A.D. 79? Or, were people in those days very similar in their outlook to people of today?

   _____

   _____

[Note: Quotes were translated by John Bostock (1773–1846) and Henry Thomas Riley (1816–1878).]

Interdisciplinary Exploration

Language Arts: Latin Parts of English Words

Latin was the language spoken in Pompeii. Many English words have Latin parts. What's the connection between Pompeii and the language on this page?

Pompeii was part of the Roman Empire. The Romans had a large army and navy and used them to conquer most of what we know as Europe today. When they took over lands, they brought their language with them. Italian, French, Spanish, and Portuguese are called "Romance" languages because they are related to the language spoken in ancient Rome. But how did Latin get into English?

Before being buried by the eruption of Vesuvius, Pompeians probably knew that their empire had recently expanded into a land known as Britannia. Roman armies conquered Britain just 36 years before the eruption. Although the Romans remained in Britain for about 400 years, Latin's major effect on English happened later.

During the fifth and sixth centuries, missionaries from Europe arrived in Britannia. Latin was the language of scholars at that time, and most books were written in Latin. Therefore, the missionaries taught from Latin books and often spoke Latin.

However, the greatest effect occurred in 1066, when Britain was conquered again. This time the invaders spoke French, which brought even more Latin into the English language. Today some people estimate that more than half of the words we use in English came from French, which in its turn came from Latin.

Look at the Latin word parts in the first column below. Now look at the meanings and examples of how they are used. Next, in the last column, write what you think the word means. Compare your answers with those of your classmates.

Word Part	Meaning	Example	What You Think It Means
1. -dict	to say something	dictate: to speak or read for a person	contradict:
2. pre-	in front of, before	prepay: to pay in advance	prearrange:
3. re-	again or anew	rewrite: to write again	rerun:
4. -ject	to throw	project: to throw forward	eject:

Interdisciplinary Exploration

Science: Comparing Pompeii With Other Archaeological Sites

1. Students likely will find some similarities in architecture and culture.
2. Age and location should be different.
3. Encourage students to imagine a day in the life of a typical resident of Pompeii and a typical resident at the other site.

Science: Formation of a Pyroclastic Flow

1. An eruption column is a column of hot gas, ash, and pumice that is propelled high into the air during an explosive eruption.
2. The force of the eruption is strong enough to propel the material upward.
3. A portion of the lower eruption column contains too much material. It is so dense that it cannot be forced upward.
4. At night, the hot material in a pyroclastic flow glows.
5. Ash and gases can choke people or cause them to suffocate from lack of oxygen. People may also die from intense heat or from the impact of the flow.

Science: Volcanic Soils

1. Fertile soil
2. Volcanic glass
3. The ash and pumice break down to form new materials, and soil develops.
4. Most of the soil in Italy is infertile, whereas the soil near Mount Vesuvius is fertile.
5. To take advantage of the fertile soil; other answers are possible.

Science: The Plaster Casts of Pompeii

1. A mold is a void that has the shape of some object. A cast is a replica of the object that is made by filling the mold.
2. plaster
3. As the dog's body decayed, the mold that formed around it remained. The cast made from this mold is a perfect replica of the dog.
4. When molds were discovered during excavation, plaster was poured into them. The plaster was allowed to harden, and the casts were excavated.
5. The casts preserve fine details of materials that normally would not have survived for such a long period of time.

Mathematics: Roman Numerals

1. MCCXI
2. CCL
3. DX
4. LII
5. MML
6. 8
7. 152
8. 2,100
9. 652
10. 1,060

Mathematics: Measuring the Explosiveness of a Volcanic Eruption

1. Toba, Indonesia; it has a VEI of 8.
2. Mount Pelée, Martinique
3. It was less explosive than most of the other eruptions.
4. About 100 times; a VEI difference of two corresponds to a difference in explosivity of about 100 (10×10).
5. About 1,000 times; a VEI difference of three corresponds to a difference in explosivity of about 1,000 ($10 \times 10 \times 10$).

Social Studies: The Scrolls of the Roman Empire

1. The process that is used to make paper today had not yet been invented.
2. A large roll of writing material.
3. The stems were cut into strips and placed side by side in two perpendicular layers to make sheets. The sheets of papyrus were pasted together and rolled into scrolls.
4. Herculaneum
5. Historians can learn about Roman life, beliefs, and culture.

Social Studies: Vulcan, Blacksmith of the Gods

1. Jupiter
2. Blacksmith
3. Venus
4. For making weapons for Jupiter's enemies
5. The island of Sicily beneath Mount Etna

Quotes From Pliny the Elder

1. By comparing the works of many popular writers, you can see that several are guilty of plagiarism.

2. The first time we see something, we may find it so novel that it amazes us; but as it becomes familiar, we are no longer amazed by it. Also, some things are thought to be impossible until someone actually does them, for example, inventing the telephone or walking on the moon.

3. People often cause their own problems.

4. Learn from the mistakes of others. Or, take advantage of the mistakes of a competitor.

5. Answers should indicate that students think that there are many parallels.

Latin Parts of English Words

1. to speak the opposite

2. to arrange in advance

3. to run again, such as a rerun of a movie or television show

4. to throw out

Interdisciplinary Exploration

Inside Earth

Multiple Choice

Write the letter of the correct answer on the line at the left.

_____ 1. What mineral has a rating of 10 on the Mohs hardness scale?
    a. granite   **b.** diamond
    c. quartz   **d.** silica

_____ 2. The pliable layer called the asthenosphere is part of the
    a. outer core.   **b.** crust.
    c. mantle.   **d.** inner core.

_____ 3. The vibrations that travel through Earth carrying the energy of an earthquake are called
    a. magnitudes.   **b.** pahoehoe.
    c. seismic waves.   **d.** tsunamis.

_____ 4. The three types of heat transfer are radiation, conduction, and
    a. subduction.   **b.** liquefaction.
    c. compression.   **d.** convection.

_____ 5. To measure horizontal movement of the ground along a fault, geologists could use a
    a. creep meter.   **b.** GPS satellite.
    c. tiltmeter.   **d.** seismograph.

_____ 6. Which of the following is NOT a way to reduce earthquake damage?
    a. Construct a building entirely of bricks.
    b. Construct a building far from a fault.
    c. Construct a building on rubber pads or springs.
    d. Construct a building made of flexible materials.

_____ 7. Magma that cools deep underground produces
    a. glassy textures.   **b.** large crystals.
    c. pahoehoe.   **d.** geothermal energy.

_____ 8. Which of the following is an example of a clastic sedimentary rock?
    a. granite   **b.** rock salt
    c. coal   **d.** conglomerate

_____ 9. Sea-floor spreading occurs on
    a. the outer rim of the Ring of Fire.
    b. both sides of the mid-ocean ridge.
    c. the continental side of a deep-ocean trench.
    d. the leading edge of a tsunami.

Inside Earth • *Book Test*

_____ **10.** Magma that is low in silica is
    a. thick.
    b. likely to erupt explosively.
    c. too sticky to flow very far.
    d. dark in color.

Completion

Fill in the line to complete each statement.

11. The point on Earth's surface directly above an earthquake's focus is called the _____.

12. A substance made of two or more elements that have been chemically combined is a(n) _____.

13. A(n) _____ volcano may awaken in the future and become active.

14. Heat and pressure deep beneath Earth's surface can change any rock to _____ rock.

15. A process in which an ore is melted to separate useful metal from other elements is called _____.

True or False

If the statement is true, write true. *If it is false, change the underlined word or words to make the statement true.*

_____ **16.** Igneous rock that formed when magma hardened beneath Earth's surface is called <u>extrusive</u> rock.

_____ **17.** The theory that states that pieces of Earth's lithosphere are in constant motion is called <u>plate tectonics</u>.

_____ **18.** The Ring of Fire is a major volcanic belt around the <u>Indian</u> Ocean.

_____ **19.** A mineral that splits easily along flat surfaces has the property called <u>cleavage</u>.

_____ **20.** Compression forces in Earth's crust produce <u>normal faults</u>.

Name _____ Date _____ Class _____

Using Science Skills: Interpreting Diagrams

Use the figure below to answer questions 21 and 22 in the spaces provided.

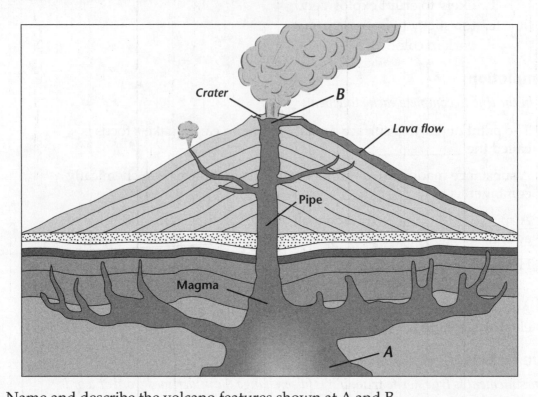

21. Name and describe the volcano features shown at A and B.

_____

_____

_____

_____

22. If this volcano had a caldera, where would it form? Explain how it would form.

_____

_____

_____

Essay

Answer each of the following on a separate sheet of paper.

23. What characteristics cause geologists to classify silver as a mineral?

24. Why is limestone that began as coral sometimes found on continents?

25. Describe the processes that work together to produce sandstone.

Using Science Skills

Use the figure below to answer questions 26 and 27. Write your answers in the spaces provided.

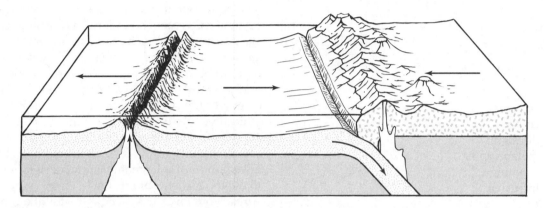

26. Interpreting Diagrams Describe the types of plate boundaries shown in the figure.

_____

_____

_____

_____

27. Inferring Why would volcanoes and earthquakes be common near these boundaries?

_____

_____

_____

_____

_____

Essay

Answer each of the following on a separate sheet of paper.

28. Describe convection in Earth's mantle, and explain how it might be related to the movement of Earth's plates.

29. What do geologists know today that would have convinced geologists of the early 1900s that Alfred Wegener's theory of continental drift was in large part correct?

30. Explain how the lava flow from a shield volcano could become part of the rock cycle and eventually become a flow of lava again.

Book Test

Book Test

1. b
2. c
3. c
4. d
5. a
6. a
7. b
8. d
9. b
10. d
11. epicenter
12. compound
13. dormant
14. metamorphic
15. smelting
16. intrusive
17. true
18. Pacific
19. true
20. reverse faults
21. A. Magma chamber, the place beneath a volcano where magma collects in a pocket.
B. Vent, the opening at the surface where molten rock and gas leave the volcano.
22. It would form at the top of the volcano. It forms when the volcanic mountain collapses because the main vent and magma chamber are empty after an enormous eruption.
23. Silver occurs naturally. It is an inorganic solid that has a crystal structure. It has a definite chemical composition. Because silver has these five characteristics, geologists classify it as a mineral.
24. Plate motions have slowly moved limestone deposits far from the tropical oceans where they formed. The sea floor where coral reefs grew eventually became dry land. Limestone formed from coral is exposed in many places on land.
25. Erosion carries sediment in water or wind. Eventually, the moving water or wind slows, and the sediment settles out. As more and more sediments are deposited, the weight of layers on top compacts the sediment layers on the bottom. As compaction is taking place, dissolved minerals in the spaces between particles of sediment crystallize and cement the particles together to form sedimentary rock.

26. The boundary to the left is a divergent plate boundary, in which plates are moving apart. The boundary to the right is a convergent plate boundary, in which plates are moving together.
27. Volcanoes occurs at divergent boundaries as lava pours out of cracks in the ocean floor. They occur at convergent boundaries as crust melts to become magma, which then rises toward the surface to produce volcanoes. Earthquakes occur at both divergent and convergent boundaries because the forces of plate motion pull or compress the crust, causing stress on rocks, which eventually causes the rocks to move.
28. Heat from Earth's mantle and core causes convection currents to form in the mantle when hot columns of solid mantle material rise slowly to the top asthenosphere, the hot material spreads out and pushes cooler material out of the way, and the cooler material sinks back into the mantle. Most geologists think that the flow of convection currents in the mantle causes the movement of Earth's plates.
29. Geologists now know that the lithosphere is broken into separate plates. They also know that sea-floor spreading occurs from the mid-ocean ridge, moving oceanic plates. In addition, they know that convection currents in the mantle cause movement of all the plates. These forces provide the pushes and pulls that account for movement of the continents according to Wegener's theory of continental drift.
30. Answers may vary, though all should describe rock as it moves through the rock cycle. A typical answer might mention that lava from a shield volcano would harden into an igneous rock. If that rock became buried, high pressure and temperatures would change it into a metamorphic rock. Then uplift would expose that rock to the surface, where it would be weathered and particles of it would be carried away and deposited with other sediments. Compaction and cementation would turn the sediments into sedimentary rock. That rock might sink beneath a trench, where it would melt in the mantle. Finally, the molten material would once again rise to the surface as lava.

Plate Tectonics

▲ Lab zone | Chapter **Project** | Make a Model of Earth

The following steps will walk you through the Chapter Project. Use the hints and detailed directions as you guide your students through design, construction, presentation, and reflection.

Chapter Project Overview

In this project, students will work in groups to make a scale model of Earth's interior, with features associated with plate tectonics added to the surface. The model should show the layers of Earth, plates and plate boundaries, sea-floor spreading, subduction, continents, and a rift valley.

In introducing the project, do the following demonstration.

1. Cut a whole melon in half, and display to the class the insides of one half. Ask students what materials they could use to make a model of the melon.

2. Then cut a quarter out of another whole melon by cutting down to the core from the top and from the side. Have students compare the quarter melon with the half melon. Which perspective gives a better view of what's inside a melon? Point out that models likewise can be of different perspectives, and in this project each group has the choice to develop its own type of model.

Distribute Chapter Project Overview. Review the project's rules. You may also want to hand out the Chapter Project Scoring Rubric so students will understand what is expected of them.

Organize the class into small groups. Make sure students understand that each member will make sketches and develop a design for a model before meeting with other members. Members will then collaborate in creating the final design. Point out that as they progress through the chapter, they will add to the design of the group's model. Each student will also make sketches to revise the group's model.

Set a deadline for the project presentation and some interim dates at the end of Sections 1, 4, and 5, and have students copy the dates in their Project Time Line.

Distribute Chapter Project Worksheet 1. After students have read the worksheet, ask if they have any questions.

Review scales used on maps and models. Explain that a scale is the proportion used in determining the relationship of a model to the object it represents.

1. Point out scales on maps and globes. To help students who have trouble with the concept, have them use a map and its scale to calculate the distance between their home town and other cities.

2. Display various three-dimensional models, such as model airplanes or boats, and invite students' opinions on whether they were "made to scale," that is, whether the parts of the models are in proportion to the things they represent.

Point out that in their models students will make the interior layers of Earth to a scale. The surface features, though, should not be made to the same scale, because they would be too small.

Materials and Preparation

Though groups will decide for themselves what materials to use to make their models, you might want to provide some basic materials and tools.

Materials that could be used to make a model include papier-maché, modeling compound, chicken wire, cardboard, plywood, particle board, plastic foam, wood blocks, wire, paints, and permanent markers.

Tools that could be used in constructing the model include plastic knives, pliers, hand saws, glue guns, and paint brushes.

Keep Students on Track— Section 1

As you review the student's sketches, encourage students who lack ideas to talk with classmates about a general direction to take. Three different possibilities students might pursue are a wedge-shaped model, a sphere with a portion cut away, and a block model. You might share these ideas to help students make their sketches. Creative thinkers might imagine other ways to model Earth's interior.

Talk with each group during its initial meeting. Make sure members take each other's sketches and ideas seriously. At this point, students should think about the materials they will use for their models and begin collecting them.

Distribute Chapter Project Worksheet 2. Make sure students understand that they will need to work on this worksheet as they learn more about Earth's structure in the rest of the chapter. As in Worksheet 1, students should individually make sketches. These sketches, though, should build upon the group's design for the layers of Earth's interior.

Keep Students on Track— Section 4

Check to see that students have begun making sketches of surface features, including the mid-ocean ridge and a deep-ocean trench. Encourage students to share their sketches and ideas in their groups. Questions students should be asking themselves at this point in the project include, How can we show sea-floor spreading on the surface of the model? What new materials do we need to find?

Groups should begin building the base of their models. A base might be made of wood, plastic foam, or some other sturdy material.

Keep Students on Track— Section 5

Students' sketches should now show the full range of surface features related to plate tectonics, including three types of plate boundaries. Check students' folders to see that everyone is contributing something to the group's design process.

Encourage students to rethink their original models—there's still time to revise the design. Encourage them to review the Chapter Project Overview to make sure that their models include everything they are supposed to include.

Chapter Project Wrap Up

As you review each group's final model, you may wish to have the members "talk you through" the presentation. Make suggestions for organizing the presentation into a logical report. When appropriate, encourage some students to take a greater role in presenting the model.

Provide class time for group presentations. Allow each group to present its model and explain what the model shows. Encourage other students to ask questions about the design of the model, the materials, and the scale.

After all presentations have been made, discuss with students which models seemed to work best, that is, which were the best looking and which incorporated all the necessary features in the most instructive way.

Encourage students to evaluate how well they accomplished what they set out to do, including how well the final model matched the design that group members had agreed upon. Invite students to make suggestions about what they think would have made the project better.

Extension

Students might want to find a place in the school or in a community building to display their models. To make the models self-explanatory to those who know little about this topic, groups might prepare annotations on three-by-five cards. Another possibility is to make audio- or videotapes that provide a further explanation for what the models show.

Plate Tectonics · *Chapter Project*

⬛ Chapter **Project** **Make a Model of Earth**

How can you make a model that shows both what's inside planet Earth and how the inside affects features on the surface? In this project, you will work in a group to design and create just such a model.

First, you will make sketches of your own design for a three-dimensional model of Earth's interior. Since your model of the interior will have to be to scale, you will need to use a scale in your sketches. Then you will meet with your group to review all members' designs and agree on a single design for a model of Earth's interior. As you and other group members learn more about plate tectonics, you will make new sketches for adding features of Earth's surface to your model. As you learn more about Earth's structure, you will want to make changes in the design of your model. At the end of the project, your group will present your finished three-dimensional model to the class.

Project Rules

- Devise a scale and make a sketch of the layers of Earth, as described in Worksheet 1. Keep any sketches you make in a Project Folder. You will show your sketch or sketches to your teacher and discuss your ideas for a model at the end of Section 1.

- With your group, review one another's sketches and ideas. Come to a consensus on a design for the model you want to build as a group, and begin collecting the materials you will need.

- Make sketches of surface features that you want to include on your model, including features associated with sea-floor spreading and plate boundaries as described in Worksheet 2. You will show your sketches to your teacher and discuss your ideas for a revised model at the end of Sections 4 and 5.

- Begin building the base of your model as soon as possible. Then, as you learn new information, you can add to your design and build the model from the core out to the surface.

- With your group, revise your initial model to include surface features, including at least three plates, three plate boundaries, and two continents.

- With your group, prepare a presentation to the class of your completed model. As part of this presentation, you will explain what your model includes, what scale you used for the interior layers, and how your model shows how Earth's interior affects its surface.

Plate Tectonics ▪ *Chapter Project*

Project Hints

- Look through textbooks and encyclopedias to find drawings that show Earth's interior and surface features. When you find one that looks interesting and informative, think of ways you could make that drawing into a three-dimensional model.

- As soon as possible, begin collecting the materials you will use to build your model. Your teacher may be able to provide some materials, but you will probably need to bring some materials and tools from home.

- Work closely with other members of your group, and listen to their ideas. You might find that someone in your group has just the right idea to make your own design a great deal better.

- Don't be afraid to change your group's design if it doesn't seem to come together well after you've begun construction.

- Make sure your model includes everything that is necessary to inform the viewer about plate tectonics.

- Try to make your model accurate and informative, but also try to make it as artistically pleasing as possible. Encourage members of your group who have artistic talents to put finishing touches on the model.

Project Time Line

Task	Due Date
1. Complete design and sketches for Worksheet 1	_____
2. Agree on a group design for model	_____
3. Collect and test materials	_____
4. Agree on how group will show surface features on model	_____
5. Finish collecting materials	_____
6. Construct final model	_____
7. Prepare class presentation	_____
8. Present the model to the class	_____

A Scale Model of Earth's Interior

This worksheet will help you get started making a design for your model of Earth's interior.

Making Layers to Scale

1. What is the distance from the surface of Earth to the center?
   _____ km

2. How large will your model be, from the outside to the center?
   _____ cm

3. Divide your answer to Question 1 by the answer to Question 2 to calculate the scale you will use when building your model.
   1 cm = _____ km

4. Name the layers of Earth that you will include in your model, and write how thick each one is. Then use another sheet of paper to compute the thickness of each layer to the scale you will be using.

Layer	Thickness	Thickness to Scale
	km	cm
	km	cm
	km	cm

Planning a Model of Earth

5. Write a description of the model you think your group should build.

   _____

   _____

   _____

6. What materials will you need to build this model?

   _____

   _____

   _____

7. On a separate sheet of paper, make a sketch of a model your group could build. Keep the sketch in your Project Folder. Take this worksheet and your sketch to your group meeting. Talk over your ideas with group members.

Adding Surface Features to the Model

Now that you've learned more about the structure of Earth, you will want to make some changes to your model design. This worksheet will help you organize these changes. Use the back of this sheet if you need more space.

Sea-Floor Spreading

1. What features must be added to show sea-floor spreading on the model?

   _____

   _____

2. What features must be added to show the process of subduction?

   _____

   _____

3. What materials could be used to add these features to the model?

   _____

   _____

Plate Tectonics

4. Briefly describe three plate boundaries that could be added to the model.

   _____

   _____

5. How could convection currents be shown in the model?

   _____

   _____

6. What other features of the surface should also be included in the model?

   _____

   _____

7. What materials could be used to add these features to the model?

   _____

   _____

8. On a separate sheet of paper, make a sketch of the revised model that your group could build. Keep the sketch in your Project Folder. Take this worksheet and your sketch to your group meeting. Talk over your ideas with group members. Then construct the final model.

Name _____ Date _____ Class _____

Plate Tectonics · *Chapter Project* **Scoring Rubric**

Lab zone Chapter Project

Make a Model of Earth

In evaluating how well you complete the Chapter Project, your teacher will judge your work in four categories. In each, a score of 4 is the best rating.

	4	3	2	1
Individual Sketches and Designs	Makes sketches that show originality of design and a thorough understanding of Earth's interior and plate tectonics.	Makes sketches that show some originality of design and a good understanding of Earth's interior and plate tectonics.	Makes sketches that show an adequate design and some understanding of Earth's interior and plate tectonics.	Makes sketches that show an incomplete or inappropriate design and little understanding of Earth's interior and plate tectonics.
Constructed Model of a Cut-Away Earth	Model is well constructed and includes Earth's layers made to scale, at least three plates and plate boundaries, two continents, and clear, accurate labels of all features on the model.	Model is constructed adequately and includes Earth's layers made to scale, at least two plates and plate boundaries, two continents, and accurate labels of all features on the model.	Model construction is a little sloppy, and model is missing one or two features. Accurate labels of most features on the model are included.	Model is poorly constructed and missing two or more major features. Labels are incomplete, inaccurate, or missing.
Presenting the Model to the Class	Makes a thorough and interesting presentation that includes a clear, accurate explanation of what the model shows about Earth's layers and plate tectonics.	Makes a thorough presentation that includes a satisfactory explanation of what the model shows about Earth's layers and plate tectonics.	Makes a presentation that includes a partial explanation of what the model shows about Earth's layers and plate tectonics.	Makes a presentation that includes an incomplete and/or inaccurate explanation of what the model shows about Earth's layers and plate tectonics.
Participating in the Group	Takes a lead in planning, constructing, and presenting the model.	Participates in all aspects of planning, constructing, and presenting the model.	Participates in most aspects of planning, constructing, and presenting the model.	Plays a minor role in planning, constructing, and presenting the model.

Earth's Interior

 2 periods, 1 block

Plate Tectonics

Objectives
F.1.1.1 Explain how geologists learn about Earth's inner structures.
F.1.1.2 Identify the characteristics of Earth's crust, mantle, and core.

Key Terms
• seismic waves • pressure • crust • basalt • granite
• mantle • lithosphere • asthenosphere • outer core
• inner core

Local Standards

PRETEACH

Build Background Knowledge
Students share their experiences digging holes in the ground and discussing what is below Earth's surface.

 *How Do Scientists Find Out What's Inside Earth?* **L1**

Targeted Resources

❑ **All in One** **Teaching Resources**
  L2 Reading Strategy Transparency F1: Using Prior Knowledge
❑ 💿 **PresentationExpress™ CD-ROM**

INSTRUCT

Exploring Inside Earth
Use visuals and leading questions to open discussion of how activity in Earth's interior affects the surface.

A Journey to the Center of Earth
Explain why changes in pressure and temperature increase with depth.

The Crust
Help students compare and contrast oceanic and continental crust.

The Mantle
Use hard candy and taffy to open discussion of characteristics of the lithosphere and asthenosphere.

The Core
Use an apple to help students compare and contrast Earth's inner core and outer core.

Targeted Resources

❑ **All in One** **Teaching Resources**
  L2 Guided Reading, pp. 47–50
  L2 Transparency F2
❑ **www.SciLinks.org** Web Code: scn-1011
❑ 💿 **Student Edition on Audio CD**

ASSESS

Section Assessment Questions
Have students use their completed graphic organizers with their paragraphs using prior knowledge to answer the questions.

Reteach
Students discuss characteristics of continental crust and oceanic crust.

Targeted Resources

❑ **All in One** **Teaching Resources**
  Section Summary, p. 46
  L1 Review and Reinforce, p. 51
  L3 Enrich, p. 52

Plate Tectonics · *Section Summary*

Earth's Interior

Key Concepts

- How have geologists learned about Earth's inner structure?
- What are the characteristics of Earth's crust, mantle, and core?

Earth's surface is constantly changing. Earth looks different today from the way it did millions of years ago. People wonder, "What's inside Earth?" The extreme conditions in Earth's interior prevent exploration far below the surface. **Geologists have used two main types of evidence to learn about Earth's interior: direct evidence from rock samples and indirect evidence from seismic waves.**

Rocks from inside Earth give geologists clues about Earth's structure. Geologists can make inferences about conditions deep inside Earth where these rocks formed. Using data from **seismic waves** produced by earthquakes, geologists have learned that Earth's interior is made up of several layers.

The three main layers of Earth are the crust, the mantle, and the core. These layers vary greatly in size, composition, temperature, and pressure. Beneath the surface, the temperature decreases for about 20 meters, then increases until the center of Earth is reached. **Pressure** results from a force pressing on an area. Pressure inside Earth increases as you go deeper.

The **crust** is the layer of rock that forms Earth's outer skin. The **crust is a layer of solid rock that includes both dry land and the ocean floor.** Oceanic crust consists mostly of rocks such as **basalt,** dark rock with a fine texture. Continental crust, the crust that forms the continents, consists mainly of rocks such as granite. **Granite** is a rock that usually is a light color and has a coarse texture.

Below a boundary 40 kilometers beneath the surface is the solid material of the **mantle,** a layer of hot rock. **Earth's mantle is made up of rock that is very hot, but solid. Scientists divide the mantle into layers based on the physical characteristics of those layers.** The uppermost part of the mantle and the crust together form a rigid layer called the **lithosphere.** Below the lithosphere is a soft layer called the asthenosphere. Beneath the **asthenosphere,** the mantle is solid. This solid material, called the lower mantle, extends all the way to Earth's core.

The core is made mostly of the metals iron and nickel. It consists of two parts—a liquid outer core and a solid inner core. The **outer core** is a layer of molten metal that surrounds the inner core. The **inner core** is a dense ball of solid metal.

Scientists think that movements in the liquid outer core create Earth's magnetic field. Because Earth has a magnetic field, the planet acts like a giant bar magnet.

Plate Tectonics • *Guided Reading and Study*

Earth's Interior (pp. 6–13)

This section explains how scientists learn about Earth's interior. The section also describes the layers that make up Earth and explains why Earth acts like a giant magnet.

Use Target Reading Skills

Before you read the passage for each heading, fill in the top box with what you know. After you have read the passage, fill in the bottom box with what you have learned.

What You Know
I. Earth's crust is made of rock.
2.
3.
4.
5.

What You Learned
I.
2.
3.
4.
5.

Exploring Inside Earth (pp. 7–8)

1. What prevents geologists from directly exploring Earth's interior?

_____

_____

2. Geologists use direct evidence from _____ to learn about Earth's interior.

3. Geologists learn about Earth's interior using indirect evidence from

_____ .

Earth's Interior *(continued)*

4. Is the following sentence true or false? Earth looks the same today as it did millions of years ago. _____

5. Seismic waves reveal the structure of Earth through their _____ and _____.

6. Circle the letter of each sentence that is true about Earth.

   a. Indirect evidence of Earth's interior comes from studying rock samples.

   b. Geologists cannot observe Earth's interior directly.

   c. It is over 6,000 kilometers from the surface to the center of Earth.

   d. Geologists learn about Earth's interior by drilling holes.

7. _____ waves are produced by earthquakes.

A Journey to the Center of Earth *(p. 9)*

8. How does the temperature change as you go from the surface toward the center of Earth? _____

   _____

   _____

9. How does pressure change as you go from the surface toward the center of Earth? _____

10. The three main layers that make up Earth are the _____, _____, and _____.

The Crust *(p. 10)*

11. The _____ is a layer of rock that forms Earth's outer skin.

12. Is the following sentence true or false? The crust is thinnest under high mountains. _____

13. The dark-colored rock that makes up most of the oceanic crust is

    _____.

14. The light-colored rock that makes up most of the continental crust is

    _____.

Plate Tectonics · *Guided Reading and Study*

The Mantle (p. 11)

Match the name of each layer of the mantle with its description.

Layer

_____ **15.** lower mantle

_____ **16.** lithosphere

_____ **17.** asthenosphere

Description

a. Rigid layer that includes the upper part of the mantle and the crust

b. Solid material beneath the asthenosphere

c. Soft layer just below the lithosphere

18. Is the following sentence true or false? The asthenosphere is not considered solid because it can bend like plastic. _____

19. Is the following sentence true or false? The mantle is nearly 3,000 kilometers thick. _____

The Core (pp. 12–13)

20. Circle the letter of each sentence that is true about Earth's outer core.

    a. It is under low pressure.

    b. It is made of solid metal.

    c. It contains iron and nickel.

    d. It is a solid.

21. Circle the letter of each sentence that is true about Earth's inner core.

    a. It consists of molten metal.

    b. It is a thick liquid.

    c. It is not very dense.

    d. It is under extreme pressure.

Plate Tectonics · *Guided Reading and Study*

Earth's Interior *(continued)*

22. In the drawing, label the three main layers of Earth.

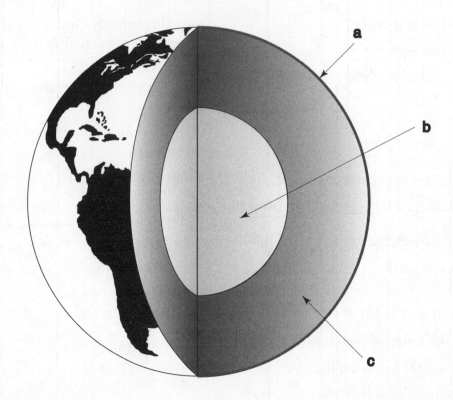

23. Describe how a compass needle aligns itself. _____

_____

24. What creates Earth's magnetic field? _____

_____

Plate Tectonics • *Review and Reinforce*

Earth's Interior

Understanding Main Ideas

Label the layers of Earth by writing the name of the layer in the blank.

1. _____

2. _____

3. _____

4. _____

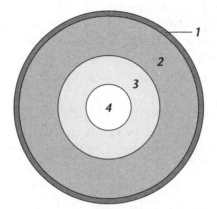

Earth's layers

Answer the following questions on a separate sheet of paper.

5. What are two types of evidence geologists use to learn about Earth's interior?

6. Compare and contrast the asthenosphere with the lithosphere.

Building Vocabulary

Match each term with its definition by writing the letter of the correct definition on the line beside the term in the left column.

_____ 7. basalt

_____ 8. asthenosphere

_____ 9. crust

_____ 10. outer core

_____ 11. lithosphere

_____ 12. granite

_____ 13. pressure

_____ 14. seismic wave

a. a rock that makes up much of the ocean floor

b. the force pushing on a surface or area

c. the layer made up of liquid iron and nickel

d. the uppermost part of the mantle

e. a rock that makes up the core of the continents

f. outer rind of rock

g. a wave produced by an earthquake

h. soft layer of rock in the mantle

Name _____ Date _____ Class_____

Plate Tectonics · *Enrich*

Differences in Arrival Time

Geologists have learned a great deal about Earth's interior by carefully studying the waves created by earthquakes, called seismic waves. Like light waves and sound waves, seismic waves travel through different kinds of materials at different rates. For example, a type of seismic wave called a P wave travels through crust material at an average speed of 6 km/s. But through the uppermost mantle material, P waves travel at an average speed of 8 km/s. Geologists use their knowledge of this difference in speeds to explore the interior of Earth. They have set up thousands of receiving stations to record the arrival of seismic waves. Computers then help in analyzing the data and creating a picture of Earth's interior.

The figure below shows two P waves from an earthquake whose travel times are recorded by a receiving station. Use the figure to answer the questions that follow.

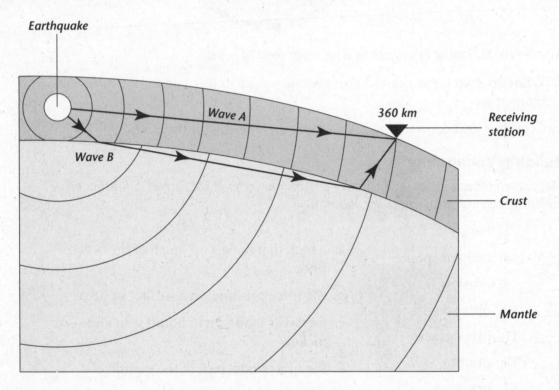

Answer the following questions on a separate sheet of paper.

1. How far away from the earthquake is the receiving station?

2. Which P wave takes a more direct route to the receiving station, Wave A or Wave B?

3. How long does Wave A take to reach the station?

4. Wave B took 51 seconds to arrive at the station. What accounts for the difference in arrival times between Wave A and Wave B?

5. Can you infer why P waves travel faster through the upper mantle than they do through the crust?

Convection and the Mantle

 1 period, 1/2 block

Objectives
F.1.2.1 Explain how heat is transferred.
F.1.2.2 Identify what causes convection currents.
F.1.2.3 Describe convection currents in Earth's mantle.

Key Terms
• radiation • conduction • convection • density
• convection current

Local Standards

PRETEACH

Build Background Knowledge
Students recall experiences about convection currents in a room.

 **Discover Activity** *How Can Heat Cause a Motion in a Liquid?* **L1**

Targeted Resources
❑ **All in One** **Teaching Resources**
   L2 Reading Strategy Transparency F3: Outlining
❑ ● **PresentationExpress™ CD-ROM**

INSTRUCT

Types of Heat Transfer
Use everyday examples to describe and explain the three mechanisms of heat transfer: radiation, conduction, and convection. Then consider everyday examples of each.

Convection Currents
Review the concepts of density and gravity to explain why convection occurs.

Convection Currents in Earth
Use a diagram to explain how temperature differences in Earth's mantle create convection currents in solid rock.

Targeted Resources
❑ **All in One** Teaching Resources
   L2 Guided Reading, pp. 55–57
   L2 Transparency F4
❑ **PHSchool.com** Web Code: cfd-1012
❑ ● **Student Edition on Audio CD**

ASSESS

Section Assessment Questions
● Have students use their completed outlines to answer the questions.

Reteach
Students consider heat transfer in a glass containing water and ice cubes.

Targeted Resources
❑ **All in One** Teaching Resources
   Section Summary, p. 54
   L1 Review and Reinforce, p. 58
   L3 Enrich, p. 59

Plate Tectonics • *Section Summary*

Convection and the Mantle

Key Concepts

■ How is heat transferred?

■ What causes convection currents?

■ What causes convection currents in Earth's mantle?

The movement of energy from a warmer object to a cooler object is called heat transfer. Heat is always transferred from a warmer substance to a cooler substance. **There are three types of heat transfer: radiation, conduction, and convection.**

The transfer of energy through empty space is called **radiation.** Heat transfer by radiation takes place with no direct contact between a heat source and an object. For example, radiation enables sunlight to warm Earth's surface.

Heat transfer by direct contact of particles of matter is called **conduction.** In conduction, the heated particles of a substance transfer heat to other particles through direct contact. An example is when a spoon heats up in a hot pot of soup.

The transfer of heat by the movement of a heated fluid is called **convection.** Fluids include liquids and gases. During convection, heated particles of a fluid begin to flow, transferring heat energy from one part of the fluid to another.

Heat transfer by convection is caused by differences in temperature and density within a fluid. **Density** is a measure of how much mass there is in a volume of a substance. When a liquid or gas is heated, the particles move faster. As they move faster, they spread apart. Because the particles of the heated fluid are farther apart, they occupy more space. The fluid's density decreases. But when a fluid cools, the particles move closer together and density increases.

An example of convection occurs in heating a pot of soup on a stove. As soup at the bottom of the pot gets hot, it expands and becomes less dense. The warm, less dense soup moves upward, floating over cooler, denser soup. At the surface, the warm soup spreads out and cools, becoming denser. Then gravity pulls this cooler, denser soup down to the bottom, where it is heated again and begins to rise. This flow that transfers heat within a fluid is called a **convection current. The heating and cooling of the fluid, changes in the fluid's density, and the force of gravity combine to set convection currents in motion.** Convection currents continue as long as heat is added to the fluid.

Convection currents flow in the mantle. The heat source for these currents is heat from Earth's core and from the mantle itself. Hot columns of mantle material rise slowly. At the top of the asthenosphere, the hot material spreads out and pushes the cooler material out of the way. This cooler material sinks back into the mantle. Convection currents like these have been moving inside Earth for more than four billion years!

Plate Tectonics · *Guided Reading and Study*

Convection and the Mantle (pp. 14–17)

This section describes how heat is transferred from Earth's hot core through the mantle.

Use Target Reading Skills

As you read about heat transfer, complete the outline to show the relationships among the headings.

Convection and the Mantle

I. _____

    A. _____

    B. Conduction

    C. _____

II. Convection Currents

III. _____

    _____

    _____

Types of Heat Transfer (pp. 15–16)

1. The movement of energy from a warmer object to a cooler object is called

   _____.

2. List the three types of heat transfer.

   a. _____ b. _____ c. _____

3. What is radiation? _____

   _____

4. What are two forms of radiation? _____

   _____

5. What is conduction? _____

   _____

6. What is an example of conduction? _____

   _____

Plate Tectonics ▪ *Guided Reading and Study*

Convection and the Mantle *(continued)*

7. What is convection? _____

_____

8. Heat transfer by convection is caused by differences of _____ and density within a fluid.

9. A measure of how much mass there is in a volume of a substance is

_____.

10. Circle the letter of the sentence that describes what happens to a fluid when its temperature increases.

   a. Its particles occupy less space.

   b. Its density decreases.

   c. Its particles move more slowly.

   d. Its particles settle together more closely.

Convection Currents (p. 16)

11. What three factors set convection currents in motion? _____

_____

12. What happens to convection currents when the liquid or gas is no longer heated? _____

_____

Plate Tectonics · *Guided Reading and Study*

Convection Currents in Earth (p. 17)

13. Complete the graphic organizer to show the relationships among heat, movement, and density in mantle rock.

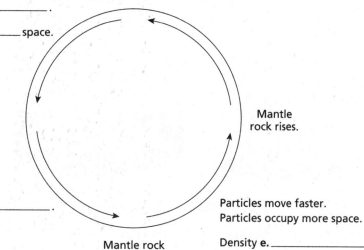

Mantle rock **a.** _____.

Particles move **b.** _____.

Particles occupy **c.** _____ space.
Density increases.

Mantle rock rises.

Mantle rock **d.** _____.

Particles move faster.
Particles occupy more space.

Density **e.** _____.

Mantle rock
is heated.

f. Why is this relationship shown as a cycle? _____
_____

g. In the cycle shown, where would mantle rock be the densest? _____
_____

14. Is the following sentence true or false? The heat source for the convection currents in the mantle is the sun. _____

Plate Tectonics · *Review and Reinforce*

Convection and the Mantle

Understanding Main Ideas

Label each figure by writing the type of heat transfer it shows.

1. _____ 2. _____ 3. _____

Answer the following questions in the spaces provided.

4. What are convection currents and what causes them?

_____

_____

_____

5. What causes convection currents in Earth's mantle?

_____

_____

_____

Building Vocabulary

If the statement is true, write true. *If it is false, change the underlined word or words to make the statement true.*

_____ 6. The transfer of energy through empty space is called <u>convection</u>.

_____ 7. The movement of energy from a warmer object to a cooler object is called <u>heat transfer</u>.

_____ 8. <u>Conduction</u> is heat transfer by direct contact of particles of matter.

_____ 9. <u>Radiation</u> is the transfer of heat by the movement of a heated fluid.

_____ 10. Density is a measure of how much <u>heat</u> there is in a volume of a substance.

Plate Tectonics · *Enrich*

What's Happening During Convection?

The figure below shows a convection cell in Earth's mantle. A **convection cell** is one complete loop of a convection current. Use the figure to answer the questions that follow.

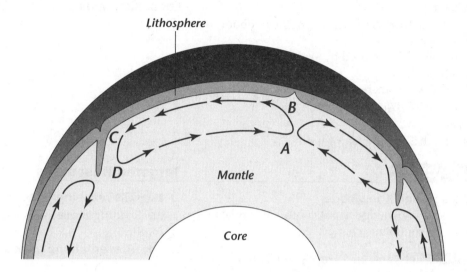

Answer the following questions on a separate sheet of paper.

1. Where does the heat come from that drives this convection current in the mantle?

2. Where is the temperature of the mantle material greater, at point A or point B? Explain why.

3. Where is the density of the material greater, at point B or point C? Explain why.

4. What causes the convection cell to turn to the left at point B?

5. What happens to the temperature and density of the material between points B and C?

6. What force causes the convection cell to turn down at point C?

7. What happens to the temperature and density of the material between points D and A?

8. What causes the convection cell to turn up at point A?

9. How do you think this convection cell might affect the crust material above it?

Drifting Continents

 *2 periods, 1 block*

Ability Levels Key
L1 Basic to Average
L2 For All Students
L3 Average to Advanced

Objectives

F.1.3.1 Explain Alfred Wegener's hypothesis about the continents.

F.1.3.2 List the evidence used by Wegener to support his hypothesis.

F.1.3.3 Explain why other scientists of Wegener's time rejected his hypothesis.

Key Terms

• continental drift • Pangaea • fossil

Local Standards

PRETEACH

Build Background Knowledge
Students recall knowledge about continents and consider whether continents change.

 **Discover Activity** *How Are Earth's Continents Linked Together?* **L1**

Targeted Resources

❏ **All in One Teaching Resources**
L2 Reading Strategy Transparency F5: Outlining
❏ **PresentationExpress™ CD-ROM**

INSTRUCT

Continental Drift
Use a jigsaw puzzle and a world map to demonstrate Wegener's hypothesis of continental drift and consider evidence that can be used to reassemble Pangaea.

Wegener's Hypothesis Rejected
Consider historic arguments against continental drift and explain why the hypothesis was not accepted by most of Wegener's contemporaries.

Targeted Resources

❏ **All in One Teaching Resources**
L2 Guided Reading, pp. 62–63
L2 Transparency F6
❏ **www.SciLinks.org** Web Code: scn-1013
❏ **Student Edition on Audio CD**

ASSESS

Section Assessment Questions
Have students use their graphic organizers showing the evidence they have identified to answer the questions.

Reteach
Students work together to create a concept map about continental drift.

Targeted Resources

❏ **All in One Teaching Resources**
Section Summary, p. 61
L1 Review and Reinforce, p. 64
L3 Enrich, p. 65

Plate Tectonics · *Section Summary*

Drifting Continents

Key Concepts

- What was Alfred Wegener's hypothesis about the continents?
- What evidence supported Wegener's hypothesis?
- Why was Alfred Wegener's theory rejected by most scientists of his day?

In 1910, a young German scientist named Alfred Wegener became curious about why the coasts of several continents matched so well, like the pieces of a jigsaw puzzle. He formed a hypothesis that Earth's continents had moved! **Wegener's hypothesis was that all the continents had once been joined together in a single landmass and have since drifted apart.** He named this supercontinent Pangaea, meaning "all lands." According to Wegener, **Pangaea** existed about 300 million years ago. Over tens of millions of years, Pangaea began to break apart. The pieces of Pangaea slowly moved toward their present-day locations, becoming the continents of today. The idea that the continents slowly moved over Earth's surface became known as **continental drift.** In a book called *The Origin of Continents and Oceans,* Wegener presented his evidence. **Wegener gathered evidence from different scientific fields to support his ideas about continental drift. He studied land features, fossils, and evidence of climate change.**

Mountain ranges and other landforms provided evidence for continental drift. For example, Wegener noticed that when he pieced together maps of Africa and South America, a mountain range running from east to west in South Africa lines up with a range in Argentina. Also, European coal fields match up with coal fields in North America.

Fossils also provided evidence to support Wegener's theory. A **fossil** is any trace of an ancient organism preserved in rock. The fossils of the reptiles *Mesosaurus* and *Lystrosaurus* and a fernlike plant called *Glossopteris* have been found on widely separated landmasses. This convinced Wegener that the continents had once been united.

Wegener used evidence from climate change to further support his theory. For example, an island in the Arctic Ocean contains fossils of tropical plants. According to Wegener, the island once must have been located close to the equator. Wegener also pointed to scratches on rocks made by glaciers. These scratches show that places with mild climates today once had climates cold enough for glaciers to form. According to Wegener's theory, Earth's climate has not changed. Instead, the positions of the continents have changed.

Wegener also attempted to explain how the drift of continents took place. **Unfortunately, Wegener could not provide a satisfactory explanation for the force that pushes or pulls the continents.** Because he could not identify the cause of continental drift, most geologists rejected his theory. For nearly half a century, from the 1920s to the 1960s, most scientists paid little attention to the idea of continental drift. Then new evidence about Earth's structure led scientists to reconsider Wegener's bold theory.

Plate Tectonics • *Guided Reading and Study*

Drifting Continents (pp. 18–22)

This section describes a theory of how the continents came to be located where they are today. The section also gives evidence for the theory and explains why the theory was not accepted for many years.

Use Target Reading Skills

As you read about the evidence that supports the theory of continental drift, complete the graphic organizer.

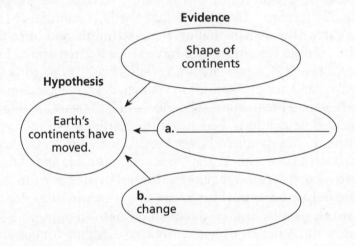

Continental Drift (pp. 19–21)

1. State Alfred Wegener's hypothesis about how Earth's continents have moved.

   _____

   _____

2. Wegener named his supercontinent _____.

3. What did Wegener think had happened to this supercontinent?

   _____

   _____

   _____

4. Wegener's idea that the continents slowly moved over Earth's surface

   became known as _____.

Plate Tectonics • *Guided Reading and Study*

5. Circle the letter of each sentence that supports Wegener's hypothesis.

   a. Some continents match up like jigsaw puzzle pieces.

   b. Different rock structures are found on different continents.

   c. Fossils of tropical plants are found near the equator.

   d. Continental glaciers once covered South Africa.

6. Give an example of evidence from land features that supported Wegener's idea of continental drift. _____

   _____

   _____

7. Any trace of an ancient organism preserved in rock is called a(n)

   _____.

8. How did Wegener explain similar fossils on different continents?

   _____

   _____

9. Is the following sentence true or false? Wegener believed that continental drift explained fossils of tropical plants found in places that today have a polar climate. _____

Wegener's Hypothesis Rejected (p. 22)

10. How did Wegener think that mountains formed? _____

    _____

    _____

11. How do the locations of mountains support Wegener's idea about how mountains form? _____

    _____

    _____

Plate Tectonics • *Review and Reinforce*

Drifting Continents

Understanding Main Ideas

Fill in the blanks in the table below.

Types of Evidence	Example of Evidence
Evidence from 1. _____	a. Mountain ranges in South America and 2. _____ line up b. European coal fields match with similar coal fields in North America
Evidence from Fossils	a. Fossils of the plant 3. _____ found in rocks on widely separated landmasses
Evidence from 4. _____	a. Fossils of tropical plants found near Arctic Ocean b. Scratches in rocks made by 5. _____ found in South Africa

Answer the following questions on a separate sheet of paper.

6. State the hypothesis of continental drift.

7. Why did most scientists reject Wegener's theory for nearly a half century?

Building Vocabulary

Fill in the blank to complete each statement.

8. All the continents were once joined together in a supercontinent called _____, meaning "all lands."

9. A(n) _____ is any trace of an ancient organism preserved in rock.

10. Wegener's theory that the continents slowly moved over Earth's surface became known as _____.

Plate Tectonics • *Enrich*

The Curious Case of *Mesosaurus*

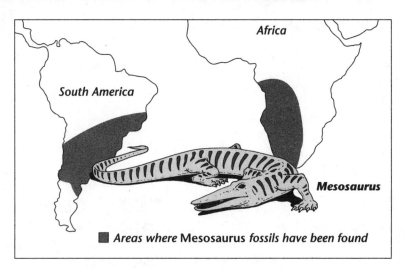

Africa

South America

Mesosaurus

■ Areas where Mesosaurus *fossils have been found*

About 265 million years ago, a reptile called *Mesosaurus* lived in just a few places on Earth. This fairly small, lizard-like reptile measured 71 centimeters from its nose to the tip of its tail—or about two thirds of a meter. Its body was long and flexible, perfect for swimming swiftly through the water. *Mesosaurus* was a hunter of small fish and other aquatic animals. Its webbed feet and long tail worked like powerful paddles as it chased and captured its food. Like all other reptiles, *Mesosaurus* breathed air, so it had to return to the surface after hunting underwater. Freshwater ponds and lakes were its habitat.

   In the 1800s, scientists began finding fossils of these ancient reptiles, which had long since become extinct. These fossils were found in only two regions, southern Africa and the southern part of South America. The shaded areas on the map show where fossils of *Mesosaurus* have been discovered. This distribution is a curious one—only two regions far from each other and separated by the Atlantic Ocean. What could explain this distribution?

Answer the following questions on a separate sheet of paper.

1. Describe the kind of environment in which *Mesosaurus* lived.

2. Is it likely that *Mesosaurus* swam back and forth across the Atlantic Ocean? Explain.

3. What could explain this distribution of *Mesosaurus* fossils?

4. Does the case of *Mesosaurus* support Wegener's theory of continental drift? Explain why or why not.

5. Does the case by itself prove the theory? Explain why or why not.

Sea-Floor Spreading

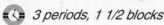 *3 periods, 1 1/2 blocks*

Ability Levels Key
L1 Basic to Average
L2 For All Students
L3 Average to Advanced

Objectives
F.1.4.1 List the evidence for sea-floor spreading.
F.1.4.2 Explain the process of sea-floor spreading.
F.1.4.3 Describe the process of subduction.

Key Terms
• mid-ocean ridge • sonar • sea-floor spreading
• deep-ocean trench • subduction

Local Standards

PRETEACH

Build Background Knowledge
Students recall prior knowledge about lava. They speculate about constructive and destructive processes affecting the sea floor.

 **Discover Activity** *What Is the Effect of a Change in Density?* **L1**

Targeted Resources

❑ **All in One** **Teaching Resources**
   L2 Reading Strategy Transparency F7: Sequencing

❑ **PresentationExpress™ CD-ROM**

INSTRUCT

Mid-Ocean Ridges
Use visuals and maps to show that mountains exist on the sea floor and explain how sonar is used to map underwater features.

What Is Sea-Floor Spreading?
Work together with the class to summarize the processes of sea-floor spreading. Develop understanding that these processes occur slowly over long periods of time.

Evidence for Sea-Floor Spreading
Use leading questions to review the evidence that led to the theory of sea-floor spreading.

Subduction at Trenches

Compare the sea floor to a giant conveyor belt in order to show how it forms at mid-ocean ridges and returns to the mantle at deep ocean trenches.

 Skills Lab *Modeling Sea-Floor Spreading* **L2**

Targeted Resources

❑ **All in One** **Teaching Resources**
   L2 Guided Reading, pp. 68–70
   L2 Transparencies F8, F9
   L2 Lab: *Modeling Sea-Floor Spreading*, pp. 73–76

❑ **PHSchool.com** Web Code: cfd-1014

❑ **Discovery SCHOOL** **Video Field Trip**

❑ **Lab Activity Video/DVD**
   Skills Lab: *Modeling Sea-Floor Spreading*

❑ **Student Edition on Audio CD**

ASSESS

Section Assessment Questions
Have students use their completed graphic organizers with their sequence of events to answer the questions.

Reteach

The class creates a concept map about sea-floor spreading.

Targeted Resources

❑ **All in One** **Teaching Resources**
Section Summary, p. 67
   L1 Review and Reinforce, p. 71
   L3 Enrich, p. 72

Plate Tectonics • *Section Summary*

Sea-Floor Spreading

Key Concepts

- What is the process of sea-floor spreading?

- What is the evidence for sea-floor spreading?

- What happens at deep-ocean trenches?

The longest chain of mountains in the world is the system of **mid-ocean ridges.** In the mid-1900s, scientists mapped the mid-ocean ridges using sonar. **Sonar** is a device that bounces sound waves off underwater objects and then records the echoes of these sound waves. The mid-ocean ridges curve along the sea floor, extending into all of Earth's oceans. Most of the mountains in the mid-ocean ridges lie hidden under hundreds of meters of water. A steep-sided valley splits the top of some mid-ocean ridges.

Earth's ocean floors move like conveyor belts, carrying the continents along with them. This movement begins at a mid-ocean ridge. A ridge forms along a crack in the oceanic crust. **At a mid-ocean ridge, molten material rises from the mantle and erupts. The molten material then spreads out, pushing older rock to both sides of the ridge.** As the molten material cools, it forms a strip of solid rock in the center of the ridge. Then more molten material splits apart the strip of solid rock that formed before, pushing it aside. This process, called **sea-floor spreading,** continually adds new material to the ocean floor.

Scientists have found strange rocks shaped like pillows in the central valley of mid-ocean ridges. Such rocks can form only if molten material hardens quickly after erupting under water. The presence of these rocks supports the theory of sea-floor spreading. More support came when scientists discovered that the rock that makes up the ocean floor lies in a pattern of magnetized "stripes." The pattern is the same on both sides of the ridge. These stripes hold a record of reversals in Earth's magnetic field. The final proof of sea-floor spreading came from rock samples obtained by drilling into the ocean floor. Scientists found that the farther from a ridge the rocks were taken, the older they were.

The ocean floor does not just keep spreading. Instead, it sinks beneath deep underwater canyons called **deep-ocean trenches.** Where there are trenches, subduction takes place. **Subduction** is the process by which the ocean floor sinks beneath a deep-ocean trench and back into the mantle. **At deep-ocean trenches, subduction allows part of the ocean floor to sink back into the mantle, over tens of millions of years.**

The processes of subduction and sea-floor spreading can change the size and shape of the oceans. Because of these processes, the ocean floor is renewed about every 200 million years. The Pacific Ocean is shrinking. Its many trenches are swallowing more ocean crust than the mid-ocean ridge is producing. The Atlantic Ocean is expanding. In most places, the oceanic crust of the Atlantic Ocean is attached to continental crust. As the Atlantic's floor spreads, the continents along its edges also move.

Plate Tectonics • *Guided Reading and Study*

Sea-Floor Spreading (pp. 23–29)

This section explains sea-floor spreading and describes evidence that it happens. The section also explains subduction and describes how subduction affects Earth's oceans.

Use Target Reading Skills

As you read about sea-floor spreading, fill in the flowchart to show the sequence of events.

Magma erupts along mid-ocean ridge

↓

Magma a._____ to form new b._____

↓

c._____ spreads away from d._____

Mid-Ocean Ridges (p. 24)

1. Circle the letter of each sentence that is true about mid-ocean ridges.

   a. The mid-ocean ridges were mapped using sonar.

   b. The mid-ocean ridges are found only below the Pacific Ocean.

   c. The mid-ocean ridges are completely under water.

   d. The tops of some mid-ocean ridges are split by a steep-sided valley.

2. A device that bounces sound waves off underwater objects is called

   _____.

3. What is sonar used for? _____

   _____

What Is Sea-Floor Spreading? (p. 25)

4. The process that continually adds new material to the ocean floor is

   called _____.

5. In sea-floor spreading, where does new crust come from? _____

   _____

Plate Tectonics • *Guided Reading and Study*

Evidence for Sea-Floor Spreading (pp. 26–27)

6. List three types of evidence for sea-floor spreading.

    a. _____

    b. _____

    c. _____

7. Circle the letter of each sentence that is true about Earth's magnetism.

    a. At times in the past, a compass needle on Earth would have pointed south.

    b. Rock that makes up the ocean floor lies in a pattern of magnetized stripes.

    c. The pattern of stripes is different on both sides of mid-ocean ridges.

    d. The magnetic memory of rock on the ocean floor changes over time.

8. How did drilling samples show that sea-floor spreading really has taken place?

_____

_____

Subduction at Trenches (pp. 28–29)

9. A long, narrow and very deep canyon where the ocean floor bends down toward the mantle is called a _____.

10. What is subduction? _____

_____

Plate Tectonics ▪ *Guided Reading and Study*

Sea-Floor Spreading *(continued)*

11. Complete the cause, events, and effect graphic organizer to show the relationships among the processes of convection currents, subduction, and sea-floor spreading.

a. _____ in Earth's mantle

↓ cause

Subduction

b. _____

↓ results in

The ocean is changed in **c.** _____

d. What process in Earth's interior causes subduction and sea-floor spreading? _____

_____

e. What effect do those two events have on Earth's surface? _____

_____

12. Is the following sentence true or false? At deep-ocean trenches, conduction allows oceanic crust to sink back into the mantle.

_____

13. Is the following statement true or false? The Pacific Ocean is shrinking.

_____

14. Why is the Atlantic Ocean expanding? _____

_____

_____

Plate Tectonics ▪ *Review and Reinforce*

Sea-Floor Spreading

Understanding Main Ideas

Use the figure below to answer the questions that follow. Answer the questions on a separate sheet of paper.

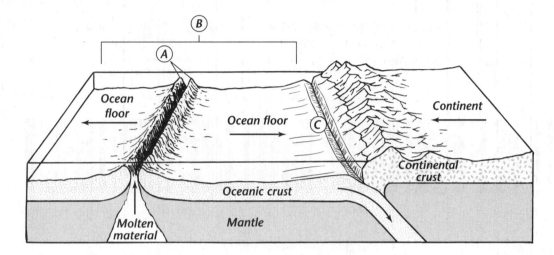

1. Name and describe the feature of the ocean floor shown at A.

2. Describe the process shown occurring at B, and explain what results from this.

3. What happens to old oceanic crust as new molten material rises from the mantle?

4. The arrows on the figure show the ocean floor spreading from the ridge. What are three kinds of evidence scientists have found to support this idea?

5. What process is shown occurring at C, and why does it occur?

Building Vocabulary

Fill in the blank to complete each statement.

6. A device that scientists use to map the ocean floor is _____.

7. The feature on the ocean floor at C is called a(n) _____.

8. The process that continually adds new material to the ocean floor is called _____.

9. The process by which the ocean floor sinks into the mantle is called _____.

10. A chain of underwater mountains along which sea-floor spreading occurs is a _____.

Plate Tectonics • *Enrich*

Magnetic Reversals Through the Ages

How often does Earth's magnetic field reverse itself? The graph below shows the record geologists have put together for the last 65 million years. As you might know, the last of the dinosaurs died about 65 million years ago. So you can think of this graph as the record of Earth's reversals since the dinosaurs became extinct.

In this graph, each dark band represents a "normal" magnetic field, as it is today. Each light band represents a reversed magnetic field. Use the graph to answer the questions that follow.

Reversals in Earth's Magnetic Field

65   40   20   (Present
                                                                    day)

Time (millions of years)

Answer the following questions on a separate sheet of paper.

1. Was Earth's magnetic field "normal" or reversed 65 million years ago?

2. About how long ago was the last time Earth's magnetic field reversed?

3. Can you see any pattern in how often Earth's magnetic field reverses? Give reasons for your answer.

4. How would this history of reversals show itself on the ocean floor?

5. From this graph, when would you predict the next reversal would occur? Give reasons for your answer.

Name _____ Date _____ Class_____

Plate Tectonics • *Skills Lab*

Modeling Sea-Floor Spreading

Problem

How does sea-floor spreading add material to the ocean floor?

Materials

scissors
metric ruler
2 sheets of unlined paper
colored marker

Procedure   *Review the safety guidelines in Appendix A.*

1. Draw stripes across one sheet of paper, parallel to the short sides of the paper. The stripes should vary in spacing and thickness.

2. Fold the paper in half lengthwise and write the word "Start" at the top of both halves of the paper. Using the scissors, carefully cut the paper in half along the fold line to form two strips.

3. Lightly fold the second sheet of paper into eighths. Then unfold it, leaving creases in the paper. Fold this sheet in half lengthwise.

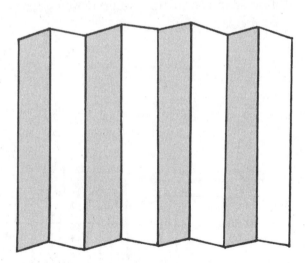

Plate Tectonics • *Skills Lab*

Modeling Sea-Floor Spreading *(continued)*

4. Starting at the fold, draw lines 5.5 cm long on the middle crease and the two creases closest to the ends of the paper.

5. Now carefully cut along the lines you drew. Unfold the paper. There should be three slits in the center of the paper.

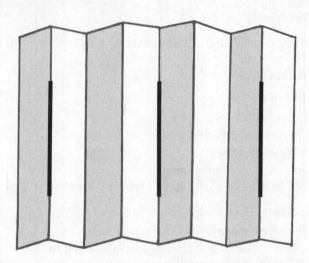

6. Put the two striped strips of paper together so their Start labels touch one another. Insert the Start ends of the strips up through the center slit, and then pull them toward the side slits.

7. Insert the ends of the strips into the side slits. Pull the ends of the strips, and watch what happens at the center slit.

8. Practice pulling the strips through the slits until you can make the two strips come up and go down at the same time.

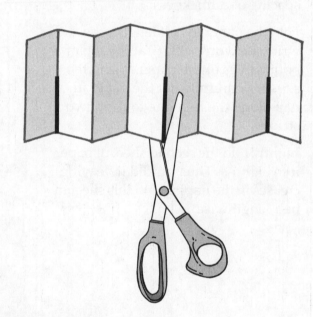

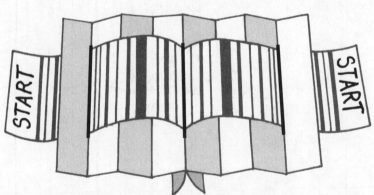

Plate Tectonics • *Skills Lab*

Analyze and Conclude

Write your answers in the spaces provided.

1. **Observing** What feature of the ocean floor does the center slit stand for? What prominent feature of the ocean floor is missing from the model at this point?

   _____

   _____

2. **Making Models** What do the side slits stand for? What does the space under the paper stand for?

   _____

   _____

3. **Comparing and Contrasting** As shown by your model, how does the ocean floor close to the center slit differ from the ocean floor as shown by the part near a side slit? How does this difference affect the depth of the ocean?

   _____

   _____

   _____

4. **Making Models** What do the stripes on the strips stand for? Why is it important that your model have an identical pattern of stripes on both sides of the center slit?

   _____

   _____

Plate Tectonics · *Skills Lab*

Modeling Sea-Floor Spreading *(continued)*

5. **Applying Concepts** Explain how differences in density and temperature provide some of the force needed to cause sea-floor spreading and subduction.

_____

_____

_____

6. **Communicating** Use your own words to describe the process of sea-floor spreading. What parts of the process were not shown by your model?

_____

_____

_____

_____

More to Explore

How could you modify your model to show an island that formed where a large amount of molten rock erupted from the mid-ocean ridge? How could you show what would happen to the island over a long period of time?

The Theory of Plate Tectonics

 2 periods, 1 block

Objectives
F.1.5.1 Explain the theory of plate tectonics.
F.1.5.2 Describe the three types of plate boundaries.

Key Terms
• plate • scientific theory • plate tectonics • fault
• divergent boundary • rift valley • convergent
boundary • transform boundary

Local Standards

Ability Levels Key
L1 Basic to Average
L2 For All Students
L3 Average to Advanced

 **PRETEACH**

Build Background Knowledge
Students create a general definition of the word *plate*.

Discover Activity *How Well Do the Continents Fit Together?* **L1**

Targeted Resources
❑ **All in One Teaching Resources**
  L2 Reading Strategy: Building Vocabulary, p. 79
❑ **PresentationExpress™ CD-ROM**

 INSTRUCT

How Plates Move
Demonstrate how tectonic plates move over the asthenosphere below.

Plate Boundaries
Show students how to use their hands to model motion along the three types of plate boundaries. Then connect these motions to different types of real-world boundaries.

Skills Lab *Modeling Mantle Convection Currents* **L2**

Targeted Resources
❑ **All in One Teaching Resources**
  L2 Guided Reading, pp. 79–81
  L2 Transparencies F10, F11, F12
  L2 Lab: *Modeling Mantle Convection Currents*, pp. 84–85
❑ **PHSchool.com** Web Code: cfp-1015
❑ **Lab Activity Video/DVD**
  Skills Lab: *Modeling Mantle Convection Currents*
❑ **Student Edition on Audio CD**

ASSESS

Section Assessment Questions
Have students use their definitions of key terms to answer the questions.

Reteach
Students make a compare and contrast table about plate boundaries.

Targeted Resources
❑ **All in One Teaching Resources**
  Section Summary, p. 78
  L1 Review and Reinforce, p. 82
  L3 Enrich, p. 83

The Theory of Plate Tectonics

Key Concepts

■ What is the theory of plate tectonics?

■ What are the three types of plate boundaries?

Earth's lithosphere is broken into separate sections called **plates.** The plates fit closely together along cracks in the crust. They carry the continents, or parts of the ocean floor, or both. **Plate tectonics** is the geological theory that states that pieces of Earth's lithosphere are in constant, slow motion, driven by convection currents in the mantle. A **scientific theory** is a well-tested concept that explains a wide range of observations. **The theory of plate tectonics explains the formation, movement, and subduction of Earth's plates.**

The plates float on top of the asthenosphere. Convection currents rise in the asthenosphere and spread out beneath the lithosphere, causing the movement of Earth's plates. As the plates move, they produce changes in Earth's surface, including volcanoes, mountain ranges, and deep-ocean trenches. The edges of different pieces of the lithosphere meet at lines called plate boundaries. **Faults**—breaks in Earth's crust where rocks have slipped past each other—form along these boundaries.

There are three types of plate boundaries: transform boundaries, divergent boundaries, and convergent boundaries. The plates move at amazingly slow rates, from about 1 to 24 centimeters per year. They have been moving for tens of millions of years. A **transform boundary** is a place where two plates slip past each other, moving in opposite directions. Earthquakes occur frequently along these boundaries. The place where two plates move apart, or diverge, is called a **divergent boundary.** Most divergent boundaries occur at the mid-ocean ridge. When a divergent boundary develops on land, two slabs of Earth's crust slide apart. A deep valley called a **rift valley** forms along the divergent boundary. The place where two plates come together, or converge, is a **convergent boundary.** When two plates converge, the result is called a collision. When two plates collide, the density of the plates determines which one comes out on top. Oceanic crust is more dense than continental crust.

When two plates carrying oceanic crust meet at a trench, the plate that is less dense dives under the other plate and returns to the mantle. This is the process of subduction. When a plate carrying oceanic crust collides with a plate carrying continental crust, the more dense oceanic plate plunges beneath the continental plate through the process of subduction. When two plates carrying continental crust collide, subduction does not take place because both plates are mostly low-density granite rock. Instead, the plates crash head-on. The collision squeezes the crust into mighty mountain ranges.

About 260 million years ago, the continents were joined together in the supercontinent Pangaea. About 225 million years ago, Pangaea began to break apart. Since then, the continents have moved to their present locations.

Plate Tectonics • *Guided Reading and Study*

The Theory of Plate Tectonics (pp. 32–36)

This section explains how the lithosphere is broken into separate sections that move.

Use Target Reading Skills

Before reading the section, write simple definitions for the words *diverge, converge,* and *transform.* You may use a dictionary. After reading the passages that contain the key terms *divergent boundary, convergent boundary,* and *transform boundary,* explain how your definitions relate to these terms.

_____

_____

_____

_____

_____

Write a definition of each Key Term in your own words below:

plate: _____

_____

scientific theory: _____

_____

plate tectonics: _____

_____

fault: _____

_____

divergent boundary: _____

_____

rift valley: _____

_____

convergent boundary: _____

_____

transform boundary: _____

_____

Plate Tectonics • *Guided Reading and Study*

The Theory of Plate Tectonics *(continued)*

Introduction (p. 32)

1. The lithosphere is broken into separate sections called

    _____.

2. Is the following sentence true or false? Plates can carry continents or parts
   of the ocean floor but not both. _____

How Plates Move (p. 33)

3. What is a scientific theory? _____

   _____

4. State the theory of plate tectonics. _____

   _____

   _____

5. Is the following sentence true or false? The theory of plate tectonics
   explains the formation, movement, and subduction of Earth's plates.

   _____

Plate Boundaries (pp. 34–36)

Match the term with its definition.

Layer	Description
____ 6. plate boundary	a. Deep valley that forms where two plates pull apart
____ 7. fault	b. Line where the edges of Earth's plates meet
____ 8. rift valley	c. Break in Earth's crust where rocks have slipped past each other

Plate Tectonics • *Guided Reading and Study*

9. Complete the compare/contrast table to show how plates move at the different types of plate boundaries.

Plate Movement	
Type of Plate Boundary	**How Plates Move**
Divergent boundary	a.
Convergent boundary	b.
Transform boundary	c.

d. How are the movement of plates at divergent boundaries and at transform boundaries similar?

_____

10. Is the following sentence true or false? Crust is neither created nor destroyed along a transform boundary. _____

11. Most divergent boundaries occur along _____.

12. When two plates converge, the result is called a(n) _____.

13. When two plates collide, what determines which plate comes out on top? _____

_____

14. Circle the letter of each sentence that is true about convergent boundaries.

   a. Where two plates carrying oceanic crust meet, subduction does not take place.

   b. An oceanic plate sinks beneath a continental plate when the two plates collide.

   c. Where two plates meet, the one that is more dense sinks under the other.

   d. Mountain ranges form where two plates carrying continental crust collide.

15. Was Pangaea the only supercontinent to have existed? Explain your answer.

_____

_____

16. Is the following sentence true or false? The pieces of the supercontinent Pangaea began to drift apart about 225 million years ago.

_____

Plate Tectonics ▪ *Review and Reinforce*

The Theory of Plate Tectonics

Understanding Main Ideas

Label each figure by writing the type of plate boundary it shows.

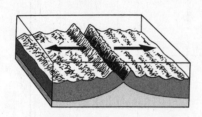 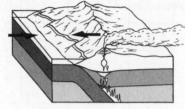 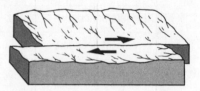

1. _____   2. _____   3. _____

Answer the following questions on a separate sheet of paper.

4. Describe what happens when (a) two plates carrying oceanic crust collide, (b) two plates carrying continental crust collide, and (c) a plate carrying oceanic crust collides with a plate carrying continental crust.

5. Explain what force caused the movement of the continents from one supercontinent to their present positions.

Building Vocabulary

Fill in the blank to complete each statement.

6. A scientific _____ is a well-tested concept that explains a wide range of observations.

7. Breaks in Earth's crust where rocks have slipped past each other are called _____.

8. The lithosphere is broken into separate sections called

   _____.

9. A(n) _____ is a deep valley on land that forms along a divergent boundary.

10. The geological theory that states that pieces of Earth's crust are in

    constant, slow motion is called _____.

Plate Tectonics · *Enrich*

The Birth of the Himalayas

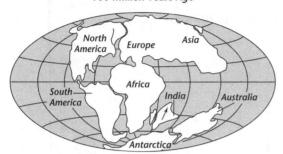
100 Million Years Ago

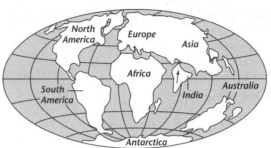
50 Million Years Ago

The greatest challenge for mountain climbers is Mt. Everest, whose peak rises 8,872 meters above sea level. This is the highest mountain in the world, though many mountains around it are almost as high. Mt. Everest is in the Himalayas, a series of massive ranges that extends 2,500 kilometers across South Asia north of India. The Himalayas cover all or part of the countries of Tibet, Nepal, and Bhutan.

A climber on the high slopes of Mt. Everest would probably be surprised to learn that the region was relatively flat about 40 million years ago. It was then that two continental plates collided. The plate carrying India had been moving northward for millions of years. The oceanic crust in front of it was slowly subducted under the Eurasian plate. But when the two continents collided, subduction stopped because India could not sink into the mantle. Instead, it pushed crust upward and downward. The Himalayas were one result. Thus, the Himalayas are actually pieces of plates broken and lifted up because of the collision. Another result of this collision was the movement of China eastward, as the movement of India northward pushed the Eurasian plate in front of it. The collision is still occurring today. In fact, the Himalayas are growing in elevation at a rate of about 1 centimeter per year.

Answer the following questions on a separate sheet of paper.

1. Where are the Himalayas?

2. What was the area of the Himalayas like 40 million years ago?

3. How did the movement of plates create the Himalayas?

4. What else resulted from the collision of those plates?

5. What type of plate boundary exists today along the Himalayas?

6. If the Himalayas continue to grow in elevation at their present rate, how tall will Mt. Everest be in one million years?

Plate Tectonics · *Skills Lab*

Modeling Mantle Convection Currents

Problem

How might convection in Earth's mantle affect tectonic plates?

Materials

- large plastic bottle
- food coloring
- small glass jar
- aluminum foil
- rubber band
- several pieces of paper about 0.5 cm square
- tap water

Procedure

1. Fill the large bottle about half full with cold tap water.

2. Partly fill the small jar with hot tap water and stir in 6 drops of food coloring. Carefully add enough hot water to fill the jar to the brim.

3. Cover the top of the jar with aluminum foil and secure with a rubber band.

4. Carefully lower the jar into the bottle of ice water.

5. Place the pieces of paper on the surface of the water.

6. Without disturbing the water, use the tip of the pencil to make two small holes about 2 mm in diameter in the aluminum foil covering the jar.

7. Predict what will happen to the colored water and to the pieces of paper floating on the surface.

8. Observe the contents of the jar as well as the paper pieces on the surface of the water.

Plate Tectonics · *Skills Lab*

Analyze and Conclude

Write your answers in the spaces provided.

1. **Observing** Describe what happened to the colored water and to the pieces of paper after the holes were punched in the material covering the jar.

   _____

   _____

2. **Drawing Conclusions** How did your prediction compare with what actually happened to the colored water and pieces of paper?

   _____

   _____

3. **Inferring** What type of heat transfer took place in the bottle? Describe how the transfer occurred.

   _____

   _____

4. **Making Models** Which part of your model represents a tectonic plate? Which part represents Earth's mantle?

   _____

   _____

5. **Communicating** How well do you think this lab modeled the movement of Earth's plates? What similarities exist between this model and actual plate movement? What factors weren't you able to model in this lab?

   _____

   _____

Designing Experiments

Repeat this activity, but develop a plan to measure the temperature of the water inside the large bottle. Is there a difference in temperature between the water's surface and the water near the top of the small jar? Do you observe any change in the convection currents as the water temperature changes? With your teacher's approval, carry out your plan.

Key Terms

Use key terms from the chapter to complete the crossword puzzle.

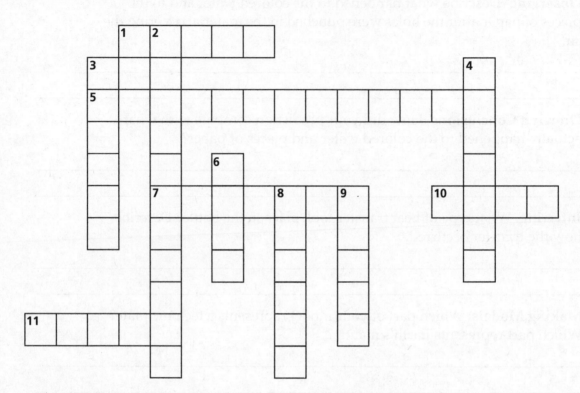

Clues across

1. Section of lithosphere that carries crust
5. Part of mantle below lithosphere
7. Kind of wave released during an earthquake
10. The innermost layer of Earth
11. Used to map mid-ocean ridge

Clues down

2. Layer that is part crust and part mantle
3. Rock that makes up oceanic crust
4. Study of planet Earth
6. Kind of valley where plates move apart
8. Earth's middle layer
9. Earth's outer layer

Plate Tectonics • *Connecting Concepts*

Connecting Concepts

Develop a concept map that uses the key concepts and key terms from this chapter. Keep in mind the big idea of this chapter: Convection currents in Earth's mantle are the driving force that causes the movement of Earth's plates. The concept map shown is one way to organize how the information in this chapter is related. You may use an extra sheet of paper.

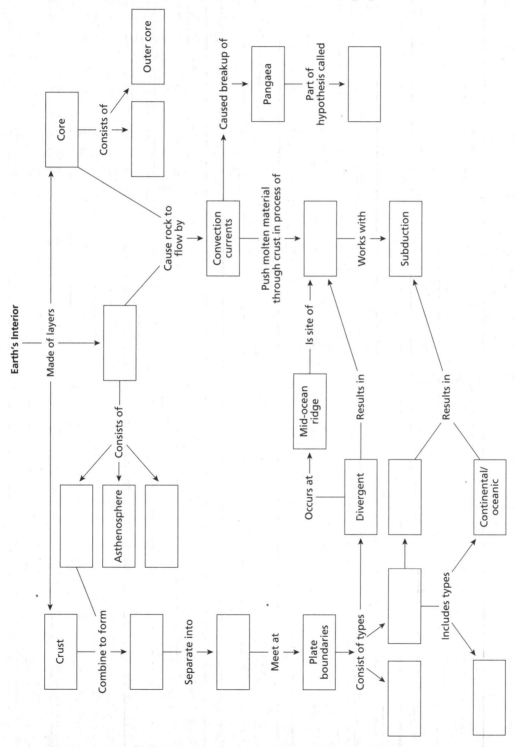

Mapping a Future World

Key Concept

Earth's continents and oceans ride on plates that are moving at a slow rate and affect many of Earth's features, such as mountains and ocean basins.

Skills Focus

making models, predicting

Time

40 minutes

Materials

2 outline maps of the world showing latitude and longitude lines
scissors
colored pencils or markers
envelope
pencil or pen
clear tape
world map or globe

Safety

Use caution in handling sharp scissors.

Advance Preparation

Make a second copy of the map for each student.

Teaching Tips

- Encourage students to choose different cities on each continent so that differences in location can be compared.

- Review proportions for the calculations. Have students set up the scale value on one side of the proportion and use 100 million as the time factor in the other part, e.g.: $x/100,000,000$ yr = 2.6 cm/1 yr. Remind students that 1 km = 100,000 cm.

- Have slabs of modeling clay available to help students visualize what happens when plates move apart or are pushed together.

Plate Tectonics ▪ *Laboratory Investigation*

Mapping a Future World

Pre-Lab Discussion

You can't feel the land underneath you moving every day, but it is! The surface of Earth is divided into continents and oceans. These landmasses and water bodies are slowly but surely changing their postitions and shapes. Scientists have measured these movements of a few centimeters per year.

What will Earth look like in the future? No one can be sure where the continents will end up. In this investigation, you will predict what Earth will look like as you map the movement of the continents.

1. What are plates in the Earth's crust?

_____

_____

2. What does *plate tectonics* mean?

_____

_____

_____

Problem

Where will the continents be in the distant future, and how will their position affect mountains and oceans around the world?

Materials *(per group)*

- 2 outline maps of the world showing latitude and longitude lines
- scissors
- colored pencils or markers
- envelope
- pencil or pen
- clear tape
- world map or globe

Safety ✂ *Review the safety guidelines in Appendix A.*

Use caution in handling sharp scissors.

Plate Tectonics · *Laboratory Investigation*

Mapping a Future World *(continued)*

Procedure

1. You will ignore the movement of Antarctica in this activity. Label the other continents and the oceans on the two outline maps.

2. You will need reference points when you start moving continents. Use a world map or globe to locate and label one city on each continent on both of the maps. In Data Table 2 in Observations, record the current latitude and longitude of each reference-point city.

3. From one map, carefully cut out the continents. Keep these pieces in an envelope when you are not using them.

4. Assemble a complete world map—the base map—by cutting out the map on one page and overlapping it with the map on the other page. The 20°W longitude lines (also called meridians) should overlay each other. Carefully tape the map together along the 20°W longitude line.

5. Lay the cutout continents on the base map in their current positions. You should be able to slide your cutouts easily over your base map.

6. Predict where the continents will be in 100 million years. Slowly move the continents to where you predict they will be. Trace their outlines lightly in pencil. Assume that the Indo-Australian Plate splits in a few million years, and India and Australia continue to move at the same rate.

7. Now, check your predictions. Use the plate speeds in Data Table 1 and the map in your textbook to find the direction and rate of movement for each plate that carries a continent. Calculate how far each continent will drift in 100 million years. Record these figures in Data Table 2 in Observations.

DATA TABLE 1

Plate	Speed (cm/yr)
African	0.66
Eurasian	0.95
Indo-Australian	8.50
North American	2.31
South American	3.55

8. Use the scale on the base map to help you decide where the continents will be in 100 million years. Slowly move the cutout continents to their new locations. Trace their outlines on your base map, using a different color for each continent. Some continents may overlap in their new positions. Trace the outlines overlapping.

9. Mark and record the new location of each reference point.

10. Compare your completed map to your predictions. Then compare it to those of your classmates and discuss any differences.

Plate Tectonics · *Laboratory Investigation*

Observations

DATA TABLE 2

Continent	Reference Point	Location Now (Latitude and Longitude)	Distance Traveled in 100 Million Years	Location in 100 Million Years (Latitude and Longitude)
Africa				
Asia				
Australia				
Europe				
North America				
South America				

Analyze and Conclude

1. How did your predicted locations of continents compare with the locations in Step 8?

   _____

2. What will happen to the location of North and South America as sea-floor spreading widens the Atlantic Ocean?

   _____

3. What will happen to the size of the Pacific Ocean as North America moves west?

   _____

4. How did the latitude and longitude of your reference point in South America change?

   _____

5. What might happen to the Himalayas over the next several million years? Give a reason for your answer.

   _____

Plate Tectonics ▪ *Laboratory Investigation*

Mapping a Future World (continued)

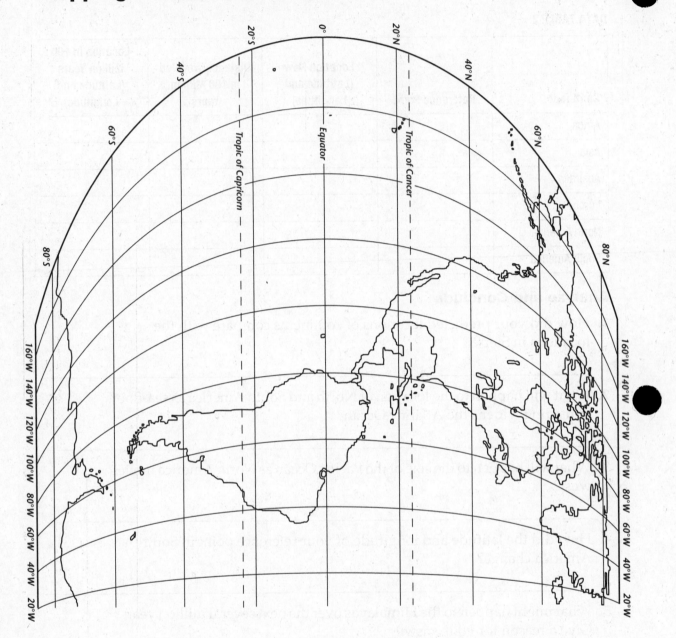

Plate Tectonics • *Laboratory Investigation*

Scale
0 1000 2000 3000 4000 km

Plate Tectonics ▪ *Laboratory Investigation*

Mapping a Future World (continued)

Critical Thinking and Applications

1. Why did many scientists not accept the early theories of continental drift?

   _____

2. Based on your movements of the continents, where do you predict new mountain ranges will be forming in 100 million years? Explain your reasoning.

   _____

3. Why do continents move at different rates?

   _____

4. Which is more important in determining the future location of a city— what continent it is on or what plate it is on? Give a reason for your answer.

   _____

More to Explore

New Problem   Near what city's location will Los Angeles, California, be in about 17 million years? (*Hint:* The rate of plate movement along the San Andreas Fault is about 3.4 cm/yr.)

Possible Materials   Use the same map and continent shapes as before. You may also need scissors again.

Safety   Use caution in handling sharp scissors.

Procedure   Predict where Los Angeles will be. Then develop a procedure to test your prediction. Get the teacher's approval before carrying out your investigation.

Observations   Record your prediction. Also record any appropriate observations on your base map.

Analyze and Conclude   Where do you think Los Angeles will be located in about 17 million years?

Modeling Plate Boundaries

Students are presented with the problem of creating a model for each of the three types of plate boundaries: transform boundary, divergent boundary, and convergent boundary. To solve this problem, students will apply the concepts they have learned about plate tectonics and plate boundaries.

Expected Outcome

Students should use the modeling compound to make three models to represent the three types of plate boundaries. For each model, students should form two flat blocks of clay to represent plates of Earth's lithosphere.

For a transform boundary, the two blocks should be shown sliding past each other, with arrows carved into the plates that show movement in opposite directions.

For a divergent boundary, the two blocks should be shown pulling apart, with a rift valley between. Arrows should indicate that the plates are moving apart.

For a convergent boundary, the two blocks should be shown colliding, with arrows on the blocks that indicate movement toward one another. An excellent model could show either subduction of one plate beneath the other or mountain building on one or both plates.

Content Assessed

This activity assesses students' understanding of plate tectonics and plate boundaries.

Skills Assessed

making models, classifying, applying concepts

Materials

Provide each student with a block of modeling compound large enough to cut into six smaller blocks to represent two plates for each type of boundary.

Advise students to make their models on the sheets of wax paper provided.

Advance Preparation

Cut the modeling compound into the number of blocks needed to give a block to each student.

Tear a sheet of wax paper from a roll for each student in the class.

Time

30 minutes

Monitoring the Task

Demonstrate how to use the knife to cut the modeling compound into plates as well as to carve arrows in the plates to show direction of movement.

Modeling Plate Boundaries

In assessing students' performance, use the following rubric.

	4	3	2	1
Making Models of the Three Types of Plate Boundaries	The student makes models that clearly and accurately show the three types of plate boundaries and what occurs at each.	The student makes models that adequately show the three types of plate boundaries and what occurs at each.	The student makes models that show at least two types of plate boundaries accurately, though does not show clearly what occurs at each.	The student makes a model that shows at least one type of plate boundary, though does not show what occurs there.
Concept Understanding	The student demonstrates a mastery of the concepts related to plate tectonics and the three types of plate boundaries.	The student demonstrates an adequate understanding of the concepts related to plate tectonics and the three types of plate boundaries.	The student demonstrates some understanding of the concepts related to plate tectonics and the three types of plate boundaries, but is confused on some points.	The student demonstrates a weak understanding of the concepts related to plate tectonics and the three types of plate boundaries.

Modeling Plate Boundaries

Problem

How can you make models of the three types of plate boundaries?

Suggested Materials

modeling compound
plastic knife
wax paper

Devise a Plan

1. Study the materials and think of a way that you could use them to make models of all three types of plate boundaries.

2. Make drawings on a separate sheet of paper of the models you could make.

3. Make the models by referring to your drawings. As you work, make adjustments in your plans so that the models clearly show how plates meet and what occurs at the three types of plate boundaries. You can use the knife to cut the modeling compound into as many separate plates as you need. You can also use the knife to carve arrows on the plates to show direction of movement.

Analyze and Conclude

On a separate sheet of paper, respond to the items that follow.

1. Make sketches of the models you made. Add as many arrows and labels as necessary to clearly show what happens at each type of plate boundary.

2. Name and describe each of the three types of plate boundaries.

3. Could you have made any of your models in another way and still have shown the same type of plate boundary? Describe any alternative models you could have made.

4. What landforms are associated with each of these boundaries?

5. Describe how these plate boundaries relate to plate tectonics.

Plate Tectonics

Multiple Choice

Write the letter of the correct answer on the line at the left.

_____ 1. A break in Earth's crust where rocks have slipped past each other is called a
   a. plate.
   b. layer.
   c. boundary.
   d. fault.

_____ 2. Continental crust consists mainly of the rock
   a. nickel.
   b. basalt.
   c. mantle.
   d. granite.

_____ 3. Scientists rejected Wegener's theory because he could not
   a. explain why continental crust was denser than oceanic crust.
   b. describe the climate of Pangaea.
   c. explain what force pushes or pulls continents.
   d. describe how seeds moved from Africa to South America.

_____ 4. Subduction is
   a. the process by which oceanic crust sinks beneath trenches.
   b. the direct transfer of heat through solid materials.
   c. the process that continually adds ocean floor.
   d. a device that bounces sound waves off underwater objects.

_____ 5. Earth's lithosphere is broken into separate sections called
   a. plates.
   b. faults.
   c. trenches.
   d. rifts.

_____ 6. Scientists who study the forces that make and shape the planet Earth are called
   a. biologists.
   b. geologists.
   c. chemists.
   d. physicists.

_____ 7. In the convection current of a pan of soup, the cooler, denser fluid
   a. rises to the top.
   b. sinks to the bottom.
   c. stays where it is.
   d. stays on top.

_____ 8. The transfer of energy through space is called
   a. subduction.
   b. convection.
   c. radiation.
   d. conduction.

_____ 9. Who first proposed the theory of continental drift?
   a. Harry Hess
   b. Alfred Wegener
   c. Pangaea
   d. J. Tuzo Wilson

____ **10.** What erupts through the valley of the mid-ocean ridge?
   a. molten material   **b.** the lithosphere
   c. deep-ocean trenches   **d.** continental drift

Completion

Fill in the line to complete each statement.

11. Heat transfer by the movement of a heated fluid is called

_____.

12. A _____ boundary is a place where two plates slip past each other.

13. The _____ is the part of the mantle that can bend like plastic.

14. The process that continually adds new material to the ocean floor is

_____.

15. Fossils of tropical plants found on an island in the Arctic Ocean are evidence for Wegener's hypothesis of _____.

True or False

If the statement is true, write true. *If it is false, change the underlined word or words to make the statement true.*

____ **16.** A rift valley forms along a <u>convergent</u> boundary on land.

____ **17.** The supercontinent that began to break apart about 225 million years ago is called <u>Antarctica</u>.

____ **18.** As oceanic crust moves away from the <u>mid-ocean ridge</u>, it cools and becomes more dense.

____ **19.** <u>Density</u> is a measure of how much mass there is in a volume of a substance.

____ **20.** The lithosphere includes all of the <u>core</u> and part of the mantle.

Essay

Answer each of the following on the lines provided.

21. Explain what sets convection currents into motion.

_____

_____

_____

Plate Tectonics *(continued)*

22. Describe the process of sea-floor spreading.

_____

_____

_____

_____

Using Science Skills: Interpreting Diagrams

Use the diagram below to answer the following questions.

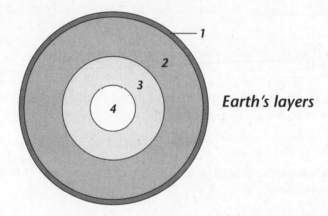

Earth's layers

23. Name each of the layers on the figure in order, from outermost to

innermost. _____

_____

24. Where would you draw a line on the figure to show the bottom of the

lithosphere? Explain. _____

_____

_____

_____

25. What is the major difference between layer 3 and layer 4?

_____

_____

_____

Plate Tectonics • *Chapter Test*

Using Science Skills

Use the figure below to answer the following questions in the spaces provided.

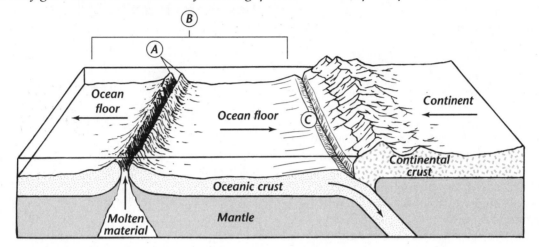

26. Classifying Classify each of the plate boundaries shown on the figure and identify the type of boundary not shown.

_____

_____

_____

27. Predicting If the boundary shown at A occurred on land instead of the ocean floor, what would be the long-term result?

_____

_____

_____

Essay

Answer each of the following on a separate sheet of paper.

28. Compare and contrast three different kinds of convergent boundaries.

29. Describe what scientists now know about Earth that would have answered the scientists who rejected Wegener's theory.

30. What accounts for the difference in density between oceanic and continental crust?

Chapter Project

Worksheet 1

1. 6,371 km
2. Model sizes will vary; a typical diameter may be 50 cm.
3. Answers will vary; a typical scale might be 1 cm = 130 km.
4. Crust, 5–40 km, 1 cm; Mantle, 2,900 km, 22 cm; Outer Core, 5,150 km, 39 cm; Inner Core, 6,371 km, 50 cm
5. Students' designs will vary. A typical design might be a wedge or a sphere with a section cut away.
6. Materials will vary, though most students will probably suggest papier-mâché or modeling compound for at least part of the model.
7. Students' sketches will vary but should include all layers of Earth's interior drawn to scale.

Worksheet 2

1. mid-ocean ridge, ocean floor
2. ocean floor, continent, deep-ocean trench
3. Materials will vary. A typical suggestion might include modeling compound
4. A divergent boundary, in which two plates pull apart from each other; a convergent boundary, in which two plates collide; a transform boundary, in which two plates slide past each other
5. Answers will vary. A typical answer might suggest using paint.
6. Other features include continents and a rift valley.
7. A typical answer will suggest using modeling compound.
8. Students' sketches will vary but should include a mid-ocean ridge, ocean floor, deep-ocean trench, continents, plates and plate boundaries, and a rift valley.

Earth's Interior
Guided Reading and Study

Use Target Reading Skills

This is one possible way to complete the graphic organizer. Accept all logical answers.

What You Know
1. Earth's crust is made of rock.
2. Earth is very hot near the center.
3. Dry land is part of the crust.
4. The mantle is very hot.
5. The core has iron in it.

What You Learned
1. Geologists use seismic waves to study Earth's interior.
2. Radioactive substances heat the interior of Earth.
3. The crust is thickest under high mountains.
4. The mantle is solid.
5. Movements in the outer core create Earth's magnetic field.

1. extreme conditions
2. rock samples
3. seismic waves
4. false
5. speed; the paths they travel
6. b, c, d
7. Seismic
8. The temperature gets cooler from the surface to about 20 meters down. After that, the temperature rises rapidly for several tens of kilometers. Then the temperature increases more slowly, but steadily.
9. The deeper you go, the greater the pressure.
10. crust, mantle, core
11. crust
12. false
13. basalt
14. granite
15. b
16. a
17. c
18. false
19. true

20. c
21. d
22a. crust
b. core
c. mantle
23. It aligns with the lines of force in Earth's magnetic field.
24. movements in the liquid outer core

Earth's Interior
Review and Reinforce

1. Crust
2. Mantle
3. Outer core
4. Inner core
5. To learn about Earth's interior, geologists use direct evidence from rock samples that formed deep inside Earth and indirect evidence from seismic waves.
6. The asthenosphere is a part of the upper mantle, whose material can bend like plastic. The lithosphere is a rigid layer that includes the crust and the top of the mantle.
7. a
8. h
9. f
10. c
11. d
12. e
13. b
14. a
15. g

Earth's Interior
Enrich

1. 360 km
2. Wave A takes the more direct route.
3. 60 seconds
4. The different speeds at which the seismic waves travel through the crust and the upper mantle account for the difference in arrival times.
5. Rock material in the upper mantle is denser than rock material in the crust, so P waves can travel faster in the denser material of the upper mantle.

Convection and the Mantle
Guided Reading and Study

Use Target Reading Skills

Convection and the Mantle
  I. *Types of Heat Transfer*
    A. *Radiation*
    B. Conduction
    C. *Convection*
  II. Convection Currents
  III. *Convection in Earth's Mantle*
1. heat transfer
2a. radiation **b.** conduction **c.** convection
3. the transfer of energy through space
4. sunlight and the heat you feel around a flame or open fire
5. heat transfer within a material or between materials that are touching
6. A spoon sitting in a pot of hot soup will heat up.
7. heat transfer by the movement of currents within a fluid
8. temperature
9. density
10. b
11. the heating and cooling of the fluid, changes in the fluids, density, and the force of gravity
12. They eventually stop.
13a. cools
  b. slower
  c. less
  d. sinks
  e. decreases
  f. A cycle means that an event occurs over and over. In this cycle, each event in the cycle causes the next event to occur.
  g. where it sinks and starts to be heated again
14. false

Convection and the Mantle
Review and Reinforce

1. convection
2. radiation
3. conduction
4. The flow that transfers heat within a fluid is called a convection current. The heating and cooling of the fluid, changes in the fluid's density, and the force of gravity combine to cause convection currents.
5. Heat from Earth's core and mantle causes convection currents in Earth's mantle.
6. radiation
7. true
8. true
9. convection
10. mass

Convection and the Mantle
Enrich

1. Earth's core and mantle
2. Point A, because it's closer to the heat source and beginning to rise
3. The density is greater at point C, because the convection current slowly cools off, and cooler material is denser than hot material.
4. The rising material hits the rigid lithosphere and cannot go up any farther.
5. The material continues to cool, and thus its temperature drops between points B and C. As the temperature drops, its density increases.
6. The force of gravity
7. The heat from the core causes the temperature of the material to rise between points D and A. As the temperature rises, the density decreases.
8. The density of the material is less than the material above it, so the material begins to rise.
9. Answers will vary. Some students might suggest that the movement of the mantle material will cause some movement in the crustal material.

Drifting Continents
Guided Reading and Study

Use Target Reading Skills

1. All the continents were once joined together in a single landmass and have since drifted apart.
2. Pangaea
3. Over tens of millions of years, Pangaea began to break apart. The pieces of Pangaea slowly moved toward their present-day locations, becoming the continents as they are today.
4. continental drift
5. a, d
6. Any one: If maps of Africa and South America are pieced together, mountain ranges on both continents line up. European coal fields match up with similar coal fields in North America.
7. fossil
8. The organisms lived on a single landmass that has since split apart.
9. true
10. He proposed that when continents collide, their edges crumple and fold. The folding continents push up huge mountains.
11. Mountains sometimes occur in narrow bands along the edges of continents where continents could collide.

Drifting Continents
Review and Reinforce

1. Landforms
2. Africa
3. *Glossopteris*
4. Climate
5. glaciers
6. Continental drift is the hypothesis that all the continents had once been joined together in a single landmass and have since drifted apart.
7. Wegener could not provide a satisfactory explanation for the force that pushes or pulls the continents.
8. Pangaea
9. fossil
10. continental drift

Drifting Continents
Enrich

1. *Mesosaurus* lived in freshwater ponds and lakes.
2. It is unlikely because this reptile lived in fresh water, not salt water, and probably could not have survived a long journey.
3. The continents of Africa and South America were once joined together.
4. It does support the theory, because it is further evidence from fossils that the continents were once joined together.
5. It does not prove the theory, since it alone does not provide enough evidence to prove the continents were joined together.

Sea-Floor Spreading
Guided Reading and Study

Use Target Reading Skills

a. cools
b. sea floor
c. sea floor
d. ridge
1. a, d
2. sonar
3. to determine distance to an object
4. sea-floor spreading
5. molten material that erupts and cools
6 a. molten material b. magnetic strips c. drilling samples.
7. a, b
8. The farther away from the ridge the samples were taken, the older the rocks were. The youngest rocks were always in the center of the ridges.

9. deep-ocean trench
10. the process by which ocean floor sinks beneath a deep-ocean trench and back into the mantle
11a. convection currents
b. sea-floor spreading
c. size and shape
d. convection currents
e. The ocean is changed in size and shape.
12. true
13. true
14. The Atlantic Ocean has only a few short trenches. The spreading ocean floor has nowhere to go.

Sea-Floor Spreading
Review and Reinforce

1. That is a mid-ocean ridge, a mountain range which extends along the sea floor.
2. The process is sea-floor spreading. It continually adds new material to the ocean floor.
3. The new material splits apart the old material and pushes it aside.
4. evidence from molten material, evidence from magnetic stripes, and evidence from drilling samples
5. Subduction at a deep-ocean trench is occurring at C. It occurs because oceanic crust becomes denser the farther it moves away from the mid-ocean ridge. Gravity eventually pulls this dense oceanic crust down beneath the trench.
6. sonar
7. deep-ocean trench
8. sea-floor spreading
9. subduction
10. mid-ocean ridge

Sea-Floor Spreading
Enrich

1. reversed
2. slightly less than one million years ago
3. Answers may vary. Some students may correctly say that there is no discernible pattern.
4. The history of reversals would show itself in the form of magnetic stripes on both sides of the mid-ocean ridge.
5. Answers will vary. A typical answer might suggest that the next reversal may be soon, since the magnetic field often reverses in less than a million years.

Skills Lab

Modeling Sea-Floor Spreading

For answers, see the Teacher's Edition.

The Theory of Plate Tectonics
Guided Reading and Study

Use Target Reading Skills

Possible answers: Diverge means to move in different directions from a common point. Converge means to come together toward one point. Transform means to change in form or appearance. Two plates move apart from a common point at a divergent boundary. Two plates come together at a convergent boundary. Two plates slip past each other in a transform boundary. Check student definitions for accuracy.
1. plates
2. false
3. a well-tested concept that explains a wide range of observations
4. Pieces of Earth's lithosphere are in slow, constant motion, driven by convection currents in the mantle
5. true
6. b
7. c
8. a
9. a. Two of Earth's plates slide apart. b. Two plates come together. c. Two plates slip past each other. d. Near the plate boundary, both types of plate move horizontally.
10. true
11. mid-ocean ridges
12. collision
13. the density of the plates

14. b, c, d
15. No; geologists have evidence that before Pangaea existed, other supercontinents formed and split apart over billions of years.
16. true

The Theory of Plate Tectonics
Review and Reinforce

1. divergent boundary
2. convergent boundary
3. transform boundary
4. a. The denser plate subducts below the other at a deep-ocean trench. b. The collision squeezes the crust into mountain ranges. c. The denser oceanic plate subducts below the continental plate.
5. The force of convection currents in the mantle caused the movements of the plates that carry the continents.
6. theory
7. faults
8. plates
9. rift valley
10. plate tectonics

The Theory of Plate Tectonics
Enrich

1. The Himalayas extend across South Asia north of India.
2. The area was relatively flat; the plate carrying India was just beginning to collide with the Eurasian plate.
3. The plate carrying India collided with the Eurasian plate. The result was crust pushed upward to form the Himalayas.
4. The movement of the plate carrying India pushed China eastward.
5. convergent boundary
6. about 8,872 meters

Skills Lab

Modeling Mantle Convection Currents

For answers, see the Teacher's Edition.

Key Terms

Across: 1. plate 5. asthenosphere 7. seismic
10. core 11. sonar
Down: 2. lithosphere 3. basalt 4. geology
6. rift 8. mantle 9. crust

Connecting Concepts

Convection currents in Earth's mantle are the driving force that causes the movement of Earth's plates. This concept map is only one way to represent the main ideas and relationships in this chapter. Accept other logical answers from students.

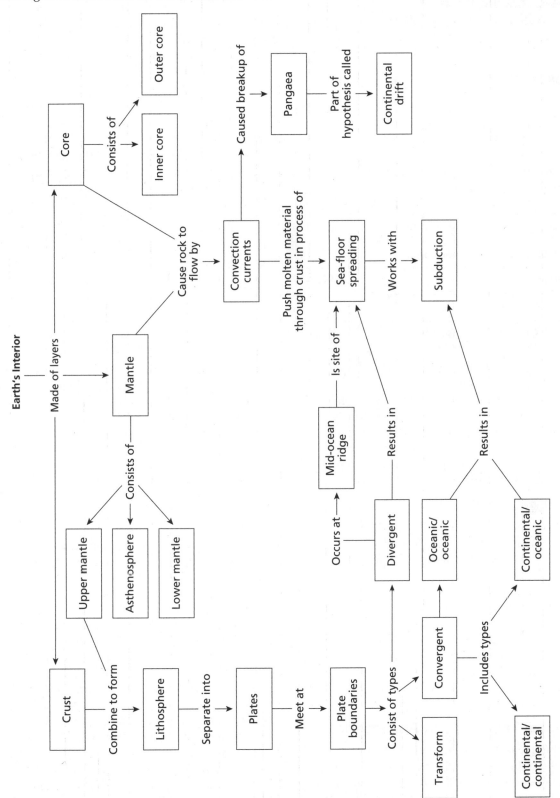

Laboratory Investigation

Mapping a Future World

Pre-Lab Discussion

1. Plates are separate sections of the lithosphere that fit closely together along cracks in the crust.

2. Plate tectonics is the theory that the movement of convection currents in the mantle slowly shifts pieces of Earth's lithosphere.

Observations

Continent	Reference Point	Location Now (Latitude and Longitude)	Distance Traveled in 100 Million Years	Location in 100 Million Years (Latitude and Longitude)
Africa	Tangier, Morocco	36°N, 6°W		40°N, 3°W
Asia	Beijing, China	40°N, 116°E		35°N, 125°E
Australia	Melbourne	39°S, 145°E		25°N, 145°E
Europe	Lisbon, Portugal	39°N, 9°W		35°N, 0°
North America	New York City	41°N, 74°W		50°N, 95°W
South America	Brasilia, Brazil	16°S, 48°W		16°S, 75°W

Assuming constant motion, in 100 million years the African plate will move 660 km, the Eurasian plate will move 950 km, the Indo-Australian plate will move 8,500 km, the North American plate will move 2,310 km, and the South American plate will move 3,550 km. Student maps should show these relative amounts of motion in the directions in the textbook map.

Analyze and Conclude

1. Predicted directions were more likely to be correct than the predicted distances.
2. North and South America will move farther west.
3. The Pacific Ocean will get smaller.
4. The latitude remains the same; the longitude is farther west.
5. Answers will vary: Sample answer: The height of the Himalayas will increase because of the Eurasian and Indo-Australian plates colliding, crumpling the crust and pushing the mountains higher.

Critical Thinking and Applications

1. There was no satisfactory explanation for the force that pushes or pulls the continents, and the movement is so slow that it is not obvious.
2. New mountain ranges probably will form in northern Africa or southern Europe as those two continents collide. Mountains might also form in northern Australia as that continent collides with Asia. Collisions will be evidenced on students' maps by overlapping outlines of the continents.

3. Answers will vary. Sample answer: Speed of movement depends on the fluidity of the underlying matter and whether the plates are colliding or pulling apart from the surrounding plates.
4. Movement of a plate determines movement of any continent on it, so location on the plate is more important. The size and shape of a continent may change over millions of years.

More to Explore

Near San Francisco. Students could best model the movement of Los Angeles by cutting their North American continent shape along the San Andreas Fault and moving the Pacific Plate northwestward. The rate of 3.4 cm/yr equals 578 km in 17 million years, which would put Los Angeles near San Francisco. Students can estimate the distance by comparing 3.4 cm/yr to their calculations for Step 6. This comparison gives a distance of 3,400 km in 100 million years. Since 17 million is about 1/6 × 3,400 = about 566 km, which is still near San Francisco.

Performance Assessment

1. Students' sketches should show a convergent boundary, a divergent boundary, and a transform boundary and describe what happens at each.

2. At a convergent boundary, two plates collide. At a divergent boundary, two plates pull apart. At a transform boundary, two plates slide past each other.

3. A model of a convergent boundary could show either one plate being subducted under the other or neither plate being subducted and mountains forming.

4. Mountains and deep-ocean trenches are associated with convergent boundaries. Rift valleys are associated with divergent boundaries.

5. Plate tectonics is the theory that plates are in constant, slow motion, driven by convection currents in the mantle. What occurs at these plate boundaries is the result of that slow motion of the plates.

Chapter Test

1. d
2. d
3. c
4. a
5. a
6. b
7. b
8. c
9. b
10. a
11. convection
12. transform
13. asthenosphere
14. sea-floor spreading
15. continental drift
16. divergent
17. Pangaea
18. true
19. true
20. crust
21. The heating and cooling of a fluid, changes in a fluid's density, and the force of gravity combine to set convection currents in motion
22. In sea-floor spreading, molten material arises from the mantle and erupts through a mid-ocean ridge. The molten material then spreads out, pushing older rock to both sides of the ridge. This process continually adds new material to the ocean floor.

23. Crust, mantle, outer core, inner core

24. You would draw the line in the mantle just below the crust, since the lithosphere includes the crust and the top part of the mantle.

25. Layer 3, the outer core, is molten, while layer 4, the inner core, is solid.

26. The plate boundary at A is a divergent boundary; the plate boundary at C is a convergent boundary; a transform boundary is not shown.

27. A divergent boundary on land would pull apart the land, creating a rift valley. Eventually the rift valley may become deep enough for the sea to fill the widening gap.

28. One kind is when two plates carrying oceanic crust collide. In this case, the denser plate subducts below the less dense plate at a deep-ocean trench. A second kind is when a plate carrying oceanic crust collides with a plate carrying continental crust. In this case, the oceanic plate plunges beneath the continental plate. In a third kind, two plates carrying continental crust collide. In this case, neither plate is subducted. Instead, the collision squeezes the crust into mountain ranges.

29. Scientists did not believe Wegener because he could not provide an explanation for the force that moves continents. Scientists now know that convection currents in the mantle cause the movements of plates on Earth's surface, and those plates carry the continents with them.

30. Oceanic crust is made mostly of basalt, while continental crust is made mostly of granite. Since basalt is denser than granite, oceanic crust is denser than continental crust.

110

Earthquakes

Lab zone Chapter Project **Design and Build an Earthquake-Safe House**

The following steps will walk you through the Chapter Project. Use the hints and detailed directions as you guide your students through designing, testing, revising, retesting, finalizing, and presenting their models.

Chapter Project Overview

When you introduce the project by having students build and test simple toothpick-and-tape models, ask them to suggest ways to make their models stronger. List their ideas on the board, and suggest that students copy the list for their reference when they build and improve the models for the project. Some ideas may not apply to the materials that students use for the actual models, but other ideas may be useful or at least adaptable for other materials and building designs.

After students have read the description in the textbook, distribute the Chapter Project Overview. Review and discuss each of the project goals. Identify the materials that you will provide, and ask students to suggest others. Also tell students that they can add other materials later as ideas occur to them.

Lead the class to discuss and agree on a list of specifications for the models. Such specifications could include minimum and maximum dimensions for the model (very low structures, for example, will not be susceptible to much earthquake damage), a prohibition on solid models or ones made from construction toys such as Legos™ and Tinker Toys™, and restrictions on the amount of bracing or support material that can be added to a model. Explain that the choice of materials affects how realistic the model will be, so, for example, the scale and strength of the materials should be proportional to the strength of the simulated earthquake. As students agree on specifications, list them on an overhead transparency or on the chalk board, and then make copies of the list to distribute to students.

Students will also need to agree on parameters for the simulated earthquakes so that all models will be subjected to the same stresses and so that earthquake intensity can be increased in each test. One easy way for students to determine and control earthquake strength is to tape a strip of adding-machine tape to the floor or to the table next to the one being used as the base and then mark the strip to show how far to shake the base back and forth for each earthquake intensity. Movements might range from 5 cm for a minor quake to 7.5 cm for a moderate quake and up to 12.5 cm for a major quake. Also let the class decide how long each earthquake will last—perhaps 5 back-and-forth shakes for a minor quake, 10 shakes for a moderate quake, and 15 shakes for a major quake.

Set a deadline for the project presentation and some interim dates for the benchmarks at the end of Sections 1, 2, and 4. Have students record these dates in the Project Time Line of the Project Overview.

At or before the end of Section 1, distribute Chapter Project Worksheet 1, which explains how to make scale drawings and provides an example for practice. Check students' worksheet answers and practice drawings. If students had difficulty with the example, review it as a class and provide additional practice examples.

Chapter Project Worksheet 2 is designed to prompt students' thinking about ways to make their models more earthquake-resistant. Use this worksheet at any point in the project. As students experiment, encourage creativity. Afterward, give students an opportunity to share their ideas and results.

Keep Students on Track— Section 1

When students discuss their initial plans with one another, encourage them to do so in a spirit of cooperative problem solving, not competition. Also remind students that their first design is not expected to be earthquake-proof. Assure them that they will have ample opportunity to test their designs, revise them, retest them, and make improvements before they present their final models to the class.

If any students are having difficulty devising a plan, meet with them individually to offer guidance and support. Also encourage them to talk further with other students to get ideas.

Keep Students on Track—Section 2

To ensure that all models are subjected to the same earthquake intensities in the test, have students review the parameters they agreed on earlier. Let students practice the shaking movements necessary to produce a minor, a moderate, and a major quake until they are able to repeat them consistently.

Make sure that students have some idea what to look for as evidence of earthquake damage (for example, a broken pretzel "support beam," a torn tape "bracket" attaching two beams, or a torn tissue-paper "wall").

Encourage students to examine other students' models that were more successful in withstanding the earthquakes to get ideas for improving their own models.

Keep Students on Track—Section 4

If necessary, replenish the supply of construction materials you have provided so that students have a wide range of materials available for improving their models. Also be sure to provide materials suitable for modeling the base-isolation construction method described in the text. Such materials might include thin pieces of foam rubber, rubber washers, cotton batting,

pieces of carpet padding, and small springs. Ask students for their ideas about other materials that could be used, and add those to the supply. Also let students use materials they have brought from home.

Remind students of the deadline for the class presentation. Also remind students that you will be rating their presentations as well as their models. Emphasize that being well prepared for the presentation is more important than devising a "perfect" model that sustains no earthquake damage at all.

Chapter Project Wrap Up

Allot sufficient time for each student to present his or her final model and to explain how and why changes were made after each test. Give each presenter positive feedback, not only on the model itself but also on the student's efforts to identify and address any weaknesses in the design as the model was tested.

After the class presentations, students might like to stage a "Quake-Off" to determine whose model is most resistant to earthquake damage. Students could begin by testing several models at a time at the lowest earthquake intensity and eliminating any models that sustain damage. In a second test, the models that survived the first round could be tested at a moderate intensity and damaged models could again be eliminated. Continue in this fashion until one or more final survivors are determined. You may want to present a "Best Earthquake-Resistant Design" to those students, but also give all students positive feedback on their efforts.

Extension

Encourage students to implement and test any ideas they have about improving their models, either ideas of their own or ideas they have gained from other students' presentations.

Earthquakes

Lab zone Chapter Project **Design and Build an Earthquake-Safe House**

What construction methods and materials make structures stronger in an earthquake? In this project, you will try to answer that question by designing, building, and testing your own model structure. You could model a house, an apartment building, an office building, a factory, a bridge, a highway overpass, or any other real-life structure.

   First, you will design a model, choose materials to build it, and discuss your plans with your classmates. After you learn more about earthquakes, you will complete your design and construct your model. You also should ask a classmate to review your model and suggest improvements. You will then test your model to see how well it withstands a simulated earthquake. After you learn about how engineers make structures earthquake-resistant, you will repair and improve your model, test it again, and make any final changes. At the end of the project, you will present your model to the class.

Project Rules

■ With your classmates, decide on rules for building the models. For example, what should be the minimum and maximum size for the models? What kinds of construction materials should *not* be used? If you and your classmates make models that are *too* strong, you won't be modeling actual structures realistically.

■ With your classmates, decide on a way to model earthquakes of different intensities. Remember, your model should be able to withstand minor, moderate, and major earthquakes. Practice making earthquakes until you can create the right intensities for each test.

■ Design your model, and discuss your plans with your classmates. Draw your model to scale, and list the materials you plan to use.

■ Construct your model. Ask a classmate to review it and suggest improvements. After you have made changes, test your model with simulated earthquakes. Make notes about how well your model survived the earthquakes. Pay particular attention to any parts of the model that did not function well and could be improved.

■ Repair and improve your model. Then test it again to see whether your changes worked. If they didn't, make additional improvements.

■ In a class presentation, explain how and why you changed your model. Then test your model for the last time. Make notes about how well it survived a major earthquake.

Earthquakes · *Chapter Project* **Overview**

Suggested Materials

Your teacher will provide a variety of materials for constructing the models. You and your classmates may have other ideas, too. Be creative!

- **To represent beams, rafters, and support columns:** You could use popsicle sticks, straight pretzels, toothpicks, wooden dowels, drinking straws, uncooked pasta, or bread sticks.

- **To represent walls, ceilings, roofs, and other surfaces:** Use materials that can crack or break under stress, rather than strong, stiff materials such as index cards or cardboard. Try thin crackers, tissue paper, or aluminum foil.

- **To join the pieces:** You could use masking tape or clear tape, glue, rubber cement, gumdrops, small marshmallows, clay, staples, or paper clips.

- **To make a base-isolated building:** Use flexible materials such as foam rubber, rubber washers, marshmallows, cotton batting, pieces of carpet padding, or small springs.

- **To simulate an earthquake:** Attach your model to a sturdy, flat base such as a tray, a piece of plywood, or a small table. Hold the base at opposite ends and shake it back and forth. (You could ask a classmate to make the earthquake for you while you watch your model.)

Hints for Building Your Model

- Before you construct the entire model, build important parts of it to see how well your design and the materials you chose work. For example, if you think that support beams will make the walls stronger, first build just one wall to try your idea.

- As you study this chapter, you will do activities that may give you ideas about how to make your model stronger. Write down your ideas so that you don't forget them. When you test your model and are ready to improve it, review your list of ideas.

Project Time Line

Task	Due Date
1. Design model and choose building materials	_____
2. Construct, test, and improve model	_____
3. Test model again; then repair and improve it	_____
4. Present model to the class	_____

Drawing Your Model to Scale

When you draw the model you plan to build, draw it to scale. "To scale" means that each measurement unit on your drawing will represent a certain measurement unit on the real model. For example, if you use a scale of 1 cm = 3 cm, each centimeter on the drawing will represent three centimeters on the real model. With a scale of 1 cm = 1 cm, your drawing would be the same size as your model.

   First, make a scale drawing of your model's floor plan to show what the model will look like from above. Then make a scale drawing of the largest wall to show what the model will look like from the side. Follow the steps below to practice making scale drawings.

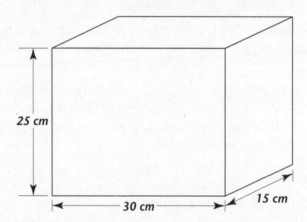

Suppose that you want to build a model with the dimensions shown in the figure above. Your graph paper is 28 centimeters long and 21.5 centimeters wide. You can't draw the model full size because it won't fit on the graph paper.

1. First decide what scale to use. What scale would let you fit both a floor plan and the largest wall drawing on the same sheet of graph paper?

   _____

   (*Hint:* Make the drawings as large as possible so that you can follow them easily when you build the model.)

2. With this scale, what would be the dimensions of the drawing?

   Length: _____ Width: _____ Height: _____

3. Use these scale dimensions to make two scale drawings—one of the floor plan and one of the largest wall. Make both drawings on the same sheet of graph paper. Use graph paper with half-centimeter squares. Label the drawings *Floor Plan* and *Largest Wall*. At the bottom of the graph paper, write the scale you used for the drawings.

Making Your Model More Earthquake-Resistant

Designers include supports in buildings to make them stronger. This activity will help you think of ways to make your model more earthquake-resistant.

Materials

6–8 drinking straws   tissue paper
scissors   glue
masking tape or clear tape   6–8 toothpicks

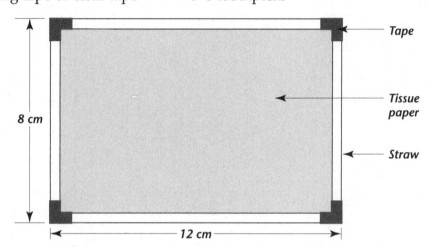

Procedure *Review the safety guidelines in Appendix A.*

1. Cut one straw into two pieces—one piece about 12 centimeters long and the other piece about 8 centimeters long. Cut another straw the same way.

2. Tape the four pieces of straw together to make a rectangular frame, as shown in the figure above. Use just one or two *small* pieces of tape at each corner.

3. Cut a piece of tissue paper the same size as the frame. Tape or glue the paper to the frame to make a model wall.

4. Lay the wall flat on your desk. Hold down one bottom corner with one hand. With the other hand, push the opposite top corner about 2 centimeters sideways. What happens to the straw frame? What happens to the paper?

5. Repeat Step 4, but this time keep pushing the top corner until the frame collapses. What happens to the paper?

6. Repair the wall, or make another one.

7. Now try to make the wall more "push-resistant." Use more straws and toothpicks. (You can cut them into smaller pieces if you like.) Try different ways to make the wall stronger. Which ways work best? What other materials could you use?

Earthquakes ▪ *Chapter Project*   **Scoring Rubric**

Design and Build an Earthquake-Safe House

In evaluating how well you complete the Chapter Project, your teacher will judge your work in three categories. In each, a score of 4 is the best rating.

	4	3	2	1
Designing, Building, Testing, and Improving the Model	Makes imaginative use of construction methods and materials; carefully tests model and notes results; uses creativity in devising improvements; final model withstands a major earthquake with little or no damage.	Makes good use of construction methods and materials; tests model at all designated stages and notes results; identifies and resolves most major design flaws and weaknesses; final model withstands only a moderate earthquake.	Makes limited use of construction methods and materials; does not carefully follow project rules for testing model design flaws; makes little or no attempt to improve model; final model sustains significant damage in a minor earthquake.	Makes poor use of construction methods and materials; does not test model and / or note design flaws; makes little or no attempt to improve model; final model sustains significant damage in a minor earthquake.
Presenting the Model	Explains all construction problems identified in testing and their resolutions; presentation is interesting, clear, and well organized.	Explains most construction problems identified in testing and their resolutions; presentation is interesting and fairly well organized.	Explains some construction problems identified in testing but does not explain their resolutions clearly; presentation lacks interest, clarity, and / or organization.	Does not explain construction problems and their resolutions; presentation is unclear and disorganized.
Working Cooperatively with Classmates	Readily offers suggestions to classmates in a noncritical manner; thoughtfully considers others' suggestions for improving own model.	Offers some suggestions to classmates; accepts others' suggestions for improving own model.	Offers few suggestions to classmates; makes little attempt to implement others' suggestions for improving own model.	Offers no suggestions to classmates; makes no attempt to implement others' suggestions for improving own model.

Forces in Earth's Crust

⏱ *3 periods, 1 1/2 blocks*

Objectives

F.2.1.1 Explain how stress in the crust changes Earth's surface.

F.2.1.2 Describe where faults are usually found and why they form.

F.2.1.3 Identify the land features that result from plate movement.

Key Terms

- stress • tension • compression • shearing
- normal fault • hanging wall • footwall
- reverse fault • strike-slip fault • anticline
- syncline • plateau

Local Standards

PRETEACH

Build Background Knowledge

Students share their experiences about earthquakes or what they have learned from media and other sources.

 **Discover Activity** *How Does Stress Affect Earth's Crust?* **L1**

Targeted Resources

❏ **All in One Teaching Resources**
  L2 Reading Strategy: Building Vocabulary

❏ ⊙ **PresentationExpress™ CD-ROM**

INSTRUCT

Types of Stress

Use visuals and paper-folding techniques to demonstrate how stress in the crust changes Earth's surface.

Kinds of Faults

Guide students to use their hands to demonstrate how types of faults depend on forces at work.

Changing Earth's Surface

Use leading questions to open discussion of the surface changes that cause landforms and the types of landforms in the United States.

Targeted Resources

❏ **All in One Teaching Resources**
  L2 Guided Reading, pp. 121–124
  L2 Transparencies F14, F15

❏ **www.SciLinks.org** Web Code: scn-1021

❏ ⊙ **Student Edition on Audio CD**

ASSESS

Section Assessment Questions

↻ Have students use their definitions of vocabulary terms in this section to answer the questions.

Reteach

Students sketch the movement of each type of fault and list the landforms created by this type of fault.

Targeted Resources

❏ **All in One Teaching Resources**
  Section Summary, p. 120
  L1 Review and Reinforce, p. 125
  L3 Enrich, p. 126

Earthquakes • *Section Summary*

Forces in Earth's Crust

Key Concepts

- How does stress in the crust change Earth's surface?

- Where are faults usually found, and why do they form?

- What land features result from the forces of plate movement?

The movement of Earth's plates creates enormous forces that squeeze or pull the rock in the crust. A force that acts on rock to change its shape or volume is **stress**. Stress adds energy to the rock. The energy is stored in the rock until it changes shape or breaks.

Three different kinds of stress can occur in the crust—tension, compression, and shearing. **Tension, compression, and shearing work over millions of years to change the shape and volume of rock. Tension** pulls on the crust, stretching rock so that it becomes thinner in the middle. **Compression** squeezes rock until it folds or breaks. **Shearing** pushes a mass of rock in two opposite directions.

When enough stress builds up in rock, the rock breaks, creating a fault. A fault is a break in the rock of the crust where rock surfaces slip past each other. **Most faults occur along plate boundaries, where the forces of plate motion push or pull the crust so much that the crust breaks. There are three main types of faults: normal faults, reverse faults, and strike-slip faults.**

Tension causes a normal fault. In a **normal fault,** the fault is at an angle, and one block of rock lies above the fault while the other block lies below the fault. The block of rock that lies above is called the **hanging wall.** The rock that lies below is called the **footwall.** Compression causes reverse faults. A **reverse fault** has the same structure as a normal fault, but the blocks move in the opposite direction. Shearing creates strike-slip faults. In a **strike-slip fault,** the rocks on either side of the fault slip past each sideways, with little up or down motion.

Over millions of years, the forces of plate movement can change a flat plain into landforms such as anticlines and synclines, folded mountains, fault-block mountains, and plateaus. A fold in rock that bends upward into an arch is an **anticline.** A fold in rock that bends downward to form a valley is a **syncline.** Anticlines and synclines are found on many parts of the Earth's surface where compression forces have folded the crust. The collision of two plates can cause compression and folding of the crust over a wide area. Where two normal faults cut through a block of rock, fault movements may push up a fault-block mountain. The forces that raise mountains can also uplift, or raise plateaus. A **plateau** is a large area of flat land elevated high above sea level.

Earthquakes • *Guided Reading and Study*

Forces in Earth's Crust (pp. 44–50)

This section explains how stresses in Earth's crust cause breaks, or faults, in the crust. The section also explains how faults and folds in Earth's crust form mountains.

Use Target Reading Skills

The first column in the chart lists key terms in this section. In the second column, write what you know about the key term. As you read the section, write a definition of the key term in your own words in the third column. Some examples are done for you.

Key Term	What You Know	Definition
Stress		
Tension	pulling, as on a rope	
Compression	squeezing together	
Shearing		
Normal fault		A fault in which one part of the rock is above another part and slips downward when movement occurs
Hanging wall		
Footwall		
Reverse fault		
Strike-slip fault		
Anticline	*anti* means "against"	
Syncline		
Plateau	flat land feature	

Earthquakes

Forces in Earth's Crust *(continued)*

1. Circle the letter of the term that refers to force that acts on rock to change its shape or volume.

   a. fault   **b.** stress   **c.** pressure   **d.** heat

2. The amount of space a rock takes up is its _____.

Types of Stress (p. 45)

3. List the three types of stress that occur in Earth's crust.

   a. _____ **b.** _____ **c.** _____

4. Complete the cause-events-effect chart to show how the different types of stress change the shape and volume of rock.

Cause	Event	Effect
Tension	**c.**	**e.**
a.	**d.**	Rock folds or breaks
b.	Pushes rock in two different directions	**f.**

   g. Which type of stress causes the crust to become thinner?

   _____

   _____

5. A break in Earth's crust is a(n) _____.

Kinds of Faults (pp. 46–47)

Match the kind of fault with its description.

Type of Fault

____ **6.** strike-slip fault

____ **7.** normal fault

____ **8.** reverse fault

Description

a. The hanging wall slides up and over the footwall.

b. There is little up-or-down motion.

c. The hanging wall slips downward below the footwall.

Earthquakes • *Guided Reading and Study*

9. Is the following sentence true or false? A strike-slip fault that forms the boundary between two plates is called a convergent boundary.

_____

10. Circle the letter of each sentence that is true about a hanging wall.

   a. It slips downward when movement occurs along a normal fault.

   b. It is the half of a fault that lies below in a reverse fault.

   c. It is the same as a footwall.

   d. It occurs when the fault is at an angle.

11. Circle the letter of each sentence that is true about both normal and reverse faults.

   a. The faults are at an angle.

   b. The faults are caused by tension.

   c. The faults are caused by compression.

   d. The faults have footwalls.

12. Complete the flowchart to show the types of faults and movements caused by stress on rock.

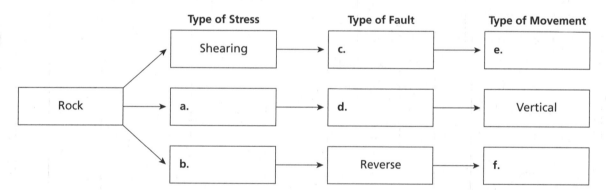

   g. Two types of faults can result in mountains. Which are they, and how do you know from examining this flowchart? _____

   _____

Name _____ Date _____ Class_____

Earthquakes • *Guided Reading and Study*

Forces in Earth's Crust *(continued)*

Match the landform with the type of fault or faults found there.

Landform

____ **13.** San Andreas Fault

____ **14.** Rio Grande rift valley

____ **15.** Rocky Mountains

Type of Fault

a. reverse fault

b. strike-slip fault

c. normal fault

Match the term with its definition.

Term

____ **16.** anticline

____ **17.** syncline

____ **18.** folded mountains

Definition

a. Fold in rock that bends upward

b. Parallel ridges and valleys

c. Fold in rock that bends downward

Changing Earth's Surface (pp. 48–50)

19. Circle the letter of the sentence that describes how a fault-block mountain is created.

a. It is created by two normal faults.

b. It is created by two reverse faults.

c. It is created by a strike-slip fault.

d. It is created by shearing.

20. Circle the letter of each mountain range that was caused by folding.

a. Alps

b. Himalayas

c. Appalachian

d. Great Basin

21. What is a plateau? _____

_____

Earthquakes · *Review and Reinforce*

Forces in Earth's Crust

Understanding Main Ideas

Use the diagrams below to answer items 1–3.

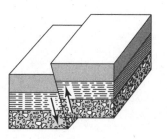
Diagram A

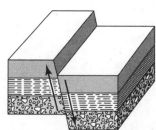
Diagram B

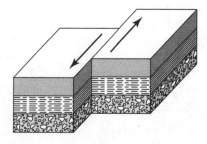
Diagram C

1. **Diagram A**

   a. Type of Fault: _____

   b. Stress Force: _____

   c. Movement Along Fault: _____

2. **Diagram B**

   a. Type of Fault: _____

   b. Stress Force: _____

   c. Movement Along Fault:_____

3. **Diagram C**

   a. Type of Fault: _____

   b. Stress Force: _____

   c. Movement Along Fault: _____

Building Vocabulary

Write a definition for each of these words. Use the back of this sheet if you need more space.

4. shearing _____

5. hanging wall _____

6. syncline _____

7. footwall _____

8. stress _____

9. anticline _____

10. plateau _____

Earthquakes ▪ *Enrich*

Evidence of Movement Along Faults

Each picture below shows how an earthquake changed the land surface at a fault. Examine the pictures carefully. Decide what kind of fault is shown in each. Then explain how movement along the fault caused the changes you see. Write your answers in the spaces provided.

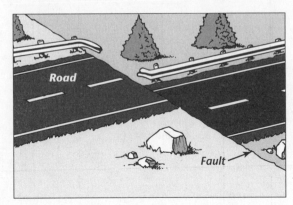

Fault 1

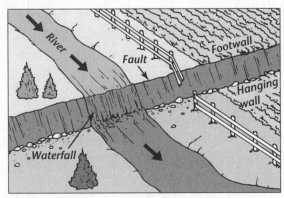

Fault 2

Fault 3

Fault 1 _____

_____

Fault 2 _____

_____

Fault 3 _____

_____

Earthquakes and Seismic Waves

3 periods, 1 1/2 blocks

Ability Levels Key
L1 Basic to Average
L2 For All Students
L3 Average to Advanced

Objectives

F.2.2.1 Describe how the energy of an earthquake travels through Earth.

F.2.2.2 Identify the scales used to measure the strength of an earthquake.

F.2.2.3 Explain how scientists locate the epicenter of an earthquake.

Key Terms

• earthquake • focus • epicenter • P wave • S wave • surface wave • Mercalli scale • magnitude • Richter scale • seismograph • moment magnitude scale

Local Standards

PRETEACH

Build Background Knowledge

Students discuss waves they have observed and describe how waves move through water.

 *Discover Activity* *How Do Seismic Waves Travel Through Earth?* **L1**

Targeted Resources

❏ **All in One Teaching Resources**
   L2 Reading Strategy Transparency F16: Identifying Main Ideas
❏ **PresentationExpress™ CD-ROM**

INSTRUCT

Types of Seismic Waves

Use the spring toy in the Discover Activity to explain the different types of seismic wave.

Measuring Earthquakes

Lead students to discuss and compare the different types of scales used to measure earthquakes.

Locating the Epicenter

Use the map in the text to open discussion of how geologists determine the epicenter by using data from several seismograms.

 Skills Lab *Finding the Epicenter* **L2**

Targeted Resources

❏ **All in One Teaching Resources**
   L2 Guided Reading, pp. 129–131
   L2 Transparency F17
   L2 Lab: *Finding the Epicenter*, pp. 134–136
❏ **Lab Activity Video/DVD**
   Skills Lab: *Finding the Epicenter*
❏ **PHSchool.com** Web Code: cfp-1022
❏ **Discovery SCHOOL** **Video Field Trip**
❏ **Student Edition on Audio CD**

ASSESS

Section Assessment Questions

Have students use their completed graphic organizers with main ideas and details to answer the questions.

Reteach

Students illustrate how seismic waves travel and how an earthquake is located by using waves.

Targeted Resources

❏ **All in One Teaching Resources**
   Section Summary, p. 128
   L1 Review and Reinforce, p. 132
   L3 Enrich, p. 133

Earthquakes

Earthquakes and Seismic Waves

Key Concepts

- How does the energy of an earthquake travel through Earth?

- What are the scales used to measure the strength of an earthquake?

- How do scientists locate the epicenter of an earthquake?

An **earthquake** is the shaking and trembling that results from the movement of rock beneath Earth's surface. The point beneath Earth's surface where rock under stress breaks to cause an earthquake is called the **focus.** The point on the surface directly above the focus is called the **epicenter.** During an earthquake, vibrations called seismic waves move out from the focus in all directions. **Seismic waves carry the energy of an earthquake away from the focus, through Earth's interior, and across the surface.**

There are three categories of seismic waves: P waves, S waves, and surface waves. **P waves** compress and expand the ground like an accordion. **S waves** vibrate from side to side and up and down. When P waves and S waves reach the surface, some become surface waves. **Surface waves** move more slowly than P waves and S waves.

Three commonly used methods of measuring earthquakes are the Mercalli scale, the Richter scale, and the moment magnitude scale. The **Mercalli scale** was developed to rate earthquakes according to the level of damage at a given place. An earthquake's **magnitude** is a number that geologists assign to an earthquake based on the earthquake's strength. The **Richter scale** is a rating of an earthquake's magnitude based on the size of the earthquake's seismic waves. The seismic waves are measured by a **seismograph.** A seismograph is an instrument that records and measures seismic waves. Geologists today often use the **moment magnitude scale,** a rating system that estimates the total energy released by an earthquake. An earthquake's magnitude tells geologists how much energy was released by the earthquake. The effects of an earthquake increase with magnitude.

Geologists use seismic waves to locate an earthquake's epicenter. When an earthquake strikes, P waves arrive at a seismograph first and S waves next. The farther away the epicenter is, the greater the difference between the two arrival times. This time difference tells scientists how far from the seismograph the epicenter is. The scientists then use the information from three different seismograph stations to plot circles on a map. Each circle shows the distance from one seismograph station to all the points where the epicenter could be located. The single point where the three circles intersect is the location of the earthquake's epicenter.

Earthquakes and Seismic Waves (pp. 51–57)

This section explains how energy from an earthquake travels through Earth, how it can be detected, and how the size of an earthquake can be measured.

Use Target Reading Skills

As you read about seismic waves, complete the graphic organizer by filling in the details.

Main Idea

Seismic waves carry the energy of an earthquake.

Detail	**Detail**	**Detail**
a.	b.	c.

Introduction (p. 51)

1. The point at which a rock under stress breaks and triggers an earthquake

   is called the _____.

2. The point on the surface directly above the focus is the

   _____.

Types of Seismic Waves (pp. 52–53)

3. What are seismic waves? _____

   _____

   _____

Earthquakes and Seismic Waves (continued)

4. Is the following sentence true or false? Seismic waves carry the energy of an earthquake away from the focus in all directions.

_____

5. Circle the letter of each term that is a category of seismic wave.

    a. P wave

    b. S wave

    c. surface wave

    d. underground wave

6. Label each drawing as *S Waves* or *P Waves*.

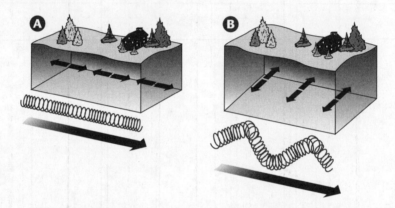

_____   _____

7. Is the following sentence true or false? Surface waves move more quickly than P waves and S waves. _____

Type of Wave	Effect
_____ **8.** P wave	**a.** shakes buildings from side to side
_____ **9.** S wave	**b.** shakes buildings violently
_____ **10.** Surface wave	**c.** causes buildings to contract and expand

11. A device that records the ground movements caused by seismic waves

    is a(n) _____.

Earthquakes · *Guided Reading and Study*

Measuring Earthquakes (pp. 54–56)

12. List the three scales that are used for measuring earthquakes.

a. _____

b. _____

c. _____

13. In your own words, write a definition of each earthquake scale.

a. _____

_____

b. _____

_____

c. _____

Locating the Epicenter (pp. 56–57)

14. Is the following sentence true or false? The closer an earthquake, the greater the time between the arrival of P waves and the arrival

of S waves. _____

15. Geologists use circles to find the epicenter of an earthquake.

a. What does the center of each circle represent? _____

_____

b. What does the radius of each circle represent? _____

_____

Earthquakes and Seismic Waves

Understanding Main Ideas

Answer the following questions in the spaces provided.

1. What are seismic waves?

_____

_____

2. In what order do the three types of seismic waves arrive at a seismograph?

_____

_____

3. Which type of seismic wave produces the most severe ground movements?

_____

4. Describe the moment magnitude scale, and explain why it is useful in measuring earthquakes.

_____

_____

_____

5. How do geologists locate the epicenter of an earthquake?

_____

_____

_____

Building Vocabulary

Match each term with its definition by writing the letter of the correct definition in the right column on the line beside the term in the left column.

_____ **6.** focus

_____ **7.** epicenter

_____ **8.** surface waves

_____ **9.** seismograph

_____ **10.** magnitude

a. records ground movements caused by seismic waves as they move through the Earth

b. slowest seismic waves that produce the most severe ground movements

c. the point beneath Earth's surface at which rock under stress breaks and triggers an earthquake

d. a measurement of earthquake strength

e. the point on the surface directly above the point at which an earthquake occurs

Earthquakes · *Enrich*

Comparing the Richter and Moment Magnitude Scales

The Richter scale rates earthquakes based on the size of their seismic waves, as measured by seismographs. The moment magnitude scale rates earthquakes based on the total amount of energy they release. To determine the moment magnitude rating, seismologists measure the surface area of the ruptured fault and how far the land moved along the fault. An earthquake's Richter rating and moment magnitude rating are not always the same. The table below shows the ratings on both scales for some famous earthquakes.

Date	Location	Magnitude	
		Richter scale	Moment magnitude scale
1811–1812	New Madrid, midwestern U.S.	8.7	8.1
1906	San Francisco, California	8.3	7.7
1960	Arauco, Chile	8.3	9.5
1964	Anchorage, Alaska	8.4	9.2
1971	San Fernando, California	6.4	6.7
1985	Mexico City, Mexico	8.1	8.1
1989	San Francisco, California	7.1	7.2
1994	Northridge, California	6.4	6.7
1995	Kobe, Japan	6.8	6.9

Answer the following questions on a separate sheet of paper.

1. Which earthquake was strongest according to the Richter scale? Which was strongest according to the moment magnitude scale?

2. Which earthquakes had the same or close to the same ratings on both scales?

3. Which earthquakes were rated more than 0.5 points stronger on the moment magnitude scale than they were rated on the Richter scale?

4. Which earthquakes were rated more than 0.5 points stronger on the Richter scale than they were rated on the moment magnitude scale?

5. Why can the same earthquake have different ratings on the two scales?

Earthquakes • *Skills Lab*

Finding the Epicenter

Problem

How can you locate an earthquake's epicenter?

Skills Focus

interpreting data, drawing conclusions

Materials

drawing compass with pencil
outline map of the United States

Procedure 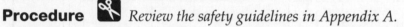 *Review the safety guidelines in Appendix A.*

1. Review the data table showing differences in earthquake arrival times.

2. The graph shows how the difference in arrival times between P waves and S waves depends on the distance from the epicenter of the earthquake. Find the difference in arrival time for Denver on the *y*-axis of the graph. Follow this line across to the point at which it crosses the curve. To find the distance to the epicenter, read down from this point to the *x*-axis of the graph. Enter this distance in the data table.

3. Repeat Step 2 for Houston and Chicago.

4. Set your compass at a radius equal to the distance from Denver to the earthquake epicenter that you recorded in your data table.

5. Draw a circle with the radius determined in Step 4, using Denver as the center. Draw the circle on the map. (*Hints:* Draw your circles carefully. You may need to draw some parts of the circles off the map.)

6. Repeat Steps 4 and 5 for Houston and Chicago.

Earthquakes · *Skills Lab*

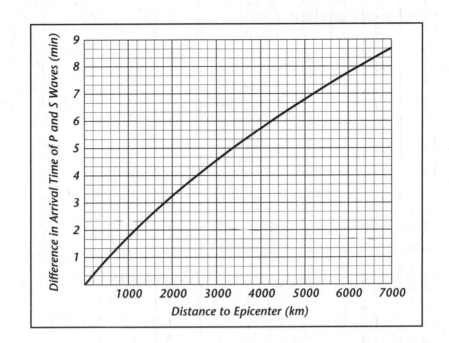

Earthquakes ▪ *Skills Lab*

Finding the Epicenter *(continued)*

DATA TABLE

City	Difference in P and S Wave Arrival Times	Distance to Epicenter
Denver, Colorado	2 min 40 s	
Houston, Texas	3 min 55 s	
Chicago, Illinois	1 min 10 s	

Analyze and Conclude

Answer the following questions on a separate sheet of paper.

1. Observe the three circles you have drawn. Where is the earthquake's epicenter?

2. Which city on the map is closest to the earthquake epicenter? How far, in kilometers, is this city from the epicenter?

3. In which of the three cities listed in the data table would seismographs detect the earthquake first? Last?

4. About how far from San Francisco is the epicenter that you found? What would the difference in arrival times of the P waves and S waves be for a recording station in San Francisco?

5. What happens to the difference in arrival times between P waves and S waves as the distance from the earthquake increases?

6. Review the procedure you followed in this lab and then answer the following question. When you are trying to locate an epicenter, why is it necessary to know the distance from the epicenter for at least three recording stations?

More to Explore

You have just located an earthquake's epicenter. Find this earthquake's location on the map of Earthquake Risk in the United States in your textbook. What is the risk of earthquakes in the area of this quake?

Now look at the map of Earth's Lithospheric Plates in your textbook. What conclusions can you draw from this map about the cause of earthquakes in this area?

Monitoring Earthquakes

2 periods, 1 block

Ability Levels Key
L1 Basic to Average
L2 For All Students
L3 Average to Advanced

Objectives
F.2.3.1 Explain how seismographs work.
F.2.3.2 Describe how geologists monitor faults.
F.2.3.3 Explain how seismographic data are used.

Key Terms
• seismogram • friction

Local Standards

PRETEACH

Build Background Knowledge
Students discuss why predicting earthquakes is important and whether predictions will ever be accurate.

 *How Can Seismic Waves Be Detected?* **L1**

Targeted Resources

❑ **All in One** **Teaching Resources**
L2 Reading Strategy Transparency F18: Sequencing
❑ ⊙ **PresentationExpress™ CD-ROM**

INSTRUCT

The Modern Seismograph
Use visuals to examine and discuss how a seismograph works.

Instruments That Monitor Faults
Guide students to compare and contrast instruments that detect phenomena that may indicate an impending earthquake.

Using Seismographic Data
Describe how friction influences movements of rocks and demonstrate the concept by interlocking their hands and then pulling free.

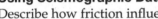 *Design a Seismograph* **L2**

Targeted Resources

❑ **All in One** **Teaching Resources**
L2 Guided Reading, pp. 139–141
L2 Transparencies F19, F20
L2 Lab: *Design a Seismograph*, pp. 144–145
❑ **www.SciLinks.org** Web Code: scn-1023
❑ 📼 **Lab Activity Video/DVD**
Technology Lab: *Design a Seismograph* pp. 144–145
❑ ⊙ **Student Edition on Audio CD**

ASSESS

Section Assessment Questions
↻ Have students use their flowchart to answer Question 1.

Reteach
Students name and describe the types of monitoring devices used to predict earthquakes.

Targeted Resources

❑ **All in One** **Teaching Resources**
Section Summary, p. 138
L1 Review and Reinforce, p. 142
L3 Enrich, p. 143

Earthquakes

Earthquakes • *Section Summary*

Monitoring Earthquakes

Key Concepts

- How do seismographs work?
- How do geologists monitor faults?
- How are seismographic data used?

Many societies have used technology to try to determine when and where earthquakes have occurred. During the early 1900s, scientists developed seismographs that were much more sensitive and accurate than any earlier devices. A simple seismograph can consist of a heavy weight attached to a frame by a spring or wire. A pen connected to the weight rests its point on a drum that can rotate. As the drum rotates slowly, the pen draws a straight line on paper that is wrapped tightly around the drum. **Seismic waves cause the seismograph's drum to vibrate. But the suspended weight with the pen attached moves very little. Therefore, the pen stays in place and records the drum's vibrations.** The pattern of lines, called a **seismogram,** is the record of an earthquake's seismic waves produced by a seismograph.

To monitor faults, geologists have developed instruments to measure changes in elevation, tilting of the land surface, and ground movements along faults. A tiltmeter measures tilting or raising of the ground. A creep meter uses a wire stretched across a fault to measure horizontal movement of the ground. A laser-ranging device uses a laser beam to detect horizontal fault movements. A network of Earth-orbiting satellites called GPS helps scientists monitor changes in elevation as well as horizontal movement along faults.

Seismographs and fault-monitoring devices provide data used to map faults and detect changes along faults. Geologists are also trying to use these data to develop a method of predicting earthquakes. Geologists use the data from seismic waves to map faults, which are often hidden by a thick layer of rock or soil. This practice helps geologists determine the earthquake risk for an area. Geologists use fault-monitoring devices to study the types of movement that occur along faults. **Friction** is the force that opposes the motion of one surface as it moves across another surface. Where friction along a fault is low, the rocks on both sides of the fault slide by each other without much sticking. Stress does not build up, and large earthquakes are unlikely. Where friction is high, the rocks lock together. Stress builds up until an earthquake occurs. Even with data from many sources, geologists can't predict when and where a quake will strike.

Earthquakes · *Guided Reading and Study*

Monitoring Earthquakes (pp. 60–65)

This section explains how geologists monitor faults to try to predict earthquakes.

Use Target Reading Skills

As you read about seismographs, make a flowchart that shows how a seismograph produces a seismogram.

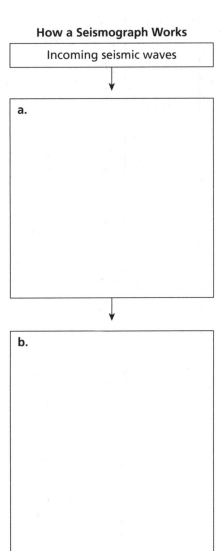

How a Seismograph Works

Incoming seismic waves

a.

b.

The Seismograph (p. 61)

1. After an earthquake, in what order are the different types of seismic waves recorded by a seismograph? _____

_____

Earthquakes • *Guided Reading and Study*

Monitoring Earthquakes *(continued)*

Instruments That Monitor Faults *(pp. 62–63)*

2. List four instruments that geologists use to monitor movements along faults.

   a. _____

   b. _____

   c. _____

   d. _____

Match the type of monitoring device with its description.

Monitoring Device

_____ 3. creep meter

_____ 4. laser-ranging device

_____ 5. tiltmeter

_____ 6. GPS satellite

Description

a. Uses a network of Earth-orbiting satellites

b. Detects changes in distance to a reflector

c. Measures movement along a slip-strike fault

d. Works like a carpenter's level

7. Label each circle in the Venn diagram with the name of the monitoring device it represents.

a. _____   b. _____

| Measures horizontal movement | Measures movement along a fault | Measures vertical movement |

Earthquakes · *Guided Reading and Study*

8. A device that bounces laser beams off a reflector to detect fault movements is a(n) _____.

9. A device that measures tiny movements of markers set up on the opposite sides of a fault is a(n) _____.

Using Seismographic Data (pp. 64–65)

10. How do seismic waves behave when they encounter a fault?

_____

11. How do the data from the movements of seismic waves help geologists determine the earthquake risk for an area? _____

_____

12. The force that opposes the motion of one surface as it moves across another surface is referred to as _____.

13. Is the following sentence true or false? Geologists can predict accurately where and when an earthquake will strike. _____

Earthquakes

Earthquakes · *Review and Reinforce*

Monitoring Earthquakes

Understanding Main Ideas

Answer the following questions on a separate sheet of paper.

1. How might monitoring faults help geologists predict an earthquake?

2. What two factors help geologists determine earthquake risk?

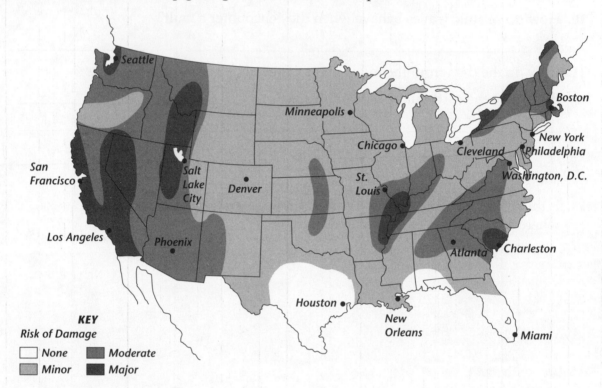

KEY
Risk of Damage

☐ None   ▨ Moderate
▦ Minor   ■ Major

3. a. Name three cities shown on the map above that have a major risk of earthquake damage.

   b. Name three cities that have a moderate risk of earthquake damage.

   c. Name three cities that have a minor risk of earthquake damage.

Building Vocabulary

Answer each item below. Write your answers on a separate sheet of paper.

4. Name four instruments that are used to detect movement along faults.

5. Briefly describe how each instrument works.

Earthquakes · *Enrich*

Earthquake Probability

This combined map and bar graph shows the probability of earthquakes in different areas along the San Andreas fault. Probability is a measure of how likely it is that some event will happen in a given time. A probability near 100 percent means that an event is very likely to happen. A probability near zero percent means that an event is very unlikely to happen.

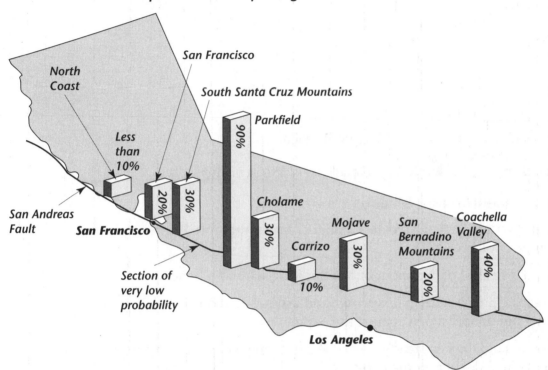

Earthquake Probability Along the San Andreas Fault

Use the figure above to answer the following questions. Write your answers on a separate sheet of paper.

1. Which area on the fault has the highest probability of an earthquake?

2. What is the probability of an earthquake in the North Coast area?

3. The fault section between the Santa Cruz Mountains and Parkfield has a very low probability. Geologists know that this area has experienced very little damaging seismic activity in the past. They also found that the blocks of rock in this section move slowly and continually. Why would slow, continual movement lead geologists to give the section a low probability?

4. What can you infer about why the probability of an earthquake is so high in the Parkfield area?

5. How do you think geologists learn about how the blocks of rock along a fault move?

Earthquakes • *Technology Lab*

Design a Seismograph

Problem

Can you design and build a seismograph that can record the movements of simulated earthquakes?

Skills Focus

designing, evaluating, troubleshooting

Materials

- large book
- pencil
- pen
- 2 strips of paper
- optional materials provided by your teacher

Procedure *Review the safety guidelines in Appendix A.*

Part 1 Research and Investigate

1. With two lab partners, create a model of a seismograph. Begin by placing a large book on a table.

2. Wind a strip of paper about one meter long around a pencil.

3. Hold the pencil with the paper wound around it in one hand. In your other hand, hold a pen against the paper.

4. As you hold the pen steady, have one lab partner slowly pull on the paper so that it slides across the book.

5. After a few seconds, the other lab partner should jiggle the book gently for 10 seconds to model a weak earthquake, and then for 10 seconds to model a strong earthquake.

6. Observe the pen markings on the paper strip. Compare how the seismograph recorded the weak earthquake and the strong earthquake. Record your observations in your notebook.

7. Repeat Steps 1–6 with a new paper strip. Compare the two paper strips to see how consistent your seismograph recordings were. Record your observations.

Earthquakes · *Technology Lab*

Part 2 Design and Build

8. Using what you learned from the seismograph model in Part 1, develop your own design for a seismograph. Your seismograph should be able to
   - record vibrations continuously for 30 seconds
   - produce a seismogram that can distinguish between gentle and strong earthquakes
   - record seismic readings consistently from trial to trial

9. Sketch your design on a sheet of paper. Then make a list of the materials you will need. Materials might include a heavy weight, a roll of paper, a pen, wood blocks, wood dowels, and duct tape.

10. Obtain your teacher's approval for your design. Then construct your seismograph.

Part 3 Evaluate and Redesign

11. Test your seismograph in a series of simulated earthquakes of different strengths. Evaluate how well your seismograph functions. Does it meet the criteria outlined in Step 8? Observe and record any problems.

12. According to your tests, decide how you could improve the design of your seismograph. Then make any necessary changes to your seismograph and test how it functions.

Analyze and Conclude

Write your answers on a separate sheet of paper.

1. **Evaluating** What problems or shortcomings did you encounter with the seismograph you tested in Part 1? Why do you think these problems occurred?

2. **Designing a Solution** How did you incorporate what you learned in Part 1 into your seismograph design in Part 2? For example, what changes did you make to improve consistency from trial to trial?

3. **Troubleshooting** As you designed, built, and tested your seismograph, what problems did you encounter? How did you solve these problems?

4. **Working with Design Constraints** What limitations did factors such as gravity, materials, costs, time, or other factors place on the design and function of your seismograph? Describe how you adapted your design to work within these limitations.

5. **Evaluating the Impact on Society** Why is it important for scientists around the world to have access to accurate and durable seismographs?

Communicate

Write an advertisement trying to "sell" your seismograph. In your ad, explain how your design and evaluation process helped you improve your seismograph. Include a labeled sketch of your design.

Earthquake Safety

 1 periods, 1/2 block

Ability Levels Key
L1 Basic to Average
L2 For All Students
L3 Average to Advanced

Objectives

F.2.4.1 Explain how geologists determine earthquake risk.

F.2..4.2 Identify the kinds of damage an earthquake can cause.

F.2.4.3 Provide suggestions to increase earthquake safety and reduce earthquake damage.

Key Terms
• liquefaction • aftershock • tsunami
• base-isolated building

Local Standards

PRETEACH

Build Background Knowledge
Students discuss structures they have seen in the context of the support the structures would lend to buildings, bridges, and the like that have been damaged by earthquakes.

 *Can Bracing Prevent Building Collapse?* **L1**

Targeted Resources

❏ **All in One** **Teaching Resources**
 L2 Reading Strategy Transparency F21: Asking Questions
❏ **PresentationExpress™ CD-ROM**

INSTRUCT

Earthquake Risk
Help students to examine plate boundaries in relation to earthquake risk.

How Earthquakes Cause Damage
Ask leading questions to open a discussion of how shaking, liquefaction, aftershocks, and tsunamis can cause damage. Apply those concepts to how damage to buildings could have been prevented.

Steps to Earthquake Safety
Guide students to discuss safety measures and brainstorm supplies needed in an emergency kit.

Designing Safer Buildings
Use models to demonstrate methods to help buildings withstand earthquakes.

Targeted Resources

❏ **All in One** **Teaching Resources**
 L2 Guided Reading, pp. 148–150
 L2 Transparency F22
❏ **PHSchool.com** Web Code: cfd-1024
❏ **PHSchool.com** Web Code: cfh-1020
❏ **Student Edition on Audio CD**

ASSESS

Section Assessment Questions
Have students use their completed graphic organizers with their questions and answers to answer the questions.

Reteach
Students list the ways that earthquakes cause damage and ways to make homes safer.

Targeted Resources

❏ **All in One** **Teaching Resources**
Section Summary, p. 147
 L1 Review and Reinforce, p. 151
 L3 Enrich, p. 152

Earthquakes • *Section Summary*

Earthquake Safety

Key Concepts

- How do geologists determine earthquake risk?

- What kinds of damage does an earthquake cause?

- What can be done to increase earthquake safety and reduce earthquake damage?

Geologists can determine earthquake risk by locating where faults are active and where past earthquakes have occurred. In the United States, the risk is highest along the Pacific Coast in the states of California, Washington, and Alaska. The eastern United States generally has a low risk of earthquakes because this region lies far from plate boundaries.

Causes of earthquake damage include shaking, liquefaction, aftershocks, and tsunamis. The shaking produced by seismic waves can trigger landslides or avalanches. The types of rock and soil determine where and how much the ground shakes. **Liquefaction** occurs when an earthquake's violent shaking suddenly turns loose, soft soil into liquid mud. As the ground gives way, buildings sink and pull apart. Sometimes, buildings weakened by an earthquake collapse during an aftershock. An **aftershock** is an earthquake that occurs after a large earthquake in the same area.

When an earthquake jolts the ocean floor, plate movement causes the ocean floor to rise slightly and push water out of its way. The water displaced by the earthquake may form a large wave called a **tsunami.** A tsunami spreads out from an earthquake's epicenter and speeds across the ocean. The height of the wave is low in the open ocean, but the wave grows into a mountain of water as the tsunami approaches shallow water.

The main danger from earthquake strikes is from falling objects and flying glass. **The best way to protect yourself is to drop, cover, and hold.** To prepare for an earthquake, store in a convenient location an earthquake kit containing canned food, water, and first aid supplies.

Most earthquake-related deaths and injuries result from damage to buildings or other structures. **To reduce earthquake damage, new buildings must be made stronger and more flexible. Older buildings may be modified to withstand stronger quakes.** The way in which a building is constructed determines whether it can withstand an earthquake. A **base-isolated building** is designed to reduce the amount of energy that reaches the building during an earthquake. During a quake, the building moves gently back and forth without any violent shaking.

Earthquakes can cause fire and flooding when gas pipes and water mains break. Flexible joints and automatic shut-off valves can be installed to prevent breaking and to cut off gas and water flow.

Earthquakes · *Guided Reading and Study*

Earthquake Safety (pp. 68–73)

This section explains how earthquakes cause damage. The section also describes how buildings can be constructed to withstand earthquakes and what people can do to help protect themselves from earthquakes.

Use Target Reading Skills

Complete the first column in the chart by previewing the red headings and asking a what, how, or where question for each. As you read the section, complete the second column with the answers.

Earthquake Safety

Question	Answer
Where is quake risk highest?	Earthquake risk is highest . . .

Earthquake Risk (p. 69)

1. What two factors do geologists take into account when they determine

   earthquake risk? _____

   _____

2. Circle the letter of the location where the risk of earthquakes is highest in the United States.

   a. along the Gulf of Mexico

   b. along the Atlantic Coast

   c. along the Great Lakes

   d. along the Pacific Coast

Earthquakes • *Guided Reading and Study*

How Earthquakes Cause Damage (pp. 70–71)

3. What kinds of damage are caused by the severe shaking of an earthquake?

_____

_____

_____

_____

4. What determines where and how much the ground shakes?

_____

5. Is the following sentence true or false? A house built on solid rock will shake more during an earthquake than a house built on sandy soil.

_____

6. The process in which an earthquake's violent shaking turns loose, soft soil into liquid mud is called _____. This process is likely to occur where the soil is full of

_____.

7. An earthquake that occurs after a larger earthquake in the same area is referred to as a(n) _____.

8. Large ocean waves usually caused by strong earthquakes below the ocean floor are called _____.

Steps to Earthquake Safety (p. 71)

9. What is the main danger to people during an earthquake?

_____

10. Is the following sentence true or false? If no desk or table is available, you should crouch against an outside wall. _____

11. Is the following sentence true or false? If you are outdoors during an earthquake, you should move under a tree or building.

_____

Earthquakes • *Guided Reading and Study*

Earthquake Safety *(continued)*

Designing Safer Buildings (pp. 72–73)

12. How can tall furniture be prevented from tipping over in an earthquake?

_____

13. How can bedrooms be made safer during an earthquake?

_____

_____

14. How can a brick or wood-frame building be modified to help it withstand an earthquake?

_____

_____

_____

15. What can be done when a new home is being built to help prevent damage caused by liquefaction?

_____

_____

16. How does a base-isolated building reduce the amount of energy that reaches the building during an earthquake?

_____

17. How can earthquakes cause fire and flooding?

_____

_____

Earthquakes • *Review and Reinforce*

Earthquake Safety

Understanding Main Ideas

Answer the following questions on a separate sheet of paper.

1. What types of damage do earthquakes cause?

2. How do ground conditions affect earthquake damage to buildings?

3. Why are aftershocks dangerous to buildings after a large earthquake?

4. Why do tsunamis grow into larger waves as they approach land?

5. If an earthquake strikes while you are indoors, what should you do?

6. Why should people living in earthquake regions prepare emergency kits?

7. What kind of building design is shown in this figure? Explain how the design helps reduce earthquake damage.

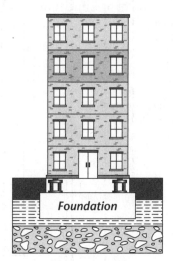

Foundation

Building Vocabulary

Write a word to complete each sentence correctly.

8. The water displaced by a strong earthquake on the ocean floor forms large waves called _____.

9. _____ occurs when an earthquake's violent shaking suddenly turns loose, soft soil into liquid mud.

10. A(n) _____ is an earthquake that occurs after a large earthquake centered in the same area.

Earthquakes · *Enrich*

Emergency Planning

Imagine that you are a member of your community's Disaster Planning Board. The board is writing earthquake safety plans for all the public buildings in the community. You are responsible for developing the safety plan for your school. You must survey the school building and identify ways to reduce the risk of damage in an earthquake. You must also prepare a list of safety guidelines to help students, teachers, and other people in the school protect themselves if an earthquake strikes.

Answer the following questions on a separate sheet of paper.

1. What types of dangerous conditions will you look for as you survey the school building?

2. Suppose you find the potential hazards listed in the table below. What should be done to eliminate or reduce each hazard? Write your answers in the table.

Hazard	Recommendation
a. Laboratory glassware and microscopes are stored on a high, open shelf.	
b. Tall bookcases might topple over.	
c. The maintenance supervisor is the only person who knows how to shut off the gas, water, and electric lines.	

3. In your list of safety guidelines for the people in the school, what is the most important guideline?

4. Will you recommend that people leave the school building as soon as an earthquake strikes? Explain.

5. What should students outside on the school grounds do to protect themselves?

6. What will you do to make sure that all students know the safety guidelines?

Key Terms

Read the clues below, and then find the key terms from the chapter that are hidden in the puzzle. The hidden terms may occur vertically, horizontally, or diagonally.

Clues

1. The shaking and trembling of Earth's crust

2. A fold in rock that bends downward

3. A stress force that squeezes rock

4. A large area of elevated flat land

5. A force that changes a rock's shape or volume

6. An earthquake that occurs after a larger earthquake in the same area

7. Large wave caused by earthquakes on the ocean floor

8. Stress that pushes rock in opposite directions

9. A fold in rock that bends upward

10. Occurs when an earthquake turns soil into liquid mud

11. The half of a fault that lies below

12. An instrument that records ground movements caused by seismic waves

```
s  t  i  o  n  s  c  o  d  d  l  n  p  m
f  a  e  a  r  t  h  q  u  a  k  e  v  l
w  a  f  t  e  r  s  h  o  c  k  n  d  i
y  t  o  n  e  e  q  u  r  c  a  f  t  q
d  u  p  c  o  s  h  e  a  r  i  n  g  u
s  w  n  o  f  s  a  z  s  e  p  t  w  e
e  g  o  m  i  p  h  o  r  v  a  d  t  f
i  n  m  p  f  g  t  p  u  l  a  c  m  a
s  o  d  r  s  y  n  c  l  i  n  e  p  c
m  w  c  e  o  m  u  a  q  a  v  b  c  t
o  v  e  s  j  m  w  u  c  k  t  i  b  i
g  l  n  s  o  t  h  u  m  b  b  e  y  o
r  a  t  i  o  k  v  o  o  x  l  e  a  n
a  w  o  o  p  l  y  i  m  s  s  a  h  u
p  u  f  n  t  t  s  u  n  a  m  i  s  s
h  a  l  e  t  a  n  t  i  c  l  i  n  e
```

Connecting Concepts

Develop a concept map that uses the key concepts and key terms from this chapter. Keep in mind the main idea of this chapter: Forces inside Earth cause rocks to move and to release energy as seismic waves during an earthquake. The concept map shown is one way to organize how the information in this chapter is related. You may use an extra sheet of paper.

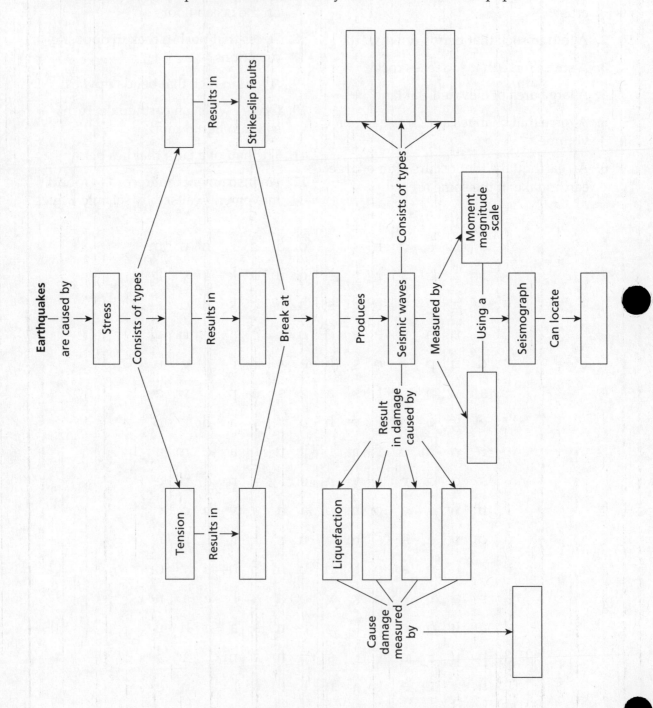

Investigating the Speed of Earthquake Waves

Key Concept

Earthquakes produce primary and secondary waves, which travel at different speeds. The time between the arrival of each wave type can be used to locate the earthquake epicenter.

Skills Focus

inferring, predicting, graphing

Time

40 minutes

Materials

pen or pencil

Advance Preparation

Have yarn, toys, and stopwatches available for More to Explore.

Teaching Tips

- Encourage students to use the Internet to learn more about earthquakes. A site at which students can track and predict earthquakes around the world is http://athena.wednet.edu/curric/land/todayqk.html

- Students may have trouble graphing seconds. Using a transparency of the grid or a grid on the chalkboard, have students locate several points to emphasize that each division is equal to 20 seconds.

Earthquakes • *Laboratory Investigation*

Investigating the Speed of Earthquake Waves

Pre-Lab Discussion

An earthquake produces waves that travel away from the earthquake's epicenter, like ripples on a pond when you throw in a pebble. An earthquake produces three types of waves, primary (P waves), secondary (S waves), and surface waves. Seismologists track how far and how fast P and S waves travel to find the epicenter of the quake.

In this investigation, you will construct a travel-time graph for P and S waves. You will use the graph to answer some questions about earthquakes.

1. What causes an earthquake?

_____

_____

2. What is the epicenter of an earthquake?

_____

_____

Problem

How can you use a graph of earthquake waves' travel distance and time to find an epicenter?

Materials *(per group)*

pen or pencil

Procedure

1. An earthquake produced P and S waves that were recorded by instruments at 20 stations. These waves are listed in the Data Table on the next page. The table shows the distance traveled and the travel time for each wave. Using these data, construct a graph showing the relationship between the distance traveled by P and S waves and their travel times. Label the curves *P wave* or *S wave*.

2. Use your graph to answer the questions.

Earthquakes ▪ *Laboratory Investigation*

Wave Type	Distance Traveled from Epicenter (km)	Travel Time (min)	(s)
P	1600	3	20
P	6500	9	50
P	5400	8	40
P	2000	4	00
P	9600	12	40
P	700	1	30
P	7000	10	20
P	3400	6	10
P	8800	12	00
P	4000	7	00
S	2200	8	00
S	4000	12	40
S	5200	15	20
S	1700	6	30
S	6000	17	00
S	1100	4	20
S	7400	19	40
S	8200	21	00
S	500	2	10
S	9000	22	10

Earthquakes

Earthquakes · *Laboratory Investigation*

Investigating the Speed of Earthquake Waves (continued)

Observations

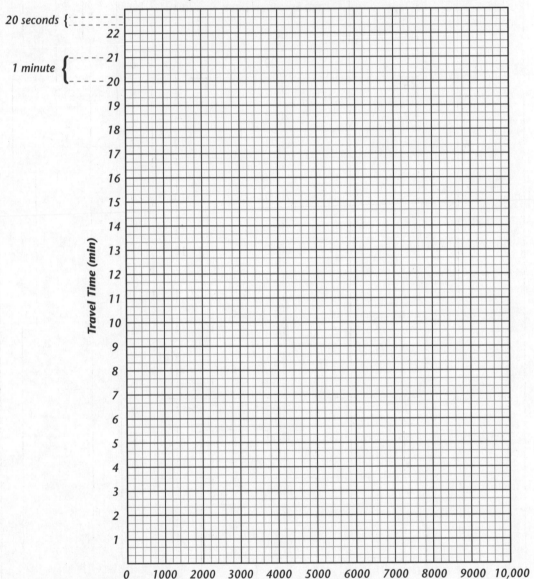

Earthquake S Wave and P Wave Travel-Time Graph

Analyze and Conclude

1. If an earthquake occurred near you, would P waves or S waves reach you first? Explain your answer.

_____

_____

Earthquakes ▪ *Laboratory Investigation*

2. How long would it take a P wave to travel 8000 km from an earthquake epicenter? How long would it take an S wave to travel the same distance?

_____

3. Approximately how far is an observer from an earthquake epicenter if he or she observed a P wave 8 min after the earthquake?

_____

4. How could you tell which of two observers was farther from an earthquake epicenter by comparing the arrival times of P and S waves for the two locations?

_____

_____

Critical Thinking and Applications

1. How far from an earthquake epicenter is an observer who measured a difference of 8 min 40 s in the arrival times of P and S waves?

_____

2. If a curve for surface waves were added to the graph, where would it appear? Explain.

_____

3. States along the West Coast, such as California and Washington, have much earthquake and volcanic activity. What does this activity indicate about the underlying rock structure of this part of the country?

_____

_____

More to Explore

Tie a piece of colorful yarn to a coil near the middle of a spring toy. Move the spring to create a P wave. Then move the spring to create an S wave. Which wave travels faster? Which kind of wave produces the most overall motion of the yarn? Which wave would cause more damage as a seismic wave?

_____

_____

_____

_____

Modeling the Effects of Fault Movements

In this activity, students are presented with the problem of creating a model to show the effects of strike-slip, normal, and reverse faults on a surface feature, such as a river, road, or fence. To solve this problem, students will apply the concepts they have learned about the different directions of movement in these types of faults.

Expected Outcome

Students should devise models in which a surface feature crosses the fault. If it does not, the feature will not be bent or broken at the fault when the blocks are moved. To show a strike-slip fault, students should move the two "rock" blocks horizontally past each other, with no upward or downward movement. The feature will be displaced sideways after movement occurs. To show a normal fault, students should move the top block (the hanging wall) downward past the bottom block (the footwall). The part of the feature on the hanging wall will sink below the part on the footwall. To show a reverse fault, students should move the hanging wall upward past the footwall. The part of the feature on the hanging wall will be raised above the part on the footwall.

Content Assessed

This activity assesses students' understanding of the different types of stress that occur in Earth's crust and the different types of faults that these stresses cause.

Skills Assessed

making models, observing, comparing and contrasting

Materials

Give each student enough modeling compound of each of two or three colors to model a block of layered rock.

Each student will need a plastic knife to cut the modeled block of layered rock to form a fault.

Provide a variety of stiff, straight objects (such as popsicle sticks, pretzels, and toothpicks), glue, and string for students' use in building model fences, telephone poles and wires, and the like.

Time

30 minutes

Safety

Caution students to handle the knife carefully. Although it is plastic, its edge could still cut a student if he or she applied too much pressure.

Monitoring the Task

Review students' drawings before they build their models. Make sure that they have shown the surface feature crossing the fault, not paralleling it on the surface of one block. If any students have not shown the surface feature crossing the fault, ask them to explain what they think will happen to the feature when the two fault blocks are moved.

Let students show more than one surface feature if they wish. For example, they could include a road crossing the fault, a row of telephone poles on one side of the road, and a fence on the other side. Students may include features that are parallel to the fault so long as at least one feature crosses it.

Also check the arrows on the drawings to make sure that students will be modeling the block movement correctly for each type of fault.

Modeling the Effects of Fault Movements

In assessing students' performance, use the following rubric.

	4	3	2	1
Planning and Constructing the Model	The student's drawing shows the surface feature crossing the fault and the arrows drawn in the correct directions for each type of fault; the model demonstrates correct block movement and appropriate deformation of the surface feature.	The student's drawing is complete but slightly flawed; the model is mostly effective in demonstrating correct block movement and appropriate deformation of the surface feature.	The student's drawing is incomplete and/or flawed but shows that a sincere attempt was made; the model does not fully demonstrate block movement and appropriate deformation of the surface feature.	The student's drawing is incomplete or mostly inaccurate, and the model fails to demonstrate block movement and appropriate deformation of the surface feature.
Concept Understanding	The student demonstrates a mastery of the concepts that underlie the model, including the different types of faults and the type of stress and direction of movement of each.	The student demonstrates an adequate understanding of the concepts that underlie the model, including the different types of faults and the type of stress and direction of movement of each.	The student demonstrates only a partial understanding of the concepts that underlie the model, including the different types of faults and the type of stress and direction of movement of each.	The student demonstrates little or no understanding of the concepts that underlie the model, including the different types of faults and the type of stress and direction of movement of each.

Earthquakes • *Performance Assessment*

Modeling the Effects of Fault Movements

Problem

How can you construct a model to show how movements along strike-slip, normal, and reverse faults affect such features as a river, a road, or a fence on the land surface?

Suggested Materials

- modeling compound in two or more colors
- plastic knife
- straight, stiff objects such as popsicle sticks, pretzels, or toothpicks
- glue
- string

Devise a Plan

1. Use the modeling compound and the knife to make two blocks of layered rock separated by a fault.

2. Think of a way that you could use the other materials to model a feature on the land surface—a road, a fence, or a row of telephone poles, for example.

3. On a separate sheet of paper, draw the model you plan to make. Label it with arrows to show how you will move the blocks for each type of fault.

4. Use your model to show what happens to the surface feature when movement occurs along a strike-slip fault.

5. Repeat Step 4 for a normal fault. (Repair the feature first, if necessary.)

6. Repeat Step 4 for a reverse fault. (Repair the feature again, if necessary.)

Analyze and Conclude

Answer the following questions on a separate sheet of paper.

1. How did you move the two blocks to show a strike-slip fault? What happened to the surface feature when the blocks moved?

2. How did you move the two blocks to show a normal fault? What happened to the surface feature?

3. How did you move the two blocks to show a reverse fault? What happened to the surface feature?

Earthquakes

Multiple Choice

Write the letter of the correct answer on the line.

_____ 1. A force that acts on rock to change its shape or volume is called
   a. stress.
   b. folding.
   c. faulting.
   d. liquefaction.

_____ 2. Which type of seismic wave arrives first at a seismograph?
   a. surface waves
   b. tsunamis
   c. S waves
   d. P waves

_____ 3. Anticlines and synclines are two types of
   a. seismic waves.
   b. folds.
   c. faults.
   d. aftershocks.

_____ 4. The point beneath Earth's surface where the crust breaks and triggers an earthquake is called the
   a. epicenter.
   b. fault.
   c. focus.
   d. magnitude.

_____ 5. Which stress force pulls on the crust and stretches rock?
   a. shearing
   b. tension
   c. liquefaction
   d. compression

_____ 6. A break in the crust where slabs slip past each other is a(n)
   a. fold.
   b. epicenter.
   c. hanging wall.
   d. fault.

_____ 7. An instrument used to measure and record ground movements during an earthquake is called a(n)
   a. seismograph.
   b. laser-ranging device.
   c. creep meter.
   d. moment magnitude scale.

_____ 8. What process occurs when an earthquake's shaking turns loose soil into mud?
   a. deformation
   b. shearing
   c. liquefaction
   d. base-isolation

_____ 9. What type of fault forms when the hanging wall moves upward past the footwall?
   a. normal fault
   b. fault-block mountain
   c. strike-slip fault
   d. reverse fault

_____ 10. The type of stress force that produces a strike-slip fault is
   a. compression.
   b. shearing.
   c. tension.
   d. liquefaction.

Earthquakes ▪ *Chapter Test*

Completion

Fill in the line to complete each statement.

11. Compression, tension, and shearing are three types of

_____ that cause changes in the crust.

12. A large area of flat land that is elevated high above sea level is known as

a(n) _____.

13. The _____ is a rating system that estimates the total energy released by an earthquake.

14. The point on Earth's surface directly above an earthquake's focus is

called the _____.

15. Water displaced by an undersea earthquake may produce

_____.

True or False

If the statement is true, write true *on the line. If it is false, change the underlined word or words to make the statement true.*

_____ **16.** A base-isolated building design <u>increases</u> the amount of energy that reaches the building during an earthquake.

_____ **17.** The type of stress that pushes masses of rock sideways in opposite directions is <u>tension</u>.

_____ **18.** S waves arrive at a seismograph <u>after</u> P waves.

_____ **19.** By drawing circles to show distances from three seismograph stations, geologists can locate the <u>magnitude</u> of an earthquake.

_____ **20.** <u>Folding</u> of the crust produces anticlines and synclines.

Essay

Write an answer for each of the following on a separate sheet of paper.

21. Name the three stress forces that cause changes in Earth's crust. Explain how each type of force affects rock. Identify the type of fault that each force produces.

22. Describe what people can do to protect themselves if they are indoors when an earthquake strikes.

Name _____ Date _____ Class_____

Using Science Skills: Applying Concepts

Use the table and graph to answer the questions below.

Location of Seismograph		
City	**Time for P Waves to Arrive**	**Time for S Waves to Arrive**
Chicago, Illinois	3 min, 45 s	7 min, 0 s
Savannah, Georgia	4 min, 50 s	8 min, 55 s
Seattle, Washington	2 min, 50 s	5 min, 30 s

23. What is the difference between P and S wave arrival times in each city?

Chicago: _____

Savannah: _____

Seattle: _____

24. What is each city's distance from the epicenter?

Chicago: _____

Savannah: _____

Seattle: _____

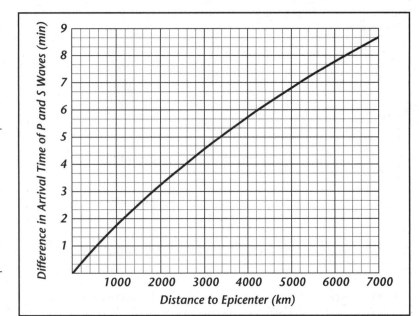

25. How could you use this information to locate the earthquake's epicenter?

_____

_____

_____

Earthquakes · *Chapter Test*

Using Science Skills

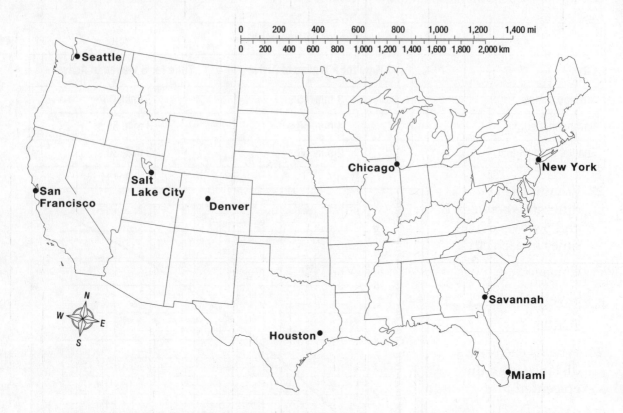

Use this map, the graph on the previous page, and your answers from Question 24 to respond to the following items.

26. Measuring Draw circles on the map to show the distance from Chicago, Savannah, and Seattle to the earthquake's epicenter.

27. Interpreting Diagrams Where was the earthquake's epicenter located?

_____

Essay

Write your responses to the following items on a separate sheet of paper.

28. Describe the differences between the Mercalli scale, the Richter scale, and the moment magnitude scale.

29. Name four instruments that geologists use to monitor movements along faults, and explain how each instrument works.

30. Why is it so difficult for geologists to predict earthquakes?

Chapter Project

Worksheet 1

1. 1 cm = 2 cm.
2. *Length:* 15 cm; *Width:* 7. 5 cm; *Height:* 12.5 cm.
3. The floor plan should be a rectangle 15 cm by 7. 5 cm. The wall elevation should be a rectangle 15 cm by 12. 5 cm. Make sure students label their drawings with the scale.

Worksheet 2

4. The frame bends sideways; the paper wrinkles or may start to tear.
5. The paper will tear.
7. Students could try placing straws horizontally, vertically, and/or diagonally within the frame; diagonal straws will offer the best support. Toothpicks or straws could be used to make diagonal braces at the corners. Students might suggest that popsicle sticks or triangular pieces cut from index cards would be even stronger as corner braces.

Forces in Earth's Crust
Guided Reading and Study

Use Target Reading Skills Check student definitions for accuracy.
1. b
2. volume
3. a. tension **b.** compression **c.** shearing
4. a. Compression **b.** Shearing **c.** Stretches rock **d.** Squeezes rock **e.** Rock becomes thinner in the middle **f.** Rock breaks and slips apart or changes its shape **g.** Tension
5. Fault
6. b
7. c
8. a
9. False
10. a, d
11. a, d
12. a. Tension **b.** Compression **c.** Strike-slip **d.** Normal **e.** Horizontal **f.** Vertical **g.** Normal and reverse; both have vertical movement. Vertical movement can push up rock.
13. b
14. c

15. a
16. a
17. c
18. b
19. a
20. a, b, c
21. A large area of flat land elevated high above sea level

Forces in Earth's Crust
Review and Reinforce

1. a. reverse fault **b.** compression **c.** hanging wall moves up
2. a. normal fault **b.** tension **c.** hanging wall moves down
3. a. strike-slip fault **b.** shearing **c.** blocks move sideways in opposite directions
4. Stress that pushes a mass of rock in two opposite directions
5. The block of rock that lies above a fault
6. A rock fold that bends downward in the middle to form a bowl
7. The rock that lies below a fault
8. A force that acts on rock to change its shape or volume
9. A rock fold that bends upward into an arch
10. A large area of flat land elevated high above sea level

Forces in Earth's Crust
Enrich

Fault 1—Strike-slip fault: The two blocks of rock on either side of the fault moved sideways in opposite directions. The road and fences broke at the fault line, and the two halves of each structure were displaced.
Fault 2—Reverse fault: The block in the foreground (the hanging wall) moved upward along the fault. The river could no longer flow across the fault. Instead, the water collected at the base of the fault (on the footwall) to form a lake. Without water flowing into it, the part of the river on the hanging wall ran dry.
Fault 3—Normal fault: The block in the foreground (the hanging wall) moved downward along the fault, creating a waterfall where the river crosses the fault.

Earthquakes and Seismic Waves
Guided Reading and Study

Use Target Reading Skills. This is one possible way to complete the graphic organizer. Accept all logical answers. **a.** P waves compress and expand the ground. **b.** S waves vibrate from side to side as well as up and down. **c.** Surface waves produce severe ground movements.

1. focus.
2. epicenter
3. vibrations that travel through Earth carrying the energy released during an earthquake
4. true
5. a, b, c
6. **A.** P waves **B.** S waves
7. false
8. c
9. b
10. a
11. seismograph
12. **a.** Mercalli scale **b.** Richter scale **c.** moment magnitude scale
13. **a.** The Mercalli scale uses a 12-point scale to rate earthquakes by how much damage they cause at particular locations. **b.** The Richter scale rates the magnitude of an earthquake based on the strength of its seismic waves. **c.** The moment magnitude scale determines an earthquake's magnitude using data on both seismic waves and fault movement.
14. false
15. **a.** a particular seismograph's location **b.** the distance from that seismograph to the epicenter

Earthquakes and Seismic Waves
Review and Reinforce

1. Seismic waves are vibrations that travel through Earth, carrying the energy released during an earthquake.
2. P waves travel fastest, so they would arrive first, followed by S waves, then surface waves.
3. surface waves
4. The moment magnitude scale provides an estimate of the total energy released by an earthquake. It can be used to rate earthquakes of all sizes, regardless of whether they occur close by or far away.
5. Geologists measure the difference between the arrival times of the P waves and S waves at three or more seismographs. Using these differences, they determine the distance of the epicenter from each seismograph and plot the distances as circles on a map. The epicenter is located where the three circles intersect.
6. c
7. e
8. b
9. a
10. d

Earthquakes and Seismic Waves
Enrich

1. *Richter scale:* New Madrid at 8.7; *moment magnitude scale:* Arauco at 9.5
2. San Fernando, Mexico City, San Francisco 1989, Northridge, Kobe
3. Arauco and Anchorage
4. New Madrid and San Francisco 1906
5. Magnitudes based on the moment magnitude and Richter scales are different because each scale uses different types of data. The Richter scale rates an earthquake based on the size of its seismic waves as measured by a seismograph. The moment magnitude scale uses additional data to rate the total energy released by an earthquake.

Skills Lab

Finding the Epicenter

For answers, see Teacher's Edition.

Monitoring Earthquakes
Guided Reading and Study

Use Target Reading Skills This is one possible way to complete the graphic organizer. Accept all logical answers. **a.** Drum rotates. **b.** Pen traces a record of the vibrations.

1. The P waves arrive first, followed by S waves, then surface waves.
2. **a.** tiltmeter **b.** creep meter **c.** laser-ranging device **d.** GPS satellite
3. c
4. b
5. d
6. a
7. **a.** GPS satellite **b.** tiltmeter
8. laser-ranging device
9. GPS satellite
10. The waves' speed and direction change slightly.
11. Geologists use the data to map the fault's length and depth. They can learn the location of hidden faults.
12. friction
13. false

Monitoring Earthquakes
Review and Reinforce

1. Fault-monitoring instruments measure changes in Earth's crust along faults. These changes may signal that an earthquake is about to occur.
2. The locations of active faults and the locations of past earthquakes.
3. **a.** *Any three:* Seattle, San Francisco, Los Angeles, Salt Lake City, Charleston, Boston **b.** Phoenix, St. Louis, Atlanta **c.** *Any three:* Denver, Minneapolis, Chicago, New Orleans, Cleveland, New York, Philadelphia
4. Creep meter, laser-ranging device, tiltmeter, satellite
5. *Creep meter:* A wire stretched across a fault measures horizontal movement of the ground. *Laser-ranging device:* A laser beam bounced off the ground detects slight fault movements. *Tiltmeter:* Detects tilting of the ground along a fault by measuring the depth of liquid in two connected bulbs. *Satellite:* Bounces radio waves off the ground to detect small changes in elevation along faults.

Monitoring Earthquakes
Enrich

1. Parkfield
2. less than 10 percent
3. Slow, continual movement prevents stress from building up in the rocks; energy is released frequently in very small amounts rather than suddenly in a severe earthquake.
4. The rocks on either side of the fault there probably lock together and do not move until enough stress builds up to overcome the friction.
5. Geologists use creep meters and laser-ranging devices to measure horizontal movements along a fault. They use tiltmeters and satellite monitors to measure distortions in the land surface. Seismographs can also provide a record of activity along a fault.

Technology Lab

Design a Seismograph

For answers, see Teacher's Edition.

Earthquake Safety
Guided Reading and Study

Use Target Reading Skills. This is one possible way to complete the graphic organizer. Accept all logical answers.

Earthquake Safety

Question	Answer
Where is the quake risk the highest?	Earthquake risk is the highest along faults and where past earthquakes have occurred.
How do earthquakes cause damage?	Earthquake damage occurs as a result of shaking, liquefaction, aftershocks, and tsunamis.
How can you stay safe during an earthquake?	The best way to stay safe during an earthquake is to drop, cover, and hold.
What makes buildings safer from earthquakes?	New buildings can be made safer from earthquakes by being built stronger and with greater flexibility. Older buildings can be modified to withstand stronger quakes.

1. where faults are active and where past earthquakes have occurred
2. d
3. The shaking can trigger landslides or avalanches. It also can damage or destroy buildings and bridges, topple utility poles, and fracture gas and water mains. It can tear buildings apart.
4. the types of rock and soil
5. false
6. liquefaction; moisture (or water)
7. aftershock
8. tsunamis
9. falling objects and flying glass
10. false
11. false
12. Fasten it to wall studs.
13. Remove heavy items from the walls above beds. Position beds away from windows.
14. Reinforce or strengthen the walls. Plywood panels can strengthen the walls. Metal connectors can strengthen the house's frame.
15. The home should be anchored to solid rock below the soil.
16. It rests on shock-absorbing rubber pads or springs.
17. Earthquakes can cause gas pipes and water mains to break.

Earthquake Safety
Review and Reinforce

1. Earthquakes can damage or destroy buildings, bridges, and other structures; topple utility poles; fracture gas and water mains; and trigger landslides, avalanches, and tsunamis.
2. Seismic waves transfer energy from hard, dense rock to loosely packed soil. The loose soil shakes more violently than the surrounding rock. The thicker the layer of soil, the more violent the shaking. Buildings constructed on solid rock will shake less and suffer less damage than buildings constructed on loose soil.
3. The buildings may have been weakened in the large earthquake and may collapse during an aftershock.
4. When tsunamis reach the shallower water near land, their wavelength decreases, causing their wave height to increase.
5. Drop, cover, and hold; crouch under a protective object such as a table or desk or against an inner wall, and cover your head and neck with your arms; avoid the outer walls, glass objects, wall hangings, and furniture that might fall over.
6. After an earthquake, people may be injured and without water, power, and food sources.
7. A base-isolated building; the pads or springs in the building's foundation act as shock absorbers, reducing the amount of energy that reaches the building during an earthquake so that it sways back and forth gently instead of shaking violently.
8. tsunamis
9. liquefaction
10. aftershock

Earthquake Safety
Enrich

1. Accept all reasonable responses. Examples: Unprotected glass; furniture and storage units that might fall over; decorative items hanging on walls or from ceilings; heavy items stored on high shelves; weak structures that need additional support.
2. a. Move the glassware and microscopes to a low cabinet with a door that latches.
b. Secure bookcases to the wall studs with sturdy brackets; remove heavy items from the upper shelves.
c. Teach several other staff members where the lines are and how to shut them off.
3. "Drop, cover, and hold." (Students may include details about what that means.)

Key Terms

1. earthquake
2. syncline
3. compression
4. plateau
5. stress
6. aftershock

7. tsunami
8. shearing
9. anticline
10. liquefaction
11. footwall
12. seismograph

Earthquakes

```
s  t  i  o  n  s  c  o  d  d  l  n  p  m
f  a  e  a  r  t  h  q  u  a  k  e  v  l
w  a  f  t  e  r  s  h  o  c  k  n  d  i
y  t  o  n  e  e  q  u  r  c  a  f  t  q
d  u  p  c  o  s  h  e  a  r  i  n  g  u
s  w  n  o  f  s  a  z  s  e  p  t  w  e
e  g  o  m  i  p  h  o  r  v  a  d  t  f
i  n  m  p  f  g  t  p  u  l  a  c  m  a
s  o  d  r  s  y  n  c  l  i  n  e  p  c
m  w  c  e  o  m  u  a  q  a  v  b  c  t
o  v  e  s  j  m  w  u  c  k  t  i  b  i
g  l  n  s  o  t  h  u  m  b  b  e  y  o
r  a  t  i  o  k  v  o  o  x  l  e  a  n
a  w  o  o  p  l  y  i  m  s  s  a  h  u
p  u  f  n  t  t  s  u  n  a  m  i  s  s
h  a  l  e  t  a  n  t  i  c  l  i  n  e
```

Connecting Concepts

Develop a concept map that uses the key concepts and key terms from this chapter. Keep in mind the main idea of this chapter: Forces inside Earth cause rocks to move and to release energy as seismic waves during an earthquake. The concept map shown is one way to organize how the information in this chapter is related. You may use an extra sheet of paper.

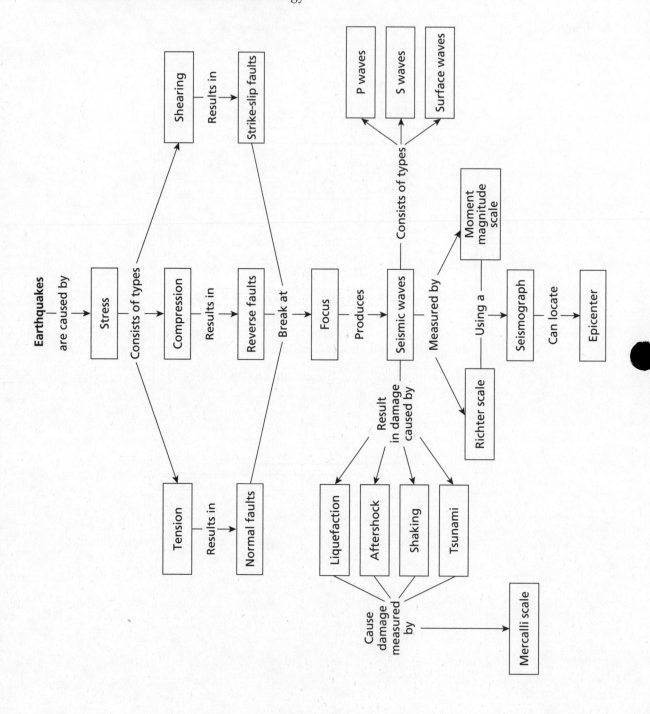

Laboratory Investigation

Investigating the Speed of Earthquake Waves

Pre-Lab Discussion

1. Stress in the subsurface rock causes the rock to break or slip, releasing energy stored in the rock.
2. The point on Earth's surface that is directly above an earthquake's focus.

Analyze and Conclude

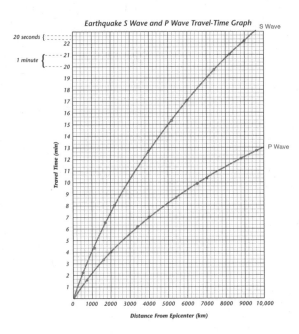

Earthquake S Wave and P Wave Travel-Time Graph

1. P waves travel faster and would arrive first. However, if you were near the epicenter, the difference might be negligible.
2. Interpolating from the graph of the data in the table, it would take 11 min 20 s for the P waves to arrive and 20 min 40 s for the S waves to arrive.
3. Interpolating from the graph of the data in the table, the observer is 4,800 km away.
4. The observer who clocked more time between the arrival of the first P and the first S waves would be farther from the epicenter.

Critical Thinking and Applications

1. 7000 km
2. The curve would be above both the P and S curves because surface waves travel slowest.
3. The underlying rock structure is close to a plate boundary and is subject to stress that may break it.

More to Explore

Students should observe that the speed of the compression wave is greater, but the overall movement of the yarn is greater in the transverse wave, reinforcing the concept that S waves cause more damage that P waves do.

Chapter Test

1. a
2. d
3. b
4. c
5. b
6. d
7. a
8. c
9. d
10. b
11. stress (*or* stress forces)
12. plateau
13. moment magnitude scale
14. epicenter
15. tsunamis
16. reduces
17. shearing
18. true
19. epicenter
20. true
21. Shearing pushes rock sideways in opposite directions, creating a strike-slip fault. Tension pulls on rock, creating a normal fault. Compression squeezes rock until it breaks, creating a reverse fault.
22. Drop, cover, and hold. Crouch beneath a table or desk and hold on to it. If a desk or table is not available, crouch against an inner wall and cover your head and neck with your arms. Avoid the outer walls of a building, as well as windows, mirrors, wall hangings, and furniture that might topple.
23. *Chicago:* 3 min 15 s; *Savannah:* 4 min 5 s; *Seattle:* 2 min 40 s
24. *Chicago:* 2,000 km; *Savannah:* 2,650 km; *Seattle:* 1,600 km
25. Draw a circle to scale on a map to show each city's distance from the epicenter. The point at which the three circles intersect is the epicenter.
26. Students must first use the map scale to convert the distances found for Question 22 to the corresponding compass settings. The correct radius of each circle is approximately: Chicago, 6.7 cm; Savannah, 8.7 cm; Seattle, 5.3 cm.

27. In northeastern Arizona

28. The Mercalli scale rates earthquakes based on the intensity of their effects on buildings and the land at a particular location. The Richter scale rates earthquakes based on the size of their seismic waves as measured by a seismograph. The moment magnitude scale rates earthquakes by estimating the total energy they release based on seismographic data and measurements of fault movements.

29. A creep meter uses a wire stretched across a fault to measure horizontal movement of the ground. A laser-ranging device bounces a laser beam off the ground to detect slight fault movements. A tiltmeter measures the depth of liquid in two connected bulbs to detect tilting of the ground. GPS uses a network of Earth-orbiting satellites to measure tiny movements of markers set up on the opposite sides of a fault.

30. *Accept all reasonable answers. Students may mention the following points:* Geologists can monitor movements of the land surface but not movements deep below ground, where earthquakes occur. Geologists hypothesize but do not know for certain that slight movements on the surface signal an impending earthquake. Even if such surface movements are reliable signals, geologists have no way of knowing how soon the earthquake may strike.

Volcanoes

Lab zone Chapter Project # Volcanoes and People

The following steps will walk you through the Chapter Project. Use the hints and detailed directions as you guide your students through the research, planning, and preparations for their documentaries about life in volcanic regions.

Chapter Project Overview

Introduce the project by having students preview some volcanoes presented in the chapter and asking them to suggest ways in which the volcanoes may have affected people living nearby. Encourage students to take notes about the effects that interest them. Suggest that they add other ideas to the list as they think of them.

Make sure students understand that they will be working in small groups to create their documentaries. Explain that group members may divide tasks among themselves any way they wish. Emphasize, though, that every group member should take part in planning the documentary and should be prepared to answer questions about the documentary's content.

After students have read the project description in their textbook, distribute the Chapter Project Overview, which presents the project rules, a list of possible research topics, and hints for researching information and taking notes. Also distribute Chapter Project Worksheet 1, which includes a list of volcanoes that students may want to consider for their documentaries. Explain that each group may choose any volcanic region and any topic the members wish, so long as they are able to find adequate source material for their research.

Set a deadline for the project presentations and interim dates for the benchmarks at the end of Sections 1, 3, and 4. Have students record these dates in the Project Time Line section at the end of the Overview.

Materials and Preparation

Provide a wide variety of age-appropriate source materials for students to use in their research, including encyclopedias, nonfiction library books, magazine articles, and films on videocassette and DVD. If students have access to the Internet in school or at home, encourage them to use that source as well. One appropriate Web site, sponsored by NASA, is Volcano World at volcano.und.nodak.edu.

Also provide index cards for taking notes and self-sticking, removable tags for flagging appropriate information in books.

When students are ready to prepare their multimedia materials, supply a variety of materials and devices—poster paper, art supplies, acetate sheets for making overhead transparencies, videocameras, and tape recorders for taping songs, background music, or sound effects. Also encourage students to use materials and devices from home.

Keep Students on Track— Section 1

Check each group's choice of a volcanic region and topic to avoid duplication. You may want to allow two groups to choose the same region so long as the groups focus on different specific topics.

Distribute Chapter Project Worksheet 2, which provides support for helping students take notes as they do their research.

Monitor students' work as they do their research, and provide assistance as needed. In particular, make sure the members of each group focus on the specific topic they have selected and do not waste time taking notes on unrelated issues.

Keep Students on Track— Section 3

At this point, students should be ready to begin planning their documentaries based on the information they have gathered. Help the groups sift through all their information, select the points they want to include, organize the content into a logical and interesting flow, and plan audiovisual materials to accompany the narrative.

If any groups are unable to find certain information they want to include, provide or suggest additional source materials.

Review the storyboard technique with the entire class. Emphasize that the storyboard should identify the presentation's major steps—each on a separate sheet of paper—so it can serve as an outline of the documentary. If necessary, help students identify and eliminate any fine-level details that do not belong in the storyboard.

Keep Students on Track— Section 4

Remind students of the deadline for the class presentations. Advise them to finish all elements in the documentary before that date so they will have enough time to rehearse and make any final improvements.

Make students responsible for gathering or providing you with a list of any special equipment, such as extension cords, television monitors, or overhead projectors, that they will need for their presentations.

Chapter Project Wrap Up

Encourage students to practice using all the documentary elements—narrative, visuals, audiotapes, videotapes, skits, and so forth—to make sure each is placed appropriately and adds to the presentation's clarity and interest.

Tell the class how much time each group will be allowed for its presentation. Encourage groups to keep this time limit in mind as they rehearse their presentations. If group members find that their presentation is running much too long, suggest that they cut some material rather than speed up the presentation to fit the time limit.

When each group presents its documentary to the rest of the class, encourage the other students to ask questions. Make sure you and the other students give each group positive feedback on its presentation.

Allow time for students to record their evaluations and their ideas for improvements in their journals. Use the textbook's final question—"Did you see any similarities between how people in different regions live with volcanoes?"—as the basis for a whole-class discussion.

Extension

Have the members of each group count off from "one" so each student has a different number. Then let students reassemble with all the "ones" in one group, all the "twos" in another group, and so on. Suggest that each new group discuss the following questions: What was the most difficult part of creating the documentary? What was the easiest part? What was the most interesting thing my group learned about the volcano we chose?

Volcanoes

Volcanoes · *Chapter Project*

Lab zone Chapter Project Volcanoes and People

How do volcanoes affect the people who live near them? In this project, you and the other members of your group will try to answer this question by making a documentary about life in a volcanic region.

First, your group will choose a volcano or volcanic region and one topic to research about how people nearby are affected. For example, your group could decide to find out how people have benefited from living near a volcano or the ways people show volcanoes in their art and stories. Your group may choose any volcano or volcanic region and any topic you want, so long as you are able to find enough information to create a good documentary.

Next, your group will research information about the volcanic region and topic you chose. As you do your research, you will need to take notes. Your group will use the notes to plan and then write your documentary. Some of the information can be presented by a speaker. Other information might be better as a visual—a poster, an overhead transparency, computer art, or a mural, for example. Some information could be presented in a video, a song, or a skit—either "live" or on tape.

Your group will have time to rehearse your documentary and practice using the audiovisual materials. After you have made final changes, your group will present the documentary to the class.

Project Rules

- With the other members of your group, choose a volcano or volcanic region to study. Also decide on one topic to research about how people there have been affected.

- Research the volcano or volcanic region and topic your group has chosen. Your teacher may provide some materials for your research. You can use other materials of your own choice. As you do your research, take notes on the information you find.

- Work with the other group members to plan your documentary. Decide which pieces of researched information best fit the topic you chose. Decide how to present each piece of information. Make a storyboard that shows each major step in your group's presentation. Identify the audiovisual materials you will use and where each will be included. Also identify which group member will present each step.

- Use the storyboard as an outline to write your documentary and create the audiovisual materials.

- Rehearse your group's presentation. Make sure it fits the time limit that your teacher has allowed. Make any final changes and improvements.

- With your group, present your documentary to the rest of the class. Be prepared to answer questions about any part of your group's presentation.

Volcanoes • *Chapter Project*   **Overview**

Topic Ideas

Here are some suggestions for topics about how volcanoes have affected people living nearby. Feel free to think of your own topic ideas, too. Your group should choose only one topic to research.

- Hot springs for recreation and health
- Tourism in a volcanic region
- Uses of and products made from volcanic materials
- Volcanic soils and agriculture
- Evacuating people from a volcanic region
- Cleaning up and rebuilding after an eruption
- Archaeological excavations in a volcanic region
- Art and literature about a volcano
- Myths and legends about a volcano
- Geothermal energy

Hints for Researching Information and Taking Notes

- Write down the topic your group has chosen on an index card. When you look through a source for information, refer back to the index card to remind yourself of the topic.

- As you examine each source, ask yourself, "Which information is directly related to my group's topic?" Take notes on only that information.

- Take notes on a separate index card or sheet of paper for each source. Also write down the name of the source.

- At the top of each index card or sheet of paper, write a key word or phrase to tell you what those notes are about. For example, if you are researching how people show volcanoes in their art and you find some information about pictures of volcanoes on pottery, write *Pottery* as the key word. Group all the *Pottery* notes together.

Project Time Line

Task	Due Date
1. Choose a volcano or volcanic region and a topic to research	_____
2. Complete your research	_____
3. Make a storyboard to plan the documentary	_____
4. Write the narrative and create the audiovisual materials	_____
5. Present the documentary to the class	_____

Volcanoes

Volcanoes · *Chapter Project*   **Worksheet 1**

Active Volcanoes and Volcanic Regions Throughout the World

Country	Volcano/Region Names
Chile	Calbuco, Llullaillaco, Villarrica
Colombia	Nevado del Ruiz, Puracé
Congo	Nyamuragira, Nyiragongo
Costa Rica	Arenal, Irazú, Poás
Ecuador	Cotopaxi, Guagua Pichincha, Reventador, Sangay
El Salvador	Izalco
Ethiopia	Erta Alè
Guadeloupe	Soufrière
Guatemala	Fuego, Pacaya, Santa María
Iceland	Askja, Heimaey, Hekla, Krafla, Laki, Surtsey
Indonesia	Agung, Colo, Dieng, Galunggung, Gamalama, Kelut, Krakatau, Merapi, Papandajan, Semeru, Tambora
Italy	Etna, Solfatara, Stromboli, Vesuvius, Vulcano
Japan	Asama, Aso, Bandai, Bayonnaise Rocks, Fuji, Oshima, Sakura-jima, Tarumai, Unzen, Usu
Kamchatka (Russia)	Bezymianny, Karymsky, Kliuchevskoi, Tolbachik
Martinique	Pelée
Mexico	Colima, El Chichón, Paricutín, Popocatépetl
Montserrat	Soufrière Hills
New Zealand	Ruapehu, Tarawera, White Island
Nicaragua	Cerro Negro, Cosegüina, Masaya
Papua New Guinea	Lamington, Rabaul
Peru	El Misti
Philippines	Pinatubo, Mayon, Taal
St. Vincent	La Soufrière
Tanzania	Ol Doinyo Lengai
USA: Alaska	Augustine, Katmai, Pavlof, Redoubt, Shishaldin
California	Lassen Peak
Hawaii	Kilauea, Mauna Loa
Oregon	Mount Hood
Washington	Mount Baker, Mount Rainier, Mount St. Helens
Wyoming	Yellowstone Caldera

Find each of the countries listed above on a world map. Use the map to answer the following questions on a separate sheet of paper.

1. Which countries are in Africa?

2. Which countries or states are islands or island chains?

3. Which countries or states are located around the rim of the Pacific Ocean?

Taking Research Notes

Pretend that your group has decided to study the volcanic region near Naples, Italy, where Mount Vesuvius is located. Your topic is how people have used volcanoes for health benefits. Suppose you found the article below about another volcano near Naples. Follow these directions to practice being an effective notetaker.

1. *Skim the article.* Which paragraphs relate to the topic?

_____

2. *Read the related paragraphs carefully and take notes.* On a separate sheet of paper, write notes about the information you find. You don't need to copy entire sentences from the article. Focus on the most important words and phrases. Remember to label your notes to identify the volcano.

3. *Read the entire article.* Identify three other topics for which this article would be a good source of information.

_____

Solfatara Volcano

Solfatara volcano is located near Naples, Italy. The ancient Romans believed that Solfatara was an entrance to the underworld. The volcano was also thought to be one of Vulcan's workshops. Vulcan was the Roman god of fire, for whom volcanoes are named.

Like many other active volcanoes, Solfatara has vents that release steam and other gases between eruptions. The temperature at some vents can reach 140°C. These vents may be good sources of geothermal energy.

Besides steam, Solfatara's vents also release sulfur gas, which smells like rotten eggs. As the sulfur gas moves away from the vents, it cools and condenses to form solid crystals. Sulfur is mined for many uses, particularly in manufacturing. For example, sul-fur is added to rubber to strengthen it—a process called vulcanization.

The steam and gases from Solfatara's vents are believed to have special healing powers. Since early Roman times, visitors have taken steam baths at Solfatara to treat arthritis and breathing problems and to get the supposed health benefits of "sweat baths."

At some of Solfatara's vents, sulfur gas bubbles up through mud that the gas itself has created. Sulfur is acidic. As the gas rises through cracks underground, it corrodes the rock around it, creating a large pool of hot mud at the surface. The mud in some pools is scorching hot. In other pools, the mud is cool enough for people to soak in it. Mud baths are a popular treatment for softening the skin.

Lab zone™ Chapter Project

Volcanoes and People

In evaluating how well you complete the Chapter Project, your teacher will judge your work in three categories. In each, a score of 4 is the best rating.

	4	3	2	1
Researching Information and Taking Notes	Consults a wide variety of appropriate source materials. Research notes are well organized and focused on the topic.	Consults an adequate variety of source materials. Research notes are fairly well organized; most notes are related to the topic.	Consults more than three source materials. Research notes are somewhat unorganized and generally unrelated to the topic.	Consults only one or two source materials. Research notes are disorganized and generally unrelated to the topic.
Planning, Creating, and Presenting the Documentary	Documentary is well organized, clear, interesting, and focused on the topic. Audiovisual materials are creative and well-integrated.	Documentary is organized, fairly clear, interesting, and focused on the topic. Audiovisual materials are used effectively.	Documentary is rather disorganized and not always focused on the topic. Uses few audiovisual materials.	Documentary is disorganized and unclear, includes much unrelated information, and makes poor use of audiovisual materials.
Working Cooperatively	Takes a lead in planning, writing, and presenting the documentary, including suggesting ideas for and creating audiovisual materials. Successfully leads group to share responsibilities; helps allocate tasks based on group members' skills and interests.	Actively participates in planning, writing, and presenting the documentary, including offering ideas for audiovisual materials. Cooperates with others in sharing responsibilities; volunteers for specific tasks.	Participates in most aspects of planning, writing, and presenting the documentary but offers few ideas. Undertakes responsibilities and tasks at others' direction.	Participates marginally in planning, writing, and presenting the documentary; may create a simple audiovisual material suggested by others. Does not carry out all responsibilities and tasks assigned by others.

Volcanoes and Plate Tectonics

 2 periods, 1 block

Objectives

F.3.1.1 Identify where Earth's volcanic regions are located and explain why they are found there.

F.3.1.2 Explain how hot spot volcanoes form.

Key Terms

• volcano • magma • lava • Ring of Fire • island arc • hot spot

Local Standards

PRETEACH

Build Background Knowledge

Students share their observations about volcanoes they have seen firsthand or on TV or film.

 **Discover Activity** *Where Are Volcanoes Found on Earth's Surface?* **L1**

Targeted Resources

❏ **All in One Teaching Resources**
   L2 Reading Strategy Transparency F24: Asking Questions
❏ **PresentationExpress™ CD-ROM**

INSTRUCT

Volcanoes and Plate Boundaries

Use board sketches to review the types of plate boundaries and to help students determine where along the boundaries volcanoes are likely to form.

Hot Spot Volcanoes

Guide students to discuss characteristics of volcanoes on Hawaii and predict what will happen when Hawaii moves away from the hot spot.

 **Skills Lab** *Mapping Earthquakes and Volcanoes* **L2**

Targeted Resources

❏ **All in One Teaching Resources**
   L2 Guided Reading, pp. 185–187
   L2 Transparencies F25, F26, F27
   L2 Lab: *Mapping Earthquakes and Volcanoes,* pp. 190–192
❏ **Lab Activity Video/DVD**
   Skills Lab: *Mapping Earthquakes and Volcanoes*
❏ **PHSchool.com** Web Code: cfd-1031
❏ **Student Edition on Audio CD**

ASSESS

Section Assessment Questions

Have students use their completed graphic organizers with their questions and answers to answer the questions.

Reteach

Students make a chart that compares the differences in how volcanoes form.

Targeted Resources

❏ **All in One Teaching Resources**
   Section Summary, p. 184
   L1 Review and Reinforce, p. 188
   L3 Enrich, p. 189

Volcanoes

Volcanoes • *Section Summary*

Volcanoes and Plate Tectonics

Key Concepts

■ Where are most of Earth's volcanoes?

■ How do hot spot volcanoes form?

A **volcano** is a weak spot in the crust where molten material, or magma, comes to the surface. **Magma** is a molten mixture of rock-forming substances, gases, and water from the mantle. When magma reaches the surface, it is called **lava.** When lava has cooled, it forms solid rock. Lava released during volcanic activity builds up Earth's surface.

Volcanoes occur in belts that extend across continents and oceans. One major volcanic belt is the **Ring of Fire,** formed by the many volcanoes that rim the Pacific Ocean. **Volcanic belts form along the boundaries of Earth's plates.** At plate boundaries, huge pieces of the crust diverge (pull apart) or converge (push together). As a result, the crust often fractures, allowing magma to reach the surface. Most volcanoes form along diverging plate boundaries such as mid-ocean ridges and along converging plate boundaries where subduction takes place. Along the rift valley, lava pours out of cracks in the ocean floor, gradually building new mountains.

Many volcanoes form near converging plate boundaries where oceanic plates return to the mantle. Volcanoes may form where two oceanic plates collide or where an oceanic plate collides with a continental plate. Many volcanoes occur near boundaries where two oceanic plates collide. Through subduction, the older, denser plate sinks beneath a deep-ocean trench into the mantle. Some of the rock above the subducting plate melts and forms magma. Because the magma is less dense than the surrounding rock, it rises toward the surface. Eventually, the magma breaks through the ocean floor, creating volcanoes. The resulting volcanoes create a string of islands called an **island arc.** Volcanoes also occur where an oceanic plate is subducted beneath a continental plate.

Some volcanoes result from "hot spots" in Earth's mantle. A **hot spot** is an area where material from within the mantle rises and then melts, forming magma. **A volcano forms above a hot spot when magma erupts through the crust and reaches the surface.** A hot spot in the ocean floor can gradually form a series of volcanic mountains. The Hawaiian Islands formed one by one over millions of years as the Pacific plate drifted over a hot spot. Hot spots can also form under the continents. Yellowstone National Park in Wyoming marks a hot spot under the North American plate.

Volcanoes · *Guided Reading and Study*

Volcanoes and Plate Tectonics (pp. 82–85)

This section explains what volcanoes are and identifies where most volcanoes occur.

Use Target Reading Skills

As you preview the headings in this section, complete the graphic organizer with questions in the left column. Then as you read, fill in the answers in the second column.

Volcanoes and Plate Tectonics

Question	Answer
Where are volcanoes found?	Most volcanoes are found along plate boundaries.

Introduction (p. 82)

1. What is a volcano? _____

_____

_____

2. A molten mixture of rock-forming substances, gases, and water from the

mantle is referred to as _____.

3. When magma reaches the surface, it is called _____.

Volcanoes

Volcanoes · *Guided Reading and Study*

Volcanoes and Plate Tectonics *(continued)*

Volcanoes and Plate Boundaries (pp. 83–84)

4. What is the Ring of Fire? _____

_____

_____

5. Where do most volcanoes form? _____

_____

_____

6. Describe how volcanoes form along the mid-ocean ridges. _____

_____

_____

7. Is the following sentence true or false? Volcanoes can form along

diverging plate boundaries on land. _____

8. Is the following sentence true or false? Many volcanoes form near
converging plate boundaries where oceanic crust returns to the mantle.

_____

9. How does subduction at converging plate boundaries lead to the

formation of volcanoes? _____

_____

_____

_____

_____

10. Volcanoes at boundaries where two oceanic plates collide create a string

of islands called a(n) _____.

11. What are three major island arcs? _____

_____

12. Circle the letter of the types of plates that collided to form the Andes Mountains on the west coast of South America.

   a. two oceanic plates

   b. a continental plate and an oceanic plate

   c. a continental plate and an island plate

   d. two continental plates

Hot Spot Volcanoes (p. 85)

13. What is a hot spot? _____

   _____

   _____

14. How did the Hawaiian Islands form? _____

   _____

15. Is the following sentence true or false? Hot spots form only under

   oceanic crust. _____

   _____

Volcanoes · *Review and Reinforce*

Volcanoes and Plate Tectonics

Understanding Main Ideas

Answer the following questions on a separate sheet of paper.

1. How do volcanoes change Earth's surface?

2. Why do so many of Earth's volcanoes occur along plate boundaries?

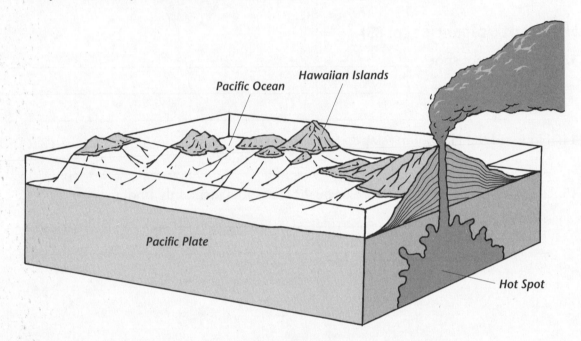

3. Explain how the hot spot shown in the diagram above created the Hawaiian Islands. Draw an arrow on the diagram to help explain the process.

Building Vocabulary

Answer the following questions on a separate sheet of paper.

4. What is the difference between magma and lava?

5. Define each of these terms in your own words.
   a. volcano
   b. Ring of Fire
   c. island arc

Volcanoes and Plates

Active Volcanoes

Volcano	Location	Volcano	Location
Arenal	Costa Rica	Mount Rainier	Washington, USA
El Chichón	Mexico	Ol Doinyo Lengai	Congo
El Misti	Peru	Pinatubo	Philippines
Erta Alè	Ethiopia	Rabaul	Papua New Guinea
Falcon	Tonga Islands	Ruapehu	New Zealand
Hekla	Iceland	Tambora	Indonesia
Katmai	Alaska, USA	Unzen	Japan
Mauna Loa	Hawaii, USA	Villarrica	Chile

Find each location listed above on a world map. Compare the location with the map of Earth's plates in your textbook. Then answer the following questions in the spaces provided.

1. Which volcanoes are located along converging plate boundaries?

_____

_____

_____

2. Which volcanoes are located along diverging plate boundaries?

_____

_____

3. Which volcanoes are located at hot spots?

_____

_____

4. Which volcano is in the middle of a continent?

_____

Volcanoes • *Skills Lab*

Mapping Earthquakes and Volcanoes

Problem

Is there a pattern in the locations of earthquakes and volcanoes?

Materials

outline world map showing longitude and latitude
4 pencils of different colors

Procedure

1. Use the information in the data table on the next page to mark the location of each earthquake on the world map that follows the data table. Use one of the colored pencils to draw a letter E inside a circle at each earthquake location.

2. Use a pencil of a second color to mark the locations of the volcanoes on the world map. Indicate each volcano with the letter V inside a circle.

3. Use a third pencil to lightly shade the areas in which earthquakes are found.

4. Use a fourth colored pencil to lightly shade the areas in which volcanoes are found.

Analyze and Conclude

Write your answers on a separate sheet of paper.

1. **Interpreting Data** How are earthquakes distributed on the map? Are they scattered evenly or concentrated in zones?

2. **Interpreting Data** How are volcanoes distributed? Are they scattered evenly or concentrated in zones?

3. **Inferring** From your data, what can you infer about the relationship between earthquakes and volcanoes?

4. **Communicating** Suppose you added the locations of additional earthquakes and volcanoes to your map. Would the overall pattern of earthquakes and volcanoes change? Explain in writing why you think the pattern would or would not change.

Name_____ Date _____ Class_____

Volcanoes ▪ *Skills Lab*

Earthquakes		Volcanoes	
Longitude	Latitude	Longitude	Latitude
120° W	40° N	150° W	60° N
110° E	5° S	70° W	35° S
77° W	4° S	120° W	45° N
88° E	23° N	61° W	15° N
121° E	14° S	105° W	20° N
34° E	7° N	75° W	0°
74° W	44° N	122° W	40° N
70° W	30° S	30° E	40° N
10° E	45° N	60° E	30° N
85° W	13° N	160° E	55° N
125° E	23° N	37° E	3° S
30° E	35° N	145° E	40° N
140° E	35° N	120° E	10° S
12° E	46° N	14° E	41° N
75° E	28° N	105° E	5° S
150° W	61° N	35° E	15° N
68° W	47° S	70° W	30° S
175° E	41° S	175° E	39° S
121° E	17° N	123° E	38° N

More to Explore

On a map of the United States, locate active volcanoes and areas of earthquake activity. Determine the distance from your home to the nearest active volcano.

Volcanoes · *Skills Lab*

Mapping Earthquakes and Volcanoes (continued)

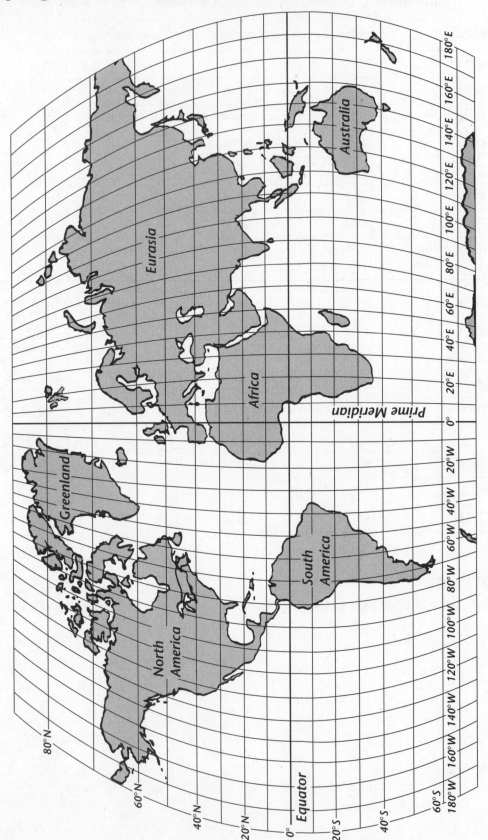

Properties of Magma

Ability Levels Key
L1 Basic to Average
L2 For All Students
L3 Average to Advanced

 1 period, 1/2 block

Objectives

F.3.2.1 Identify some physical and chemical properties of matter.

F.3.2.2 Define viscosity.

F.3.2.3 Explain what factors determine the viscosity of magma.

Key Terms

• element • compound • physical property • chemical property • viscosity • silica • pahoehoe • aa

Local Standards

PRETEACH

Build Background Knowledge

Students discuss the differences in eruptions that flow rapidly and slowly in volcanoes that they have observed on TV or on film.

 How Fast Do Liquids Flow? **L1**

Targeted Resources

❏ **All in One Teaching Resources**
L2 Reading Strategy Transparency F27: Identifying Main Ideas

❏ ⊙ **PresentationExpress™ CD-ROM**

INSTRUCT

Physical and Chemical Properties

Lead a discussion of the differences between these types of properties and classify examples.

What Is Viscosity?

Help students classify liquids as having high or low viscosity.

Viscosity of Magma

Lead a discussion to develop an understanding of the factors that affect viscosity.

Targeted Resources

❏ **All in One Teaching Resources**
L2 Guided Reading, pp. 195–197

❏ **www.SciLinks.org** Web Code: scn-1032

❏ ⊙ **Student Edition on Audio CD**

ASSESS

Section Assessment Questions

Have students use their completed graphic organizers with main ideas and details to answer the questions.

Reteach

Students suggest examples of liquids that have high viscosity and ones that have low viscosity.

Targeted Resources

❏ **All in One Teaching Resources**
Section Summary, p. 194
L1 Review and Reinforce, p. 198
L3 Enrich, p. 199

Volcanoes

Volcanoes · *Section Summary*

Properties of Magma

Key Concepts

- Why is it helpful to know the physical and chemical properties of a substance?

- What causes some liquids to flow more easily than others?

- What factors determine the viscosity of magma?

Like all substances, magma and lava are made up of elements and compounds. An **element** is a substance that cannot be broken down into other substances. A **compound** is a substance made of two or more elements that have been chemically combined. **Each substance has a particular set of physical and chemical properties. These properties can be used to identify a substance or to predict how it will behave.**

A **physical property** is any characteristic of a substance that can be observed or measured without changing the composition of the substance. Examples of physical properties include density, hardness, melting point, boiling point, and whether a substance is magnetic. A **chemical property** is any property that produces a change in the composition of matter. Examples of chemical properties include a substance's ability to burn and its ability to combine, or react, with other substances.

The physical property of liquids called **viscosity** is the resistance of a liquid to flowing. **Because liquids differ in viscosity, some liquids flow more easily than others.** In some liquids, there is a greater degree of friction among the liquid's particles. These liquids have higher viscosity.

The viscosity of magma depends upon its silica content and temperature. The major ingredient in magma is **silica,** a compound made up of particles of the elements oxygen and silicon. The amount of silica in magma helps to determine its viscosity. The more silica magma contains, the higher its viscosity. Magma that is high in silica produces light-colored lava that is too sticky to flow very far. The less silica magma contains, the lower its viscosity. Low-silica magma flows readily and produces dark-colored lava.

Viscosity increases as temperature decreases. The hotter magma is, the lower its viscosity and the more rapidly it flows. Cooler types of magma have high viscosity and flow very slowly. Temperature differences produce two different types of lava. **Pahoehoe** is fast-moving, hot lava that has low viscosity. **Aa** is lava that is cooler and slower-moving. It has higher viscosity than pahoehoe.

Volcanoes • *Guided Reading and Study*

Properties of Magma (pp. 87–90)

This section explains physical and chemical properties, the property of viscosity, and the factors that determine the viscosity of magma.

Use Target Reading Skills

As you read about the viscosity of magma, fill in the detail boxes that explain the main idea in the graphic organizer below.

Main Idea

Magma's viscosity depends on . . .

Detail   **Detail**   **Detail**

Physical and Chemical Properties (pp. 87–88)

1. A substance that cannot be broken down into other substances is called

   a(n) _____.

2. Is the following sentence true or false? When frozen water melts, it is

   undergoing a physical change. _____

3. Circle the statements that indicate a chemical property.

   a. Water boils at 100°C under normal conditions.

   b. When paper is burned, it forms ashes.

   c. An iron chair will develop rust if oxygen combines with the iron.

   d. A basketball is larger than a baseball.

Volcanoes · *Guided Reading and Study*

Properties of Magma *(continued)*

What Is Viscosity? (p. 88)

4. Fill in the blanks: The greater the viscosity, the _____ a liquid flows. The _____ the viscosity, the more easily a liquid flows.

5. Circle the liquids that have a relatively low viscosity.

   a. milk

   b. molasses

   c ketchup

   d. orange juice

   e. milkshake

Viscosity of Magma (pp. 89–90)

6. What factors determine the viscosity of magma? _____

   _____

7. Circle the letter of each sentence that is true about silica.

   a. It is formed from oxygen and nitrogen.

   b. It makes magma thicker.

   c. It is rarely found in the crust.

   d. It produces light-colored lava.

8. The rock _____ forms from light-colored lava.

9. Low-silica magma forms rocks like _____.

10. What happens to viscosity as temperature increases? _____

    _____

11. Hot, fast-moving lava is called _____.

12. Cool, slow-moving lava is called _____.

13. Complete the compare/contrast table to organize the physical and chemical properties of the different types of magma.

Viscosity of Magma	Temperature	Silica Content
High	b.	c.
a.	Higher	d.

e. State the relationship between temperature and silica content in types of magma that have high viscosity and types of magma that have low viscosity.

_____

_____

_____

_____

_____

Properties of Magma

Understanding Main Ideas

Classify each of the following properties by writing Physical *or* Chemical *in the blank beside it.*

_____ 1. Density

_____ 2. Boiling point

_____ 3. Ability to burn

_____ 4. Ability to react with other substances

_____ 5. Hardness

_____ 6. Magnetic quality

Answer the following questions.

7. Why is it helpful to know the physical and chemical properties of a substance? _____

_____

8. Explain why molasses has a higher viscosity than water. _____

_____

_____

9. What is the difference in silica content and viscosity between light-colored and dark-colored magma? _____

_____

_____

10. How does temperature affect viscosity of magma?

_____

Building Vocabulary

Fill in the blank to complete each statement.

11. A substance made of two or more elements that have been chemically combined is called a(n) _____.

12. A(n) _____ is a substance that cannot be broken down into other substances.

13. Fast-moving, hot lava that has low viscosity is called

_____.

14. Lava that is cooler and slower-moving is called _____.

Volcanoes • *Enrich*

Pegmatites

Can you imagine a mineral crystal as big as a truck? Such crystals do exist. They sometimes are found in pegmatites, which are a type of mineral deposit. Pegmatites form from low-viscosity, watery magma. As the magma cools and starts to harden beneath Earth's surface, the magma that's left becomes more and more watery. All of this water lowers the viscosity of the magma, which makes it more fluid. In some cases, the last magma to cool and harden can have a lot of water. In the more fluid magma, atoms are able to move long distances. These atoms combine to form the large crystals found in pegmatites. Pegmatites often contain gems and rare elements. The rare elements are concentrated in the watery magma that forms pegmatites. The table below includes the locations of some important pegmatites in the United States.

Some Important Pegmatites in the United States	
Location	**Characteristic**
Black Hills, South Dakota	Contains crystals more than 10 m long
Petaca, New Mexico	Contains the mineral uraninite, an ore of uranium
Oxford County, Maine	Deposit is mined to obtain lithium, a rare element
Kings Mountain, North Carolina	Includes gem-quality minerals, such as aquamarine

Answer the following questions on a separate sheet of paper.

1. What effect does water have on the viscosity of magma?

2. How do the crystals in pegmatites form?

3. According to the table, which pegmatite in the United States contains uranium ore?

4. Which pegmatite has a lot of aquamarine, a valuable gem?

5. Why are pegmatites important to society?

Volcanoes

Volcanic Eruptions

🕐 *3 periods, 1 1/2 blocks*

Objectives

F.3.3.1 Explain what happens when a volcano erupts.
F.3.3.2 Describe the two types of volcanic eruptions.
F.3.3.3 Identify a volcano's stages of activity.

Key Terms

• magma chamber • pipe • vent • lava flow • crater
• pyroclastic flow • dormant • extinct

Local Standards

PRETEACH

Build Background Knowledge
Students share their observations of what lava looks like as a volcano is erupting and what else comes out of a volcano during an eruption.

 Discover Activity *What Are Volcanic Rocks Like?* **L1**

Targeted Resources

❑ **All in One** Teaching Resources
L2 Reading Strategy Transparency F28: Using Prior Knowledge
❑ ⊙ **PresentationExpress™ CD-ROM**

INSTRUCT

Magma Reaches Earth's Surface
Use the figure A Volcano Erupts and the common meanings of the terms *chamber*, *pipe*, and *vent* to describe the parts of a volcano.

Kinds of Volcanic Eruptions
Describe the interaction of gas pressure and viscosity and show how this interaction determines whether an eruption is quiet or explosive.

Stages of Volcanic Activity
Use the life cycle concept to help students understand the stages of a volcano and develop the definition for each stage.

Targeted Resources

❑ **All in One** Teaching Resources
L2 Guided Reading, pp. 202–206
L2 Transparency F29
❑ **PHSchool.com** Web Code: cfp-1033
❑ ⊙ **Student Edition on Audio CD**

ASSESS

Section Assessment Questions
↺ Have students use their graphic organizers that they completed using prior knowledge to answer the questions.

Reteach
Students list characteristics of quiet and explosive eruptions.

Targeted Resources

❑ **All in One** Teaching Resources
Section Summary, p. 201
L1 Review and Reinforce, p. 207
L3 Enrich, p. 208

Volcanoes ▪ *Section Summary*

Volcanic Eruptions

Key Concepts

■ What happens when a volcano erupts?

■ What are the two types of volcanic eruptions?

■ What are a volcano's stages of activity?

Lava begins as magma in the asthenosphere. Magma flows upward through cracks in the rock until it becomes trapped or reaches the surface to form a volcano.

Inside a volcano, magma collects in a pocket called a **magma chamber.** The magma moves through a **pipe,** a long tube that connects the magma chamber to Earth's surface. There, the magma leaves the volcano through an opening called a **vent.** The area covered by lava as it pours out of a vent is called a **lava flow.** Lava may collect in a **crater,** a bowl-shaped area around a volcano's central vent. As magma rises toward the surface, the pressure decreases and the dissolved gases begin to expand and exert an enormous force. **When a volcano erupts, the force of the expanding gases pushes magma from the magma chamber through the pipe until it flows or explodes out of the vent.**

Geologists classify volcanic eruptions as quiet or explosive. If the magma has a low silica content, it flows easily and the volcano erupts quietly. The gases bubble out gently and the lava oozes quietly. Quiet eruptions can produce both pahoehoe and aa. A volcano erupts explosively if its magma is high in silica. The high-viscosity magma does not flow out of the chamber, but builds up in the pipe. The trapped gases build up pressure until they explode with incredible force. A **pyroclastic flow** occurs when an explosive eruption hurls out ash, cinders, and bombs. Volcano hazards include lava flows, clouds of ash and deadly gases, landslides, and avalanches of mud, snow, or rock.

Geologists often use the terms active, dormant, or extinct to describe a volcano's stage of activity. An active volcano is one that is erupting or has shown signs that it may erupt in the near future. A **dormant** volcano is not active now but may become active in the future. An **extinct** volcano is unlikely to erupt again. Geologists monitor changes in and around volcanoes to try to predict eruptions. But geologists cannot be certain about the type of eruption or how powerful it will be.

Volcanoes

Volcanoes • *Guided Reading and Study*

Volcanic Eruptions (pp. 91–98)

This section explains how volcanoes erupt and describes types of volcanic eruptions as well as other types of volcanic activity. The section also describes how geologists monitor volcanoes and what hazards are associated with volcanoes.

Use Target Reading Skills

As you preview the section headings, write what you know about the topic in the box "What You Know." As you read the section, complete the "What You Learned" box.

What You Know
I. Lava flows out of a volcano.
2.
3.

What You Learned
I.
2.
3.

Introduction (p. 91)

1. Is the following sentence true or false? Magma forms in the lithosphere.

   _____

2. Is the following sentence true or false? Liquid magma rises until it reaches the surface, or until it becomes trapped beneath layers of rock.

   _____

Volcanoes • *Guided Reading and Study*

Magma Reaches Earth's Surface (pp. 92–93)

3. Circle the letter of each feature that all volcanoes share.

    a. pocket of magma beneath the surface

    b. crack to the surface

    c. side vents

    d. crater

4. Label the drawing with the following terms: magma chamber, pipe, vent, and crater.

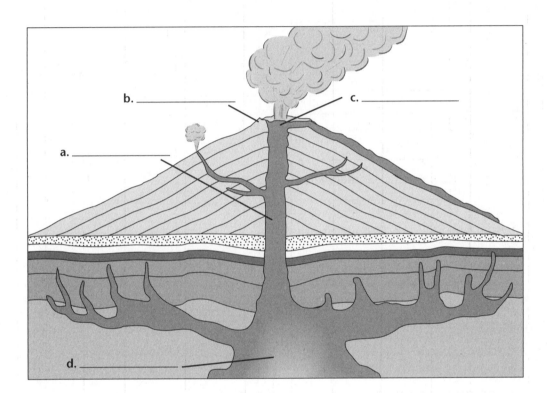

5. What is a lava flow? _____

_____

6. Where does a crater form? _____

_____

7. Is the following sentence true or false? The pipe of a volcano is a horizontal crack in the crust. _____

Volcanoes · *Guided Reading and Study*

Volcanic Eruptions *(continued)*

8. Complete the flowchart showing in what sequence magma moves through a volcano.

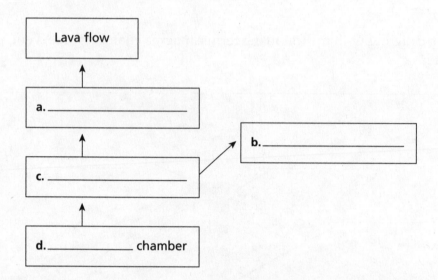

    f. What does the graph show about where magma goes after it leaves the pipes?

_____

9. Circle the letter of the sentence that describes the best model of a volcano erupting.

    a. Carbon dioxide dissolved in soda pop rushes out when the pop is opened.

    b. A car goes faster when the accelerator is pushed.

    c. Water in a pot gets hotter when the pot is heated on a stove.

    d. Clay hardens when it is baked in an oven.

10. What happens during a volcanic eruption? _____

_____

_____

11. What factors determine the force of a volcanic eruption?

_____

Name _____ Date _____ Class_____

Kinds of Volcanic Eruptions (pp. 94–96)

12. Is the following sentence true or false? A volcano erupts quietly if its magma is thick and sticky. _____

Match the type of lava with its description.

Type of Lava

_____ **13.** volcanic ash

_____ **14.** cinders

_____ **15.** bombs

Description

a. Pebble-sized particles

b. Particles ranging from the size of a baseball to the size of a car

c. Fine rocky particles as small as a speck of dust

16. What is a pyroclastic flow? _____

_____

17. Is the following sentence true or false? Volcanic eruptions cause damage only when they are close to the crater's rim. _____

18. What kinds of damage can volcanoes cause?

_____

_____

_____

Stages of Volcanic Activity (pp. 97–98)

19. Is the following sentence true or false? The activity of a volcano may last from less than a decade to more than 10 million years.

_____

20. Is the following sentence true or false? Most long-lived volcanoes erupt continuously. _____

Volcanic Eruptions *(continued)*

21. Complete the compare/contrast table showing the different stages of a volcano.

Volcanic Stages	
Stage	**Description**
a.	Unlikely to erupt ever again
b.	Erupting or showing signs that it soon will erupt
c.	No longer active but may become active again

d. Rank the volcanic stages from least likely to erupt to most likely to erupt: _____

22. Is the following sentence true or false? The length of time between eruptions of a dormant volcano is always less than a thousand years.

_____

23. Why might people living near a dormant volcano be unaware of the danger? _____

_____

24. Circle the letter of each sentence that is true about predicting volcanic eruptions.

    a. Geologists are more successful in predicting volcanic eruptions than earthquakes.

    b. There is never any warning when a volcano will erupt.

    c. Geologists can predict how powerful a volcanic eruption will be.

    d. Geologists cannot predict what type of eruption a volcano will produce.

Name _____ Date _____ Class_____

Volcanoes • *Review and Reinforce*

Volcanic Eruptions

Understanding Main Ideas

Answer the following questions on a separate sheet of paper.

1. Why does magma in the mantle rise through the crust above it?

2. As magma rises toward the surface, what happens to the gases in it? Why?

3. Contrast the viscosity of magma in quiet and explosive eruptions.

4. How does an explosive eruption produce a pyroclastic flow?

5. Identify three hazards of volcanic eruptions.

6. Describe the stages of volcanic activity.

Building Vocabulary

Label the figure below with the names of a volcano's parts.

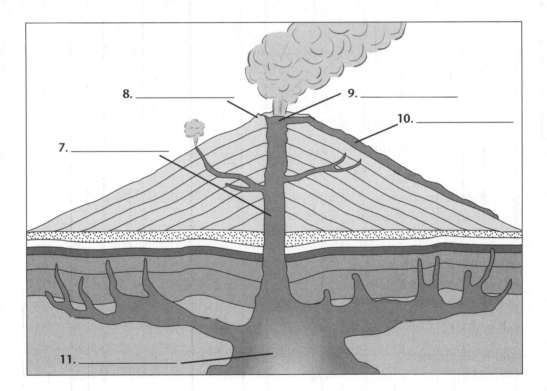

Volcanoes ▪ *Enrich*

Modeling an Eruption

Materials

clear plastic bottle, about 300–350 mL

cup, at least 200 mL

red food coloring

funnel

plastic spoon

baking soda, about 150–175 cc

large, shallow container, such as dishpan or baking pan

vinegar, about 150–175 mL

damp soil or sand

Procedure *Review the safety guidelines in Appendix A.*

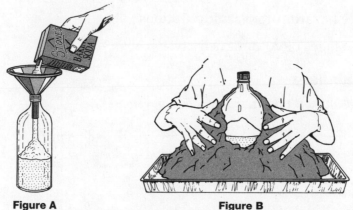

Figure A   Figure B

1. Put the funnel in the mouth of the bottle as shown in Figure A.

2. Pour baking soda into the funnel until the bottle is about half full. Remove the funnel and rinse it clean.

3. Pour vinegar into the cup. The amount of vinegar should be about the same as the amount of baking soda in the bottle.

4. Add a few drops of red food coloring to the vinegar. Stir with the spoon. Add enough food coloring to make the vinegar bright red.

5. Put the bottle in the middle of the shallow container. Shape damp soil or sand around the bottle to make a volcano-shaped mountain as shown in Figure B.

6. Put the funnel in the bottle's mouth again. Pour in the vinegar, then immediately take the funnel out. Stand back and watch what happens.

Analyze and Conclude

Answer the following questions on a separate sheet of paper.

1. What happened when you added vinegar to the bottle?

2. How is this model similar to a real volcanic eruption?

3. How is the model different from a real volcanic eruption?

Volcanic Landforms

 1 period, 1/2 block

Ability Levels Key
L1 Basic to Average
L2 For All Students
L3 Average to Advanced

Objectives

F.3.4.1 List the landforms that lava and ash create.
F.3.4.2 Explain how the magma that hardens beneath Earth's surface creates landforms.
F.3.4.3 Identify other distinct features that occur in volcanic areas.

Key Terms

• shield volcano • cinder cone • composite volcano
• caldera • volcanic neck • dike • sill • batholith
• geothermal activity • geyser

Local Standards

PRETEACH

Build Background Knowledge
Student volunteers draw on the board what they think volcanoes look like.

 **Discover Activity** *How Can Volcanic Activity Change Earth's Surface?* **L1**

Targeted Resources

❏ **All in One Teaching Resources**
L2 Reading Strategy Transparency F30: Outlining

❏ **PresentationExpress™ CD-ROM**

INSTRUCT

Landforms From Lava and Ash
Use blackboard sketches to show how lava with varying viscosities creates different types of landforms.

Landforms From Magma
Show how magma cools and forms rock beneath Earth's surface and describe the magmatic landforms that ultimately emerge from this process.

Geothermal Activity
Ask leading questions to help students compare and contrast hot springs and geysers, and explain how heated groundwater is useful to people.

 Skills Lab *Gelatin Volcanoes* **L2**

Targeted Resources

❏ **All in One Teaching Resources**
L2 Guided Reading, pp. 211–214
L2 Transparencies F31, F32, F33
L2 Lab: *Gelatin Volcanoes*, pp. 216–217

❏ **Lab Activity Video/DVD**
Skills Lab: *Gelatin Volcanoes*

❏ **www.SciLinks.org** Web Code: scn-1034

❏ **Discovery SCHOOL** **Video Field Trip**

❏ **Student Edition on Audio CD**

ASSESS

Section Assessment Questions
Have students use their graphic organizers that they completed using prior knowledge to answer the questions.

Reteach
Students compare quiet and explosive eruptions.

Targeted Resources

❏ **All in One Teaching Resources**
Section Summary, p. 210
L1 Review and Reinforce, p. 215
L3 Enrich, p. 216

Volcanoes

Volcanoes • *Section Summary*

Volcanic Landforms

Key Concepts

- What landforms do lava and ash create?
- How does magma that hardens beneath the surface create landforms?
- What other distinctive features occur in volcanic areas?

Some volcanic landforms are formed when lava flows build up mountains and plateaus on Earth's surface. **Volcanic eruptions create landforms made of lava, ash, and other materials. These landforms include shield volcanoes, composite volcanoes, cinder cone volcanoes, and lava plateaus.**

At some places on Earth's surface, thin layers of lava pour out of a vent. More layers of such lava harden on top of previous layers. The layers gradually build a wide, gently sloping mountain called a **shield volcano.** If a volcano's lava has high viscosity, the lava may explode into the air and harden into ash, cinders, and bombs. These materials pile up around the vent, forming a steep, cone-shaped hill or mountain called a **cinder cone.** Sometimes lava flows alternate with explosive eruptions of ash, cinders, and bombs. The alternating layers form a tall, cone-shaped mountain called a **composite volcano.** Some eruptions of thin, runny lava flow out of cracks and travel a long distance before cooling and hardening. Over millions of years, these layers of lava build up over a large area to form a lava plateau.

An enormous eruption may empty a volcano's main vent and magma chamber. With nothing to support it, the top of the mountain collapses inward. The huge hole left by the collapse of a volcanic mountain is called a **caldera.**

Over time, the hard surface of a lava flow breaks down to form soil. Some volcanic soils are among the most fertile soils in the world. People have settled close to volcanoes to take advantage of the fertile soil.

Sometimes magma rises upward through cracks in the crust but does not reach Earth's surface. The magma cools and hardens into rock beneath the surface. **Features formed by magma include volcanic necks, dikes, and sills, as well as batholiths and dome mountains.** A **volcanic neck** forms when magma hardens in a volcano's pipe. The softer rock around the pipe wears away, exposing the hard rock of the volcanic neck. A **dike** forms when magma forces itself across rock layers and hardens. A **sill** forms when magma squeezes between layers of rock and hardens. When a large body of magma cools inside the crust, a mass of rock called a **batholith** forms. Smaller bodies of hardened magma can form dome mountains.

In **geothermal activity,** magma a few kilometers beneath Earth's surface heats underground water. **Hot springs and geysers are types of geothermal activity that are often found in areas of present or past volcanic activity.** Hot springs collect in a natural pool. A **geyser** is a fountain of water and steam that erupts from the ground.

Volcanic Landforms (pp. 99–105)

This section describes landforms and soils that are created by volcanoes, and types of geothermal activity.

Use Target Reading Skills

As you read about volcanic landforms, use the headings to complete the outline below.

Volcanic Landforms

I. Landforms From Lava and Ash

    A. Shield Volcanoes

    B. _____

    C. _____

    D. Lava Plateaus

    E. _____

    F. _____

II. Landforms From Magma

    A. _____

    B. _____

    C. _____

    D. Dome Mountains

III. _____

    A. Hot Springs

    B. _____

    C. Geothermal Energy

Volcanoes

Volcanoes · *Guided Reading and Study*

Volcanic Landforms *(continued)*

Landforms From Lava and Ash (pp. 100–102)

1. List four landforms created from lava and ash.

    a. _____

    b. _____

    c. _____

    d. _____

2. Circle the letter of each sentence that is true about shield volcanoes.

    a. They form from many thin layers of lava.

    b. They result from quiet eruptions.

    c. They are very steep mountains.

    d. They are formed from ash, cinders, and bombs.

3. Is the following sentence true or false? The Hawaiian Islands are cinder cone volcanoes. _____

4. Name two examples of composite volcanoes. _____

_____

5. Is the following sentence true or false? A composite volcano has both quiet and explosive eruptions. _____

Volcanoes ▪ *Guided Reading and Study*

Match the landform with its description.

Landform	Description
____ **6.** shield volcano	**a.** High, level area formed by repeated lava flows
____ **7.** cinder cone	
____ **8.** composite volcano	**b.** Mountain formed by lava flows alternating with explosive eruptions
____ **9.** lava plateau	
____ **10.** caldera	**c.** Cone-shaped mountain formed from ash, cinders, and bombs
	d. Hole left by the collapse of a volcanic mountain
	e. Gently sloping mountain formed by repeated lava flows

11. When volcanic ash breaks down, it releases _____ and

_____, both of which are needed by plants.

Landforms From Magma (pp. 103–104)

12. List five features formed by magma.

a. _____

b. _____

c. _____

d. _____

e. _____

Volcanoes

Volcanoes • *Guided Reading and Study*

Volcanic Landforms *(continued)*

13. Complete the Venn diagram using the following phrases: forms from magma, forms across rock layers, forms between rock layers.

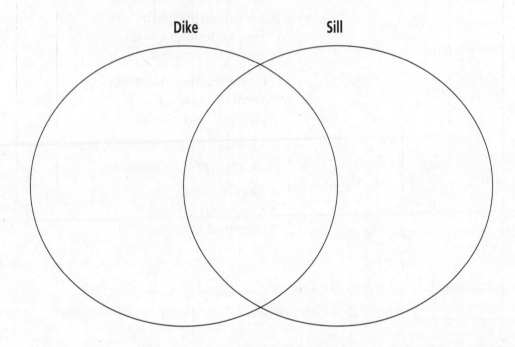

Dike   Sill

14. A mass of rock formed when a large body of magma cools inside the crust is called a(n) _____.

15. What is an example of a batholith in the United States? _____

_____

16. Is the following sentence true or false? A dome mountain forms when hardened magma is uplifted and pushes up horizontal layers of rock.

_____

Geothermal Activity (pp. 104–105)

17. Is the following sentence true or false? Some types of volcanic activity do not involve the eruption of lava.

18. When groundwater heated by a nearby body of magma rises to the surface and collects in a natural pool, it is called a(n) _____ .

19. A fountain of water and steam that erupts from the ground is referred to as a(n) _____ .

20. How can geothermal energy be converted to electricity? _____

_____

Name _____ Date _____ Class_____

Volcanoes ▪ *Review and Reinforce*

Volcanic Landforms

Understanding Main Ideas

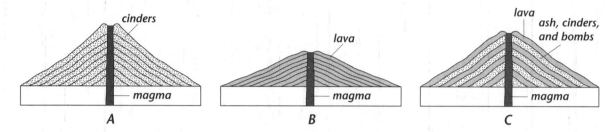

Answer the following questions on a separate sheet of paper.

1. Name each type of volcano shown in the diagrams. How is each formed?

2. How does a lava plateau form?

3. What happens to create a caldera?

4. Why is volcanic soil so fertile?

5. What are two uses of geothermal energy?

Building Vocabulary

Define each of the following terms in the spaces provided.

6. batholith _____

_____

7. dike _____

_____

8. volcanic neck _____

_____

9. sill _____

_____

10. geyser _____

_____

Volcanoes · *Enrich*

Modeling a Lava Plateau

Materials

small, disposable aluminum pan water

clay 3 large paper cups

knife 3 plastic spoons

meat baster red, blue, and yellow food coloring

plaster of Paris

Procedure *Review the safety guidelines in Appendix A of your textbook. This lab will take three to four days to complete.*

1. Cover the bottom of the pan with clay about 1 cm thick. Cut a slit in the clay and pan just wide enough for the meat baster's tip to fit through it.

2. In one cup, make a mixture of plaster of Paris and water that will flow easily. Add red food coloring to the mixture and stir.

3. Fill the baster with the red mixture. Push the baster's tip up through the slit. Squeeze the bulb so the mixture flows out onto the surface. Repeat until the layer is at least 0.5 cm deep.

4. Wash out the baster. Set the pan aside until the plaster is completely dry, preferably overnight.

5. Repeat steps 2, 3, and 4. This time, add blue food coloring to the mixture.

6. Repeat steps 2, 3, and 4 again, this time with a yellow mixture.

7. When the top layer is dry, cut your model in half. Examine the layers.

Analyze and Conclude

Answer the following questions in the spaces provided.

1. What does the wet plaster mixture represent?

_____

2. What do the three colored layers of dry plaster represent?

_____

_____

3. In what ways does this model show how a lava plateau is formed?

_____

_____

Volcanoes • *Skills Lab*

Gelatin Volcanoes

Problem

How does magma move inside a volcano?

Skills Focus

developing hypotheses, making models, observing

Materials

plastic cup

plastic knife

aluminum pizza pan with holes punched at 2.5-cm intervals

tray or shallow pan

unflavored gelatin mold in bowl

red food coloring and water

plastic syringe, 10 cc

three small cardboard oatmeal boxes

rubber gloves

unlined paper

Procedure 🔖 *Review the safety guidelines in Appendix A of your textbook.*

1. Before magma erupts as lava, how does it travel up from underground magma chambers? Record your hypothesis.

2. Remove the gelatin from the refrigerator. Loosen the gelatin from its container by briefly placing the container of gelatin in a larger bowl of hot water.

3. Place the pizza pan over the gelatin so the mold is near the center of the pizza pan. While holding the pizza pan against the top of the mold, carefully turn the mold and pizza pan upside down.

4. Carefully lift the bowl off the gelatin mold to create a gelatin volcano.

5. Place the pizza pan with the gelatin mold on top of the oatmeal boxes as shown in the photograph in your textbook.

Volcanoes · *Skills Lab*

Gelatin Volcanoes *(continued)*

6. Fill the syringe with the red water ("magma"). Remove air bubbles from the syringe by holding it upright and squirting out a small amount of water.

7. Insert the tip of the syringe through a hole in the pizza pan near the center of the gelatin volcano. Inject the magma into the gelatin very slowly. Observe what happens to the magma.

8. Repeat steps 6 and 7 as many times as possible. Observe the movement of the magma each time. Note any differences in the direction the magma takes when the syringe is inserted into different parts of the gelatin volcano. Record your observations.

9. Look down on your gelatin volcano from above. Make a sketch of the positions and shapes of the magma bodies. Label your drawing "Top View."

10. Carefully use a knife to cut your volcano in half. Separate the pieces and examine the cut surfaces for traces of the magma bodies.

11. Sketch the positions and shapes of the magma bodies on one of the cut faces. Label your drawing "Cross Section."

Analyze and Conclude

Write your answers on a separate sheet of paper.

1. **Observing** Describe how the magma moved through your model. Did the magma move straight up through the center of your model volcano or did it branch off in places? Explain why you think the magma moved in this way.

2. **Developing Hypotheses** What knowledge or experience did you use to develop your hypothesis? How did the actual movement compare with your hypothesis?

3. **Inferring** Were there differences in the direction the magma flowed when the syringe was inserted in different parts of the gelatin volcano?

4. **Making Models** How does what you observed in your model compare to the way magma moves through real volcanoes? How could you change your model to be more like a real volcano?

5. **Communicating** Prepare your model as a display to teach other students about volcanoes. Make a list of the volcanic features in your model. For each feature, write a description of how the feature would form in a real volcano.

More to Explore

Plan to repeat the experiment using a mold made of two layers of gelatin. Before injecting the magma, predict what effect the layering will have on magma movement. Record your observations to determine if your hypothesis was correct. What volcanic feature is produced by this version of the model? Can you think of other volcanic features that you could model using gelatin layers? *Obtain your teacher's permission before carrying out your investigation.*

Volcanoes · *Key Terms*

Key Terms

Solve the clues by filling in the blanks with key terms from the chapter. Then write the numbered letters in the correct order to find the hidden message.

Clues	Key Terms
1. Molten mixture of rock-forming substances, gases, and water	$\overline{}_{1} \, \_ \, \_ \, \_ \, \overline{}_{2}$
2. Bowl-shaped area that forms around a volcano's central vent	$\_ \, \overline{}_{3} \, \_ \, \_ \, \_$
3. Material found in magma that is formed from oxygen and silicon	$\overline{}_{4} \, \_ \, \_ \, \_ \, \_ \, \_$
4. Hot, fast-moving type of lava	$\_ \, \overline{}_{5} \, \_ \, \_ \, \_ \, \_$
5. Cool, slow-moving type of lava	$\overline{}_{6} \, \_$
6. Type of hot spring that erupts as a fountain of water and steam	$\_ \, \_ \, \_ \, \overline{}_{7} \, \_$
7. Weak spot in the crust where magma has come to the surface	$\overline{}_{8} \, \_ \, \_ \, \_ \, \_ \, \overline{}_{9}$
8. Magma that reaches the surface	$\overline{}_{10} \, \_ \, \_$
9. Erupting or showing signs of erupting in the near future	$\_ \, \overline{}_{11} \, \_ \, \_ \, \_$
10. Large hole formed when a volcano's magma chamber empties and collapses	$\_ \, \overline{}_{12} \, \_ \, \_ \, \_ \, \_$
11. Unlikely to erupt again	$\_ \, \_ \, \_ \, \overline{}_{13} \, \_ \, \_$
12. Mass of rock formed when magma cooled inside the crust	$\_ \, \_ \, \_ \, \overline{}_{14} \, \_ \, \_ \, \_$
13. Slab that forms when magma forces itself across rock layers	$\_ \, \_ \, \_ \, \overline{}_{15}$
14. Slab that forms when magma squeezes between layers of rock	$\_ \, \_ \, \_ \, \overline{}_{16}$

Hidden Message

$\overline{}_{1} \, \overline{}_{2} \, \overline{}_{3} \, \overline{}_{4} \quad \overline{}_{5} \, \overline{}_{6} \, \overline{}_{7} \quad \overline{}_{8} \, \overline{}_{9} \, \overline{}_{10} \, \overline{}_{11} \, \overline{}_{12} \, \overline{}_{13} \, \overline{}_{14} \, \overline{}_{15} \, \overline{}_{16}$.

Volcanoes

Connecting Concepts

Develop a concept map that uses the key concepts and key terms from this chapter. Keep in mind the big idea of this chapter: Forces inside Earth cause magma to heat, move, and push through the crust to erupt as volcanoes that pose hazards and form land features. The concept map shown is one way to organize how the information in this chapter is related. You may use an extra sheet of paper.

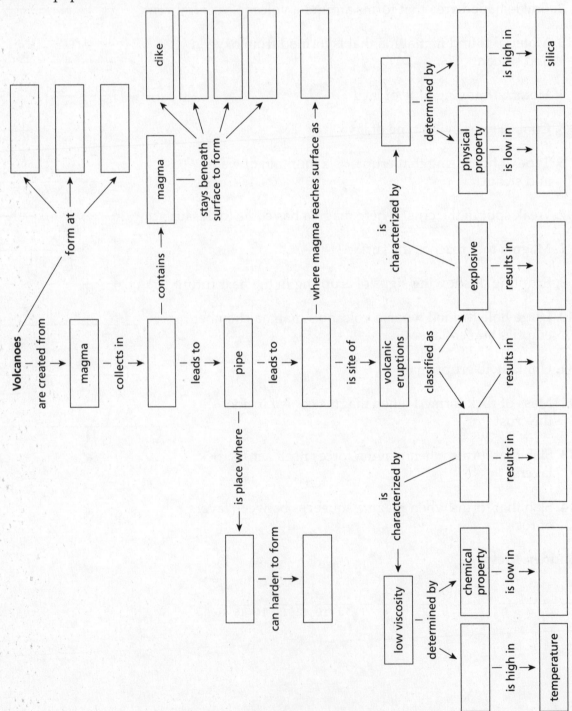

Predicting Lava Flows

Key Concept

The fluidity of magma and lava depend on both their temperature and the amount of silica they contain. The type of volcano produced by an eruption depends in part on the fluidity of the lava that forms it.

Skills Focus

observing, inferring, making models, communicating, designing experiments, creating data tables

Time

40 minutes

Possible Materials

molasses, about 20 mL

cornstarch, about 25 mL

spoon

watch or clock with second hand

cookie sheet or food tray

graduated cylinder, 100 mL

water

paper towels

newspaper

meter stick

3 paper cups or beakers, at least 100 mL each

Alternative Materials

If graduated cylinders are not available, a metric measuring cup can be used.

Teaching Tips

- [Step 1] Lab groups should be no smaller than three students. Be sure students protect themselves and all surfaces from spills. Caution students to add water gradually to the cornstarch, a little at a time, so that the result is somewhat runny.

- [Step 3] Ask students to relate to other examples of when the thickness (viscosity) of something matters. Answers might include motor oil, which can vary in viscosity depending on its use and temperature, and concrete, which varies in thickness before it sets, depending on its use and environmental conditions.

Volcanoes ▪ *Laboratory Investigation*

Predicting Lava Flows

Pre-Lab Discussion

You know that a liquid becomes a solid if its temperature is lowered enough that the substance freezes. If you freeze a mixture of cream, eggs, and flavoring in an ice-cream maker, the result is ice cream. When the molten wax on a candle cools, it turns into a solid. The type of material that results depends on the liquid you started out with.

Volcanic rocks form on Earth's surface when lava cools and "freezes." But are all rocks formed from lava the same?

Because different types of lava are made from different materials, they also behave differently when they flow on Earth's surface and harden into rock. Two main types of lava differ in how easily they flow because of their silica content. In this investigation, you will relate the ease of flow of different types of lava to the shapes of the volcanoes they form.

1. In addition to silica content, what is another difference between different types of lava?

_____

_____

2. If you are comparing how easily different types of lava flow, why do you have to make sure that the temperature of each is the same?

_____

_____

Problem

How do the temperature and composition of lava affect the way it flows?

Possible Materials *(per group)*

- molasses, about 20 mL
- cornstarch, about 25 mL
- spoon
- watch or clock with second hand
- cookie sheet or food tray
- graduated cylinder, 100 mL
- water
- paper towels
- newspaper
- meter stick
- 3 paper cups or beakers, at least 100 mL each

Volcanoes · *Laboratory Investigation*

Safety   *Review the safety guidelines in Appendix A of your textbook.*

Wear a lab apron and safety goggles while doing this activity.

Procedure

Part A: Modeling Types of Lava

1. Add about 25 mL of cornstarch to a cup or beaker. Add about 25 mL of water, a small amount at a time, to the cornstarch while mixing. A runny mixture, about the thickness of milk, should result. This mixture is a model of low-silica lava.

2. To model high-silica lava, use a spoon to place about 5 mL of molasses into a different cup or beaker.

3. Compare and contrast the thickness of the two types of "lava." Predict which type will move faster down a slope. Explain your reasoning.

_____

_____

Design an experiment to test your prediction. Write your procedure on another sheet of paper.

4. Decide what types of data you will need to collect. Add columns, rows, and headings to the Data Table in Observations as appropriate.

5. After the teacher has approved your procedure and Data Table, conduct your investigation.

Part B: Modeling Lava at Different Temperatures

1. Use molasses to investigate the effect of temperature on lava flow.

2. Predict whether a hot sample or a room-temperature sample of molasses will move faster down a slope. Explain your reasoning.

_____

_____

3. Design an experiment to test your prediction. Write down your procedure on a separate sheet of paper. Repeat Steps 4 and 5 from Part A. Obtain a sample of hot molasses from your teacher.

4. Follow any special instructions the teacher gives you about cleaning up your work area. Throw any "lava" materials, paper towels, and newspaper into the trash can. Do not wash any materials down the drain. Wash your hands after everything else is cleaned up.

Volcanoes

Volcanoes • *Laboratory Investigation*

Predicting Lava Flows (continued)

Observations

DATA TABLE

Analyze and Conclude

1. In Part A, which type of "lava" flowed slower, high-silica or low-silica "lava"? In Part B, which type of "lava" flowed slower, hot "lava" or room-temperature "lava"?

    _____

2. Compare two types of lava: pahoehoe and aa. How are they similar? How are they different? How were these two types of lava represented in this experiment?

    _____

    _____

    _____

3. In the space below, on the left, sketch and name the type of volcano that would be formed from low-silica lava. Next to it, sketch and name the type of volcano that would be formed from high-silica lava.

4. Describe the kind of eruptions you would expect as a volcano forms from low-silica lava.

    _____

5. Describe the kind of eruptions you would expect as a volcano forms from high-silica lava. _____

Volcanoes · *Laboratory Investigation*

Critical Thinking and Applications

1. How does the shape of a volcano help you draw conclusions about the type of magma near the surface beneath the volcano?

   _____

   _____

   _____

2. What type of magma occurs near the surface beneath a composite volcano? Give a reason for your answer.

   _____

   _____

   _____

More to Explore

New Problem How does the gas content in magma affect the shape of a volcano?

Possible Materials *(per group)*

modeling clay
vinegar
baking soda
paper towels

Safety Wear safety goggles and laboratory aprons.

Procedure Develop a plan to determine how volcano shape depends on the gas content of the magma. Write the steps of your plan on another sheet of paper. Have the teacher approve your plan before you carry out your investigation. (*Hint*: Vinegar and baking soda will react to form a gas.)

Observations Record your observations in a data table on a separate sheet of paper.

Analyze and Conclude Based on your observations, write a statement of how the gas content of magma is related to the shape of the volcano.

_____

_____

_____

Volcanoes

Thick and Thin Lava

In this activity, students are presented with the problem of modeling lava with different thicknesses to determine how thickness affects flow rate. To solve this problem, students will apply the concepts they have learned about the factors affecting magma's thickness.

Expected Outcome

To solve this problem, students first must recall the factors that affect magma's thickness—gas content, temperature, and silica content. Since the materials listed on the student page do not include any means for modeling gas content or temperature changes, students must select the one factor that can be modeled: silica content. Students should determine that they can use the soap or detergent to represent thin, runny lava and the flour to represent silica, preparing "lava" samples that contain different amounts of "silica" (the manipulated variable). Students can then test the flow speed of each sample by propping up one end of the cookie sheet or tray, pouring the sample into the raised end, and timing how long it takes for the sample to flow to the bottom. Students should hold all other variables—the slope of the cookie sheet or tray, the amount of "lava" poured each time, the rate at which it is poured, and so forth—constant throughout all tests. (Students can do two samples at the same time, which will ensure that the other variables will be held constant.) Students should label the samples to distinguish among them and record the results of each test in a table so they can compare the flow speeds.

Content Assessed

This activity assesses students' understanding of how silica content affects lava's thickness and how lava's thickness affects its flow speed.

Skills Assessed

designing experiments, interpreting data, drawing conclusions

Materials

Give each student a cookie sheet or comparable-size tray.

Provide the other materials listed on the student page in a distribution center for students to share.

Make newspaper available for covering work surfaces and paper towels for wiping up spills.

Advance Preparation

Assemble the necessary materials.

Time

40 minutes

Safety

Caution students to wear lab aprons and safety goggles during the activity.

Monitoring the Task

As students complete Step 2 of Devise a Plan, review their drawings to make sure they have provided for testing *at least two* (preferably three or four) "lava" samples of different thicknesses. If any of the experimental designs involve pouring the samples one after the other in one test, ask students how they will be able to time the different flow speeds.

Caution students not to raise the end of the cookie sheet or tray too high.

Provide a large container for students to dispose of the "lava" mixtures when they have completed the activity.

Thick and Thin Lava

In assessing students' performance, use the following rubric.

	4	3	2	1
Designing and Conducting the Experiment	Student prepares four or more "lava" mixtures of distinctly different thicknesses; tests each mixture in a separate test that holds all other variables constant; times flow speeds accurately; records results precisely in a well-organized table.	Student prepares at least three "lava" mixtures of different thicknesses; tests each mixture in a separate test with the surface held constant; times flow speeds fairly accurately; records results in a table.	Student prepares at least two "lava" mixtures of different thicknesses or prepares three or more mixtures that do not vary significantly in thickness; tests each mixture in a separate test with the surface held constant; does not time flow speeds accurately and/or records results in notes rather than in a table.	Student prepares two or fewer "lava" mixtures or prepares two or more mixtures that do not vary significantly in thickness; tests all mixtures in one test or does not keep variables constant; does not time flow speeds and/or record results accurately.
Concept Understanding	Student demonstrates mastery of the concepts that underlie the model, including the relationship between lava's silica content and its thickness and between its thickness and its flow speed.	Student demonstrates a satisfactory understanding of the concepts that underlie the model, including the relationship between lava's silica content and its thickness and between its thickness and its flow speed.	Student demonstrates a partial understanding of the concepts that underlie the model, including the relationship between lava's silica content and its thickness and between its thickness and its flow speed.	Student demonstrates a weak understanding of the concepts that underlie the model, including the relationship between lava's silica content and its thickness and between its thickness and its flow speed.

Volcanoes · *Performance Assessment*

Problem

How can you model how lava's thickness affects its flow speed?

Suggested Materials

measuring cup

measuring spoons

paper cups

liquid soap or detergent

flour

plastic spoons

cookie sheet or tray

books or wooden blocks

stopwatch or watch with second hand

Devise a Plan

1. Study the materials. Think of a way you could use them to test how lava's thickness affects the speed at which it flows. Consider what you learned about the factors that affect magma's thickness.

2. On a separate sheet of paper, write down the procedure and draw the setup you plan to use.

3. Try your plan. Experiment with the materials until you have a good model to test lava's flow speed. Record your results in a table.

Analyze and Conclude

Respond to the following items on a separate sheet of paper.

1. What factors affect magma's thickness? Which of these factors did you model?

2. Draw your model. Label your drawing to explain what each part of your model represents.

3. Identify the variable you changed and describe how you changed it.

4. Analyze your results. What can you conclude about the relationship between lava's thickness and its flow speed?

Volcanoes

Completion

Fill in the line to complete each statement.

1. The molten mixture of rock-forming substances, gases, and water deep in Earth's mantle is called _____.

2. The _____ is a belt of volcanoes around the rim of the Pacific Ocean.

3. The more _____ that magma contains, the thicker the magma is.

4. A(n) _____ happens when an explosive eruption hurls ash, cinders, bombs, and gases out of a volcano.

5. A(n) _____ is a wide, gently sloping mountain made of hardened layers of low-silica lava.

6. A(n) _____ forms when magma hardens in a volcano's pipe and is later exposed.

7. A substance that cannot be broken down into other substances is a(n)

   _____.

8. A substance's ability to burn is an example of a(n) _____.

True or False

If the statement is true, write true. If it is false, change the underlined word or words to make the statement true.

_____ 9. A <u>caldera</u> is a weak spot in the crust where magma comes through.

_____ 10. Liquid magma flows upward through the crust because it is <u>less</u> dense than the solid material around it.

_____ 11. Pahoehoe and aa are produced during <u>explosive</u> eruptions.

_____ 12. A <u>hot spring</u> is hot water and steam that erupts from the ground.

_____ 13. When the top of a volcanic mountain collapses, a <u>crater</u> forms.

_____ 14. A <u>batholith</u> is a mass of rock that formed when a large body of magma cooled inside Earth's crust.

Volcanoes • *Chapter Test*

Multiple Choice

Write the letter of the correct answer on the line.

_____ 15. An area where magma melts through the crust in the middle of a plate is called a(n)

    a. island arc.   **b.** hot spot.

    c. geyser.   **d.** pipe.

_____ 16. Inside a volcano, magma collects in a pocket called a

    a. pipe.   **b.** caldera.

    c. vent.   **d.** magma chamber.

_____ 17. Which is *not* a physical property of magma from an explosive eruption?

    a. thick and sticky   **b.** high viscosity

    c. flows easily   **d.** high in silica

_____ 18. Volcanic soils are fertile because they contain

    a. silica.   **b.** sulfur and liquid nitrogen.

    c. basalt.   **d.** potassium and phosphorus.

_____ 19. Layers of thin, runny lava that flow over a wide area before they cool and harden can build up a

    a. lava plateau.   **b.** cinder cone volcano.

    c. composite volcano.   **d.** volcanic neck.

_____ 20. A volcano that is erupting or has shown signs that it may erupt in the future is called

    a. sleeping.   **b.** extinct.

    c. active.   **d.** dormant.

Essay

Answer each of the following on a separate sheet of paper.

21. Explain why ash, cinders, and bombs are produced only in explosive eruptions, not in quiet eruptions.

_____

_____

_____

22. What is geothermal energy? How is it used?

_____

_____

_____

Volcanoes • *Chapter Test*

Using Science Skills

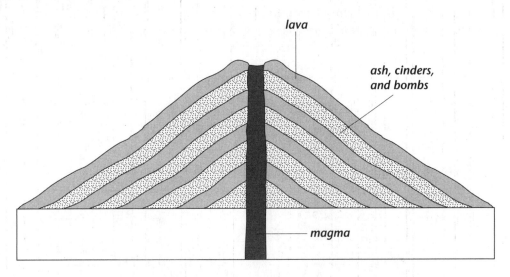

23. Classifying Which type of volcanic mountain is shown above?

_____

24. Comparing and Contrasting How does this type of volcano compare to the volcanoes that formed the Hawaiian islands?

_____

_____

_____

_____

_____

25. Predicting What kind of material is likely to erupt next? Explain why.

_____

_____

_____

_____

Volcanoes

Volcanoes • *Chapter Test*

Using Science Skills: Interpreting Graphs

The graph below shows the amount of material that was ejected in some famous volcanic eruptions. Use the graph to answer the following questions.

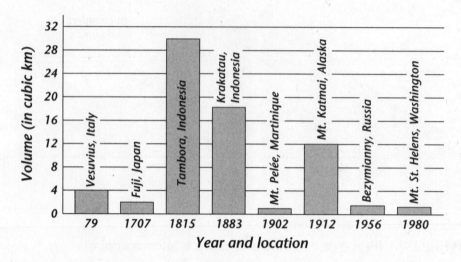

26. Which eruption ejected the most material? _____

27. Which eruption ejected the least material? _____

28. About how much material was ejected in each eruption?

    a. Vesuvius: _____ km^3

    b. Tambora: _____ km^3

    c. Mt. Katmai: _____ km^3

    d. Krakatau: _____ km^3

Essay

Answer the following on a separate sheet of paper.

29. Identify and explain the factors that affect the force of a volcanic eruption.

30. The most recent earthquake in Yellowstone National Park changed the volcanic activity there. Some geysers now erupt at different intervals than they did before. A few geysers have stopped erupting, and some new geysers have formed. Explain what might have happened during the earthquake to change the geyser activity.

Chapter Project

Worksheet 1

1. Ethiopia, Tanzania, Zaire.
2. Guadeloupe, Iceland, Indonesia, Japan, Martinique, Montserrat, New Zealand, Papua New Guinea, Philippines, St. Vincent, USA (Hawaii).
3. USA (Alaska, California, Oregon, Washington), Chile, Colombia, Costa Rica, Ecuador, El Salvador, Guatemala, Indonesia, Japan, Kamchatka (Russia), Mexico, New Zealand, Nicaragua, Papua New Guinea, Peru, Philippines.

Worksheet 2

1. paragraphs 4 and 5.
2. Students' notes will vary. Example: Solfatara (Naples, Italy). Steam and sulfur gas believed to have special healing powers. Since the Romans, people take steam baths for arthritis, breathing problems, benefits of "sweat baths," soak in mud pools to soften skin.
3. Myths and legends; geothermal energy; uses of volcanic materials in manufacturing

Volcanoes and Plate Tectonics Guided Reading and Study

Use Target Reading Skills This is one possible way to complete the graphic organizer. Accept all logical answers.

Volcanoes and Plate Tectonics

Question	Answer
Where are volcanoes found?	Volcanoes form along the boundaries of Earth's plates.
What is a hot spot?	An area where material from deep within the mantle rises and then melts, forming magma

1. a weak spot in the crust where molten material, or magma, comes to the surface
2. magma
3. lava
4. a major volcanic belt formed by the many volcanoes that rim the Pacific Ocean
5. along diverging plate boundaries such as mid-ocean ridges and along converging plate boundaries where subduction takes place

6. Along the rift valley, lava pours out of cracks in the ocean floor, gradually building new mountains.
7. true
8. true
9. When the older, denser plate sinks beneath a deep-ocean trench into the mantle, some of the rock above the subducting plate melts and forms magma. Because the magma is less dense than the surrounding rock, it rises toward the surface. Eventually, the magma breaks through the ocean floor, creating volcanoes. Volcanoes can also form where oceanic crust is subducted beneath continental crust.
10. island arc
11. Any three: Japan, New Zealand, Indonesia, the Philippines, the Aleutians, the Caribbean islands
12. b
13. an area where material from within the mantle rises and the melts, forming magma
14. They formed over millions of years as the Pacific plate drifted over a hot spot.
15. false

Volcanoes and Plate Tectonics Review and Reinforce

1. When lava that has erupted from a volcano cools, it forms solid rock. In this way, volcanoes add new rock to existing land and form new islands.
2. At the boundaries where plates diverge (pull apart) or converge (push together), the crust is weak and fractured, allowing magma to reach Earth's surface.
3. Lava erupted from the hot spot and built a volcanic island. The Pacific plate is slowly moving over the hot spot, so it carried the island away from the spot. (To indicate this, students should draw an arrow from right to left on the diagram.) Another volcanic island formed at the hot spot and then was carried away. Over time, a chain of islands formed.
4. Magma is molten, rock-forming material underground. Magma that reaches the surface is called lava.
5. **a.** a weak spot in Earth's crust where magma comes to the surface **b.** a belt of many volcanoes that rim the Pacific Ocean **c.** a chain of volcanic islands that forms at the boundary where two oceanic plates push together and one plate subducts under the other plate

Volcanoes and Plate Tectonics
Enrich

1. Arenal, El Chichón, El Misti, Katmai, Mount Rainier, Pinatubo, Rabaul, Ruapehu, Tambora, Unzen, Villarrica
2. Erta Alè, Hekla
3. Falcon, Mauna Loa
4. Ol Doinyo Lengai

Skills Lab

Mapping Earthquakes and Volcanoes

For answers, see the Teacher's Edition.

Properties of Magma
Guided Reading and Study

Use Target Reading Skills This is one possible way to complete the graphic organizer. Accept all logical answers. **Details:** Magma is made of elements and compounds, among them silica. Viscosity is a property of magma. Viscosity depends on silica content and temperature.

1. element
2. true
3. b, c
4. slower; lower
5. a, d
6. temperature and silica content
7. b, d
8. rhyolite
9. basalt
10. It decreases
11. pahoehoe
12. aa
13. **a.** low **b.** lower **c.** higher **d.** lower **e.** Possible answer: The lower the temperature and the higher the silica content of magma is, the higher the viscosity of the magma. The higher the temperature and the lower the silica content of magma is, the lower the viscosity of the magma.

Properties of Magma
Review and Reinforce

1. Physical
2. Physical
3. Chemical
4. Chemical
5. Physical
6. Physical
7. Each substance has a particular set of physical and chemical properties. These properties can be used to identify a substance or to predict how it will behave.
8. There is a greater degree of friction among the liquid's particles.
9. Light-colored magma is high in silica. It has a higher viscosity and does not flow very far. Dark-colored magma is lower in silica. It has a lower viscosity and flows readily.
10. Viscosity increases as temperature decreases.
11. compound
12. element
13. pahoehoe
14. aa

Properties of Magma
Enrich

1. Water lowers the viscosity of magma.
2. The crystals in pegmatites form from atoms that are able to move long distances because the magma is watery.
3. Petaca, New Mexico
4. Kings Mountain, North Carolina
5. Pegmatites are important because they provide a source for rare elements and gems.

Volcanic Eruptions
Guided Reading and Study

Use Target Reading Skills This is one possible way to complete the graphic organizer. Accept all logical answers.

What You Know
1. Lava flows out of a volcano.
2. Eruptions are not all the same.
3. Some volcanoes are dormant.

What You Learned
1. Magma rises toward Earth's surface through a pipe that leads to a vent.
2. Differences in gas and silica content cause some eruptions to be explosive and others to be quiet.
3. Dormant volcanoes can become active at any time.

1. true
2. true
3. a, b
4. a. pipe **b.** crater **c.** vent **d.** magma chamber
5. the area covered by lava as it pours out of a vent
6. at the top of the volcano around the central vent
7. false
8. a. crater **b.** vent **c.** pipe **d.** magma **e.** side vent **f.** to the vent or a side vent
9. a
10. The force of the expanding gases pushes magma from the magma chamber through the pipe until it flows or explodes out of the vent.
11. the magma's silica content and viscosity
12. false
13. c
14. a
15. b

16. an explosive eruption that hurls out a mixture of hot gases, ash, cinders, and bombs
17. false
18. Volcanic ash can bury entire towns. If it becomes wet, the heavy ask can cause roofs to collapse. If a jet plane sucks ash into its engine, the engine may stall. Eruptions can cause landslides and avalanches of mud, melted, snow, and rock.
19. true
20. false
21. a. extinct **b.** active **c.** dormant **d.** extinct, dormant, active
22. false
23. The time between volcanic eruptions may span hundreds to many thousands of years.
24. a, d

Volcanoes

Volcanic Eruptions
Review and Reinforce

1. The liquid magma is less dense than the solid material around it, so it rises.

2. The gases begin to expand, forming bubbles, because the pressure decreases as the magma rises.

3. A volcano erupts quietly if its magma is low in silica. Low-silica magma has low viscosity and flows easily. A volcano erupts explosively if its magma is high in silica. High-silica magma has high viscosity, making it thick and sticky.

4. Thick, sticky lava builds up in the volcano's pipe and plugs it. The trapped gases build up pressure until they explode. The erupting gases force the magma out with great force, which breaks the lava into fragments that quickly cool and harden into pieces of different sizes.

5. (*Any three*) Lava flows set fire to and then bury objects in their path. Hot clouds of volcanic gases destroy objects and kill people, animals, and plants. Volcanic ash buries towns, damages crops, and clogs car and airplane engines. Eruptions can cause landslides and avalanches.

6. An active volcano is one that is erupting or may erupt in the near future. A dormant volcano is "sleeping," that is, it is likely to awaken in the future and become active. An extinct, or dead, volcano is unlikely to erupt again.

7. pipe

8. vent

9. crater

10. lava flow

11. magma chamber

Volcanic Eruptions
Enrich

1. Red foam gushed out of the top of the "volcano" and flowed down its sides.

2. The model volcano erupted because of the pressure of gases inside it.

3. Accept all reasonable responses. *Examples:* The foam is not hot and fiery and is not made of the same materials as lava. The foam erupted because a chemical reaction occurred to create pressure; in a real volcano, lava erupts because an opening develops in weak rock so the gases can rush out.

Volcanic Landforms
Guided Reading and Study

Use Target Reading Skills

Volcanic Landforms
I. Landforms From Lava and Ash
  A. Shield Volcanoes
  B. *Cinder Cone Volcanoes*
  C. *Composite Volcanoes*
  D. Lava Plateaus
  E. *Calderas*
  F. *Soils From Lava and Ash*
II. Landforms From Magma
  A. *Volcanic Necks*
  B. *Dikes and Sills*
  C. *Batholiths*
  D. Dome Mountains
III. *Geothermal Activity*
  A. Hot Springs
  B. *Geysers*
  C. Geothermal Energy

1. a. shield volcanoes **b.** cinder cone volcanoes **c.** composite volcanoes **d.** lava plateaus

2. a, b

3. false

4. Mount Fuji in Japan and Mount St. Helens in Washington State

5. true

6. e

7. c

8. b

9. a

10. d

11. potassium, phosphorus

12. a. volcanic necks **b.** dikes **c.** sills **d.** batholiths **e.** dome mountains

13. Left circle: forms across rock layers; Middle area: forms from magma; Right circle: forms between rock layers

14. batholith

15. the Sierra Nevada mountains in California

16. true

17. true

18. hot springs

19. geyser

20. Steam from underground is piped into turbines. Inside a turbine, the steam spins a wheel. The moving wheel in the turbine turns a generator that changes the energy of motion into electrical energy.

Volcanic Landforms
Review and Reinforce

1. A: Cinder cone volcano; lava explodes out of the volcano and hardens to form ash, cinders, and bombs that pile up in layers around the vent, forming a steep, cone-shaped mountain. **B:** Shield volcano; thin layers of lava pour out of a vent and harden on top of previous layers, gradually building a wide, gently sloping mountain. **C:** Composite volcano; lava flows alternate with explosive eruptions of ash, cinders, and bombs, forming a tall, cone-shaped mountain.

2. Thin, runny lava flows out of several long, cracks and travels far before cooling and hardening. Floods of such lava build up on top of other floods. Over millions of years, these layers of lava form a plateau.

3. A volcano's eruption empties its main vent and magma chamber. Without support from below, the top of the mountain collapses inward, leaving a huge hole.

4. When volcanic ash or rock breaks down, it releases potassium, phosphorus, and other plant nutrients.

5. Water heated by magma can be piped into homes to heat them. Steam can be used to drive turbines that generate electricity.

6. A mass of rock formed when a large body of magma cools inside the crust

7. Hardened magma in a crack that crosses rock layers

8. A landform produced when magma hardens in a volcano's pipe and is then exposed when the softer rock around it wears away

9. Hardened magma in a crack between rock layers

10. A fountain of water and steam that erupts from the ground

Volcanic Landforms
Enrich

1. Lava

2. Layers of lava that flowed from the volcano in different eruptions

3. "Lava" flowed from a crack and spread out over a wide surface; layers of hardened "lava" from different eruptions built up.

Skills Lab
Gelatin Volcanoes

For answers, see Teacher's Edition.

Use Key Terms

1. magma.
2. crater.
3. silica
4. pahoehoe
5. aa
6. geyser
7. volcano
8. lava
9. active
10. caldera
11. extinct
12. batholith
13. dike
14. sill
Hidden message: Mars has volcanoes.

Connecting Concepts

Forces inside Earth cause magma to heat, move, and push through the crust to erupt as volcanoes that pose hazards and form land features.

This concept map is only one way to represent the main ideas and relationships in this chapter. Accept other logical answers from students.

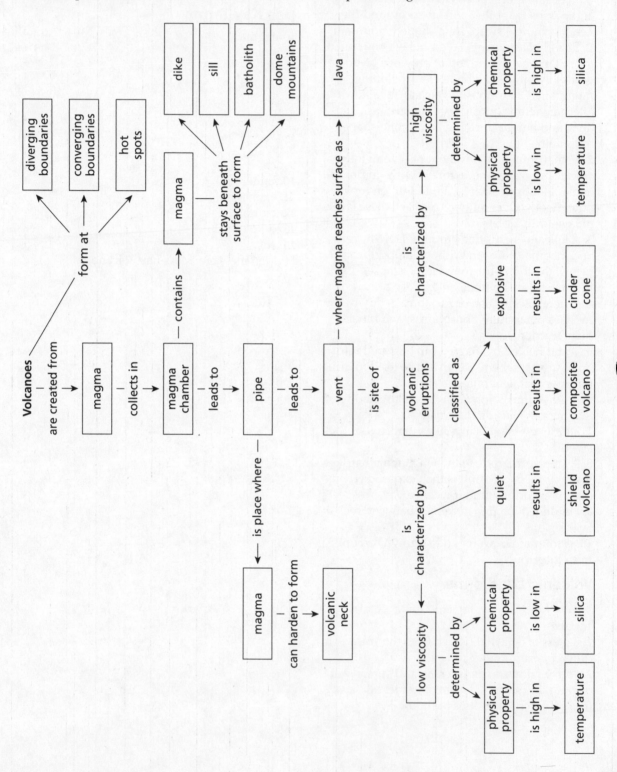

Laboratory Investigation

Predicting Lava Flow

Pre-Lab Discussion

1. Temperature

2. Ease of flow depends on temperature. Cooler lava is thicker than hotter lava. To make an appropriate comparison, you can vary only one factor at a time.

Procedure

Part A 3. Students may predict that the "low-silica lava" will flow faster because it is thinner.
Part B 2. Answers may vary. Sample: The hot molasses will flow faster because it will be thinner than the cool molasses.

Observation

Data Table Students should observe that "low-silica lava" is thinner and flows faster than does "high-silica lava." They should also observe that the hotter "lava" flows faster than does cooler "lava."

Analyze and Conclude

1. high-silica lava, room temperature
2. They are similar in that they are both low-silica lava. They differ in temperature: pahoehoe is hotter than aa and flows more easily. The hot molasses represented pahoehoe; the room-temperature molasses represented aa.
3. Students' sketches should show a volcano with gentle slopes—a shield volcano—on the left and a volcano with steep slopes—a cinder cone volcano—on the right.
4. The eruptions would be relatively quiet, with spurting and flowing lava but not explosions.
5. The eruptions would be more explosive than with low-silica lava.

Critical Thinking and Applications

1. The shape of the volcano indicates the amount of silica in the magma that erupted to the surface.
2. Because the magma beneath composite volcanoes is high in silica, these volcanoes alternate between explosive eruptions and eruptions of thick lava.

More to Explore

Analyze and Conclude Observations should show that the more baking soda used, the more gas formed, and the more explosive the eruption. Observations should indicate that the more explosive the eruption, the steeper the slope that formed.

Performance Assessment

1. Magma's thickness is affected by the amount of gas dissolved in it, its temperature, and its silica content. Silica content was modeled.
2. Students' drawings should explain each part of the model as follows: soap/detergent represents lava; flour, silica; cookie sheet/tray, slope of the surface over which the lava flows.
3. The variable that was changed should be the amount of flour (representing silica) in the lava, with little or no "silica" in one sample and increasing amounts in the other samples. Exact amounts may vary.
4. The more silica lava contains, the thicker it is, and the thicker lava is, the slower its flow speed.

Chapter Test

1. magma
2. Ring of Fire
3. silica
4. pyroclastic flow
5. shield volcano
6. volcanic neck
7. element
8. chemical property
9. volcano
10. true
11. quiet
12. geyser
13. caldera
14. true
15. b
16. d
17. c
18. d
19. a
20. c

21. In order for ash, cinders, and bombs to form, lava must be ejected forcefully from a volcano, so it is broken into fragments that cool and harden quickly to form pieces of different sizes.

22. Geothermal energy is energy derived from water that has been heated by magma underground. Hot water is piped to buildings as a heat source and steam is piped into turbines to generate electricity.

23. composite volcano

24. A composite volcano is a tall, cone-shaped mountain in which layers of lava alternate with layers of ash, while the volcanoes that formed the Hawaiian islands are shield volcanoes. These are wide, gently sloping mountains formed by thin layers of lava.

25. Ash, cinders, and bombs, because the last layer is lava, and in a composite volcano, the two types of materials form alternating layers.

26. Tambora

27. Mt. Pelée

28. a. 4 **b.** 29.5 **c.** 12 **d.** 18

29. The force of a volcanic eruption depends on its viscosity. The viscosity is determined by its temperature and its silica content. The hotter the magma is, the thinner it is and the quieter its eruption. The more silica the magma contains, the thicker it is and the more explosive its eruption.

30. Accept all reasonable explanations. Example: Earthquakes are produced by movement of Earth's crust along faults. During the most recent earthquake in Yellowstone, underground movements may have changed the channels (cracks in the rock) through which heated water reached geysers on the surface. Some channels may have been blocked, cutting off geysers. Some new channels may have opened, creating new geysers. Other channels may have widened or narrowed, changing their geysers' eruption intervals.

Minerals

Lab zone Chapter Project — Growing a Crystal Garden

The following steps will walk you through the Chapter Project. Use the hints and detailed directions as you guide your students through the creation of their crystal gardens, data collection, presentation, and reflection.

Chapter Project Overview

In this project, students will work either individually or in small groups to design and create a crystal garden and then observe and compare growth of several types of crystals. Each garden should include an attractive garden scene using common materials as well as at least two kinds of crystals.

To introduce the project, focus students' attention on pictures of mineral crystals, either in their text or in books about minerals. Explain that in this project they will be growing similar crystals from chemicals in solutions. Then show students pictures of garden scenes, such as famous English or Japanese gardens. Point out how the shapes and colors create an attractive whole.

Distribute the Chapter Project Overview. Review the project's rules. You may also want to hand out the Chapter Project Scoring Rubric so students will understand what is expected of them.

If appropriate, organize the class into pairs or small groups. The advantages of using groups include fewer materials needed and more collaboration among students of differing abilities. The advantage of individual gardens is that each student will gain more experience with growing crystals.

Set a deadline for the project presentation and some interim dates at the end of Sections 1 and 2. Have students copy the dates in their Project Time Line.

Distribute Chapter Project Worksheet 1. After students have read the worksheet, ask if they have any questions.

Materials and Preparation

Perhaps the best container for a crystal garden is a clear plastic shoe box. Gather enough of these for each student or group, or ask that students find their own containers. Any large, clear container could be appropriate.

The objects used for crystal substrates can be practically anything, though materials that are porous work best to hold the solutions and crystals. Good objects include charcoal, plastic foam, sponges, and cotton swabs. Many such materials can be made into shapes that will make attractive or representational scenes.

With Worksheet 2, students will create a salt solution to begin making crystals. Point out that they can do the procedure more than once, each time adding a different color of food coloring. In that way they can create a more attractive garden, though the salt crystals will always be the same shape.

Prepare ahead of time several other solutions for students' use. Various chemicals that you can purchase at a pharmacy or grocery store can be used. These include sugar (sucrose), Epsom salts, alum (aluminum potassium sulfate), and magnesium sulfate. Each chemical will produce a different crystal shape, from cubes to long, thin needles.

To prepare an alum or Epsom salts solution, follow this procedure. The resulting solution will be enough for five or six groups, depending on the size of their garden containers.

1. Heat 600 mL of water. Do not bring to boil.
2. Add 120 g of alum or 70 g of Epsom salts to warm water. Stir occasionally until the chemical has dissolved.
3. Pour the solution into a 1-L jar and seal it with a lid. Allow to cool over 24 hours. Then add a pinch of alum or Epsom salts to initiate precipitation. Shake twice a day. Add different colors of food coloring to different batches of solution.
4. When groups' gardens are ready, pour the solution (minus any precipitate) into a new jar and warm it again. Add an additional 24 g of alum or 10 g of Epsom salts to make sure the solution is saturated.

Prepare additional solutions with other chemicals in a similar way. Remember, the goal is to make saturated solutions that will readily grow crystals. Water temperature is the key to creating such a solution. Warmer water will dissolve more solute; as the solution cools, precipitation will occur.

Keep Students on Track—Section 1

As you review each student's materials list and sketches from Worksheet 1, encourage those who lack ideas to talk to classmates to gather more ideas.

Distribute Chapter Project Worksheet 2. Then provide each student or group with the materials needed to prepare the salt solution. An alternative to using the hot plate is to have students use hot tap water.

Demonstrate how to use the plastic dropper to add solution to an object in a garden scene.

Emphasize that students need to make an accurate map of their gardens and the places where each solution has been added. Without a map, students will forget what kind of crystal is growing where.

Provide different kinds of solutions for students to add to their scenes. Make sure each plastic dropper is used for only one kind of solution.

Keep Students on Track—Section 2

As you check the gardens, make sure students are having some success in growing crystals. Help any who are having trouble.

Make sure students are keeping a daily record of crystal growth, complete with sketches of the different kinds of crystals.

Discuss how students could compare the growth of different kinds of crystals. This might be a line or bar graph or a detailed paragraph.

Chapter Project Wrap Up

Examine each student's or group's crystal garden before their presentation. Have students "walk you through" what they will say, and make suggestions about logical sequence or any missing information in their report. If this is a group project, make sure all group members plan to participate.

Provide class time for the presentations. Allow each student or group to present the garden, with an emphasis on the materials used and the crystals grown. Encourage other students to ask questions.

After all presentations have been made, discuss with students which crystal gardens were best, both in design and results.

Encourage students to evaluate how well they created the garden they planned to create, how attractive their garden scenes were, and how well their crystals grew. Stress that they should identify in their journals ways in which they could have made their gardens better.

Extension

Have interested students draw from scenes of a variety of students or groups to make a large crystal garden in an aquarium. Then find a place in the school to display their creation.

Minerals • *Chapter Project*   **Overview**

▲ Chapter **Project** Growing a Crystal Garden

If you've ever seen a well-made garden, you've seen a work of art. A good gardener doesn't just plant flowers and bushes in any old place. Instead, each plant is considered for its color and shape as the gardener strives to make a pleasing whole impression. In this project, you have a chance to design and create a garden, but with crystals rather than plants.

First, you'll build a three-dimensional garden scene, using materials supplied by your teacher as well as materials you bring from home. This garden scene can be either a model of some landscape you've seen or an artistic creation of your own. Next, you'll prepare and add solutions to the objects in your garden scene, recording on a detailed map where each solution was added. From these solutions crystals will grow. You'll keep track of the growth of each kind of crystal, making sketches and recording growth data. At the end of the project, you'll present your crystal garden to the class.

Project Rules

- Complete Worksheet 1 by making a list of materials you could use to create a three-dimensional garden scene and by making a sketch of a possible garden.

- Collect the materials you will use to create your garden.

- Create a garden scene. This could be either a representation of a real landscape or an artistic creation using shapes and colors to make a pleasing effect.

- Follow Worksheet 2 to make a salt solution, and add it to your garden scene. Then add other solutions supplied by your teacher.

- Make a detailed map of your garden that includes exactly where you "planted" each kind of crystal. If your map is not accurate or doesn't include enough labels, your observations of crystal growth will be flawed.

- As your crystals grow, make sketches that accurately show the shape of each kind. At first, your sketches might be rough. Toward the end of the project, make a good sketch of each kind of crystal you've grown.

- Take and record measurements of each kind of crystal. You can do this with a metric ruler or some other measuring device. Record your measurements in a data table or a daily journal. You'll want to record when crystals begin growing, how much they grow each day, and when they stop growing.

- Make a comparison of the growth of the different crystals. You could do this in writing or with some kind of graph, depending on the data you've kept.

Minerals • *Chapter Project*

- Prepare a presentation to the class of your crystal garden. As part of this presentation, you will describe the materials you used to build your garden and the types of crystals grown. You will also show sketches of your crystals and present a comparison of the growth of each kind of crystal.

Project Hints

As soon as possible, begin collecting the materials you will use to create your garden. These include a container and various objects on which your crystals will grow. Your teacher may be able to provide some materials, but you will probably want to bring some materials from home.

Be as creative as you can in planning and building your garden scene. Remember, if your materials are unique to your garden, your garden will be different from all others in the class.

You can make your garden scene like a realistic landscape, with mountains, rivers, forests, and so on. Or you could make an attractive scene just by using artistic shapes and colors, like a modern painting.

Talk with your teacher and other class members about ways to take measurements of crystal growth and ways to compare those measurements.

As you prepare for your presentation, think of what you want to say and the order in which you want to present the information. You may want to make notes on index cards to help you remember what you want to say.

Project Time Line

Task	Due Date
1. Complete Worksheet 1	_____
2. Gather materials needed for garden scene	_____
3. Create three-dimensional garden scene	_____
4. Review plans with your teacher	_____
5. Prepare solution with Worksheet 2	_____
6. Add solutions to garden, recording on map	_____
7. Prepare comparison of crystal growth rates	_____
8. Make sketches of crystals grown	_____
9. Present your crystal garden to class	_____

Minerals

Creating a Crystal Garden

To get started on creating a crystal garden, you need to think about the materials you will use and the garden scene you will make.

Materials

What materials can you use to make an attractive garden scene? Make a list below of possibilities of objects on which you could grow crystals. Porous materials, such as charcoal, plastic foam, and sponges will work best.

1. Possible container:

   _____

2. Possible materials:

   _____

   _____

   _____

Garden Scene

What will your garden scene look like when completed? Make a sketch in the space below of an attractive garden scene that you would like to create.

If you're working in a group, take this design to a group meeting and present your ideas to the other members for consideration. If you're creating your garden alone, show this design to other classmates and ask for advice and criticism. Then show it to your teacher.

Getting Started With Salt Crystals

Your crystal garden must contain at least two different kinds of crystals, though it may contain more. Your teacher will provide solutions to grow some kinds of crystals. The procedure here will give you a chance to prepare your own salt solution from which you can grow salt crystals.

Materials

hot plate

pan

salt

tablespoon

food coloring

water

clean jar with lid

plastic dropper

Procedure   *Review the safety guidelines in Appendix A.*

1. Cover the bottom of the pan with water, and heat the water almost to boiling on the hot plate.

2. Pour salt into the hot water, stirring as you pour. Add salt until no more salt dissolves into the water.

3. Allow the salt solution to cool slightly, and then pour it into the jar and screw on the lid. Allow the water to cool for 24 hours.

4. Remove with a spoon any salt crystals that have formed overnight. Or, you can shake the jar twice a day until no more salt crystals form.

5. Pour the solution back into the pan and reheat on the hot plate. When the water is hot but not boiling, add a tablespoon of salt to the solution and stir.

6. Use a plastic dropper to add food coloring, and stir the solution.

7. Use a plastic dropper to cover objects in your garden scene with the salt solution. Add enough solution to saturate the objects, but do not add so much that you create standing puddles. Remember that you will want to cover some objects with other kinds of solutions.

8. Observe the growth of crystals within two to four days.

Minerals

Minerals • *Chapter Project* — **Scoring Rubric**

Growing a Crystal Garden

In evaluating how well you complete the Chapter Project, your teacher will judge your work in the following categories. In each, a score of 4 is the best rating.

	4	3	2	1
Creating a Crystal Garden Scene	Garden scene is creatively designed and attractive and contains well-formed examples of at least four kinds of crystals.	Garden scene is carefully designed and attractive and contains well-formed examples of at least three kinds of crystals.	Garden scene is partially designed and fairly attractive and contains examples of at least two kinds of crystals.	Garden scene does not appear to be well planned and contains examples of only one or two kinds of crystals.
Recording Crystal Growth	Makes well-drawn sketches of each kind of crystal as well as accurate measurements and comparisons of crystal growth.	Makes sketches of each kind of crystal as well as measurements and comparisons of most crystal growth.	Makes sketches of each kind of crystal as well as some measurements and comparisons of crystal growth.	Makes sketches of some crystals; measurements and comparisons of crystal growth are incomplete.
Presenting the Crystal Garden	Makes a thorough and interesting presentation that includes a good explanation of materials used and a logical comparison of crystals grown.	Makes an adequate presentation of the system that includes a clear explanation of materials used and a comparison of crystals grown.	Makes a presentation of the system that includes a partial explanation of materials used and some comparison of crystals grown.	Makes a presentation of the system that includes a weak explanation of materials used and an incomplete comparison of crystals grown.
Participating in the Group (optional)	Takes a lead in planning, creating, and presenting the crystal garden.	Participates in all aspects of planning, creating, and presenting the crystal garden.	Participates in most aspects of planning, creating, and presenting the crystal garden.	Participates minimally in planning, creating, and presenting the crystal garden.

Properties of Minerals

 2 periods, 1 block

Ability Levels Key
L1 Basic to Average
L2 For All Students
L3 Average to Advanced

Objectives
F.4.1.1 Define a mineral.
F.4.1.2 Explain how minerals are identified.

Key Terms
• mineral • inorganic • crystal • streak • luster
• Mohs hardness scale • cleavage • fracture

Local Standards

PRETEACH

Build Background Knowledge
Students share their knowledge about the definition of minerals and where they can find minerals in nature.

 **Discover Activity** *What Is the True Color of a Mineral?* **L1**

Targeted Resources

❑ **All in One** **Teaching Resources**
  L2 Reading Strategy Transparency F35: Outlining
❑ **PresentationExpress™ CD-ROM**

INSTRUCT

What Is a Mineral?
Use objects and samples to demonstrate the differences between rocks and minerals on the basis of the definition of a mineral.

Identifying Minerals
Bring students together for a discussion of the physical properties of minerals and to examine a mineral identification table.

 Skills Lab *Finding the Density of Minerals* **L2**

Targeted Resources

❑ **All in One** **Teaching Resources**
  L2 Guided Reading, pp. 251–254
  L2 Transparency F36
  L2 Lab: *Finding the Density of Minerals,* pp. 257–259
❑ **Lab Activity Video/DVD**
  Skills Lab: *Finding the Density of Minerals*
❑ **PHSchool.com** Web Code: cfd-1041
❑ **PHSchool.com** Web Code: cfp-1041
❑ **Student Edition on Audio CD**

ASSESS

Section Assessment Questions
Have students use their completed graphic organizers with their outlines to answer the questions.

Reteach
Students create a concept map that includes the definition of a mineral and mineral properties.

Targeted Resources

❑ **All in One** **Teaching Resources**
  Section Summary, p. 250
  L1 Review and Reinforce, p. 255
  L3 Enrich, p. 256

Minerals

Minerals • *Section Summary*

Properties of Minerals

Key Concepts

- What is a mineral?

- How are minerals identified?

A mineral is a naturally occurring, inorganic solid that has a crystal structure and a definite chemical composition. For a substance to be a **mineral,** it must have all five of these characteristics. To be classified as a mineral, a substance must be formed by processes that occur in the natural world. A mineral must also be **inorganic.** This means that the mineral cannot form from materials that were once part of a living thing. A mineral is always a solid, with a definite volume and shape. The particles of a mineral line up in a pattern that repeats over and over. The repeating pattern of a mineral's particles forms a solid called a **crystal.**

A mineral has a definite chemical composition or range of compositions. This means that a mineral always contains certain elements in definite proportions. Almost all minerals are compounds. Some elements occur in nature in a pure form, and not as part of a compound with other elements. Elements such as copper, silver, and gold are also minerals.

Each mineral has characteristic properties that can be used to identify it. Color can be used to identify only those few minerals that always have their own characteristic color. A streak test can provide a clue to a mineral's identity. The **streak** of a mineral is the color of its powder. Another simple test to identify a mineral is to check its luster. **Luster** is the term used to describe how light is reflected from a mineral's surface. Each mineral has a characteristic density. When you identify a mineral, one of the best clues you can use is the mineral's hardness. The **Mohs hardness scale** ranks ten minerals from softest to hardest. A mineral can scratch any mineral softer than itself, but can be scratched by any mineral that is harder. The crystals of each mineral grow atom by atom to form that mineral's particular crystal structure. Geologists classify these structures into six groups based on the number and angle of the crystal faces.

The way a mineral breaks apart can help to identify it. A mineral that splits easily along flat surfaces has the property called **cleavage.** Most minerals do not split apart evenly. Instead, they have a characteristic type of **fracture,** which describes how a mineral looks when it breaks apart in an irregular way.

Some minerals can be identified by special physical properties. Magnetism occurs naturally in a few minerals. Minerals that glow under ultraviolet light have a property known as fluorescence.

Minerals • *Guided Reading and Study*

Properties of Minerals (pp. 114–122)

This section explains what minerals are and how they can be identified.

Use Target Reading Skills

As you read about properties of minerals, use the headings to complete the outline below.

Properties of Minerals
I. What Is a Mineral?
A. Naturally Occurring
B. Inorganic
C. _____
D. _____
E. _____
II. Identifying Materials
A. Color
B. _____
C. _____
D. Density
E. _____
F. _____
G. _____
H. Special Properties

What Is a Mineral? (pp. 114–115)

1. Because minerals are formed by processes that occur in the natural world, they are said to be _____.

2. Complete the concept map that shows characteristics of minerals.

Minerals

Minerals • *Guided Reading and Study*

Properties of Minerals *(continued)*

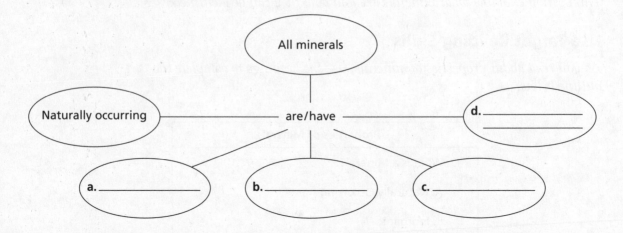

e. Use the concept map to write a definition of a mineral in your own words. You may use more than one sentence.

_____

_____

3. Because minerals do not come from living things, they are said to be

_____.

4. A substance that keeps its shape because its particles can't flow freely is

a(n) _____.

5. A solid with flat sides that meet at sharp edges and corners is called a(n)

_____.

6. Is the following sentence true or false? A mineral always contains certain elements in definite proportions. _____

7. Is the following sentence true or false? Very few minerals are compounds. _____

8. A substance formed when two or more elements combine and lose their distinct properties is a(n) _____.

9. In what two ways can elements occur in nature?

_____

10. What are some examples of minerals that occur as elements instead of compounds? _____

Identifying Minerals (pp. 116–122)

11. Is the following sentence true or false? Geologists have identified about 300 minerals. _____

12. Is the following sentence true or false? Each mineral has its own specific properties. _____ _____

13. Why can't color alone be used to identify most minerals?

_____

_____

14. The color of a mineral's powder is its _____.

15. The term that describes how a mineral reflects light from its surface is _____.

16. Is the following sentence true or false? Minerals containing metals often have a shiny luster. _____

17. Circle the letter of each sentence that is true about the density of a mineral.

    a. A given mineral can have varying densities.

    b. The larger the sample of a mineral, the greater its density.

    c. Each mineral has a characteristic density.

    d. The density of a mineral is its mass divided by its volume.

Properties of Minerals *(continued)*

18. What is the Mohs hardness scale? _____

    _____

19. The softest known mineral is _____. The hardest known

    mineral is _____.

20. Is the following sentence true or false? A mineral can scratch any

    mineral harder than itself. _____

21. Is the following sentence true or false? Each piece of a mineral has the

    same crystal structure. _____

22. How do geologists classify crystal structures? _____

    _____

    _____

Match the term with its definition.

Term	Definition
____ 23. cleavage	**a.** A mineral's ability to split easily along flat surfaces
____ 24. fracture	**b.** A mineral's ability to glow under ultraviolet light
____ 25. fluorescence	**c.** The way a mineral looks when it breaks

Minerals • *Review and Reinforce*

Properties of Minerals

Understanding Main Ideas

Fill in the blanks in the table below.

Mineral Property	Test
1. _____	Perform scratch test
Color	Observe surface of mineral
2. _____	Observe color of powder on unglazed tile
Luster	Observe how mineral reflects light
3. _____	Find mass per unit volume
4. _____	Observe number and angle of crystal faces
Cleavage and Fracture	Break mineral apart to see if it splits along flat surfaces

Answer the following questions on a separate sheet of paper.

5. List the five characteristics necessary for a substance to be a mineral.

6. Explain why each mineral has its own properties, different from every other mineral.

Building Vocabulary

Match each term with its definition by writing the letter of the correct definition on the line beside the term in the left column.

_____ 7. cleavage

_____ 8. streak

_____ 9. luster

_____ 10. fracture

_____ 11. Mohs hardness scale

_____ 12. crystal

_____ 13. element

a. how a mineral reflects light from its surface

b. a substance composed of a single kind of atom

c. the property of splitting evenly along flat surfaces

d. how a mineral breaks apart when it does not split evenly

e. the repeating pattern of a mineral's particles in a solid

f. the color of a mineral's powder

g. a ranking of minerals from softest to hardest

Minerals

Minerals • *Enrich*

Crystal Shapes

Geologists classify crystals into six groups according to the number and angle of the crystal faces. You can make models of two of those crystal shapes by using the patterns below.

Procedure

1. Cut the pattern out by cutting along the solid lines.

2. Fold the pattern along the dashed lines. Make side A opposite side AA, side B opposite side BB, and so on. Tape the shape into place using clear tape to tape the tabs onto the sides.

3. Follow the same steps to make the hexagonal shape.

4. Try to make your own paper models for the four other types of crystal shapes.

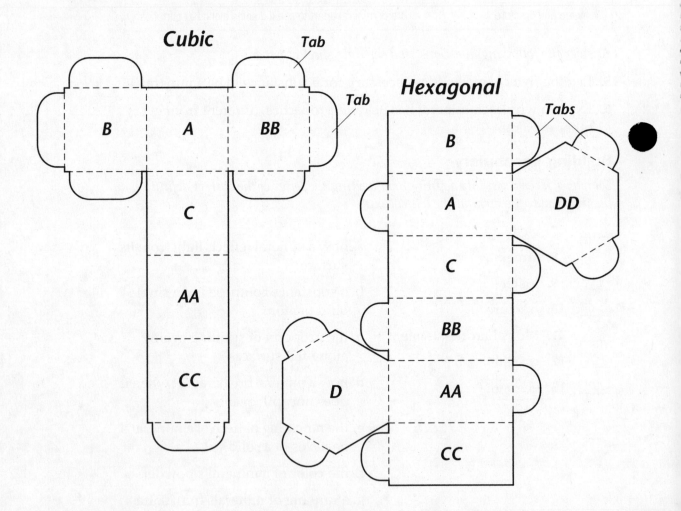

Minerals • *Skills Lab*

Finding the Density of Minerals

Problem

How can you compare the density of different minerals?

Materials

graduated cylinder, 100 mL

3 mineral samples: pyrite, quartz, and galena

water

balance

Procedure   *Review the safety guidelines in Appendix A.*

1. Check to make sure the mineral samples are small enough to fit in the graduated cylinder.

2. Place the pyrite on the balance and record its mass in the data table on the next page.

3. Fill the cylinder with water to the 50-mL mark.

4. Carefully place the pyrite into the cylinder of water. Try not to spill any of the water.

5. Read the level of the water on the scale of the graduated cylinder. Record the level of the water with the pyrite in it.

6. Calculate the volume of water displaced by the pyrite. To do this, subtract the volume of water without the pyrite from the volume of water with the pyrite. Record your answer.

7. Calculate the density of the pyrite by using this formula.

$$\text{Density} = \frac{\text{Mass of mineral}}{\text{Volume of water displaced by the mineral}}$$

(*Note:* Density is expressed as g/cm^3. One mL of water has a volume of $1\ cm^3$.)

8. Remove the water and mineral from the cylinder.

9. Repeat Steps 2–8 for quartz and galena.

Minerals

Minerals · *Skills Lab*

Finding the Density of Minerals (*continued*)

DATA TABLE

	Pyrite	Quartz	Galena
Mass of Mineral (g)			
Volume of Water without Mineral (mL)	50	50	50
Volume of Water with Mineral (mL)			
Volume of Water Displaced (mL)			
Volume of Water Displaced (cm^3)			
Density (g/cm^3)			

Analyze and Conclude

Write your answers in the spaces provided.

1. **Interpreting Data** Which mineral had the highest density? The lowest density?

   _____

   _____

2. **Measuring** How does finding the volume of the water that was displaced help you find the volume of the mineral itself?

   _____

   _____

   _____

3. **Drawing Conclusions** Does the shape of a mineral sample affect its density? Explain.

   _____

   _____

   _____

4. **Predicting** Would the procedure you used in this lab work for a substance that floats or one that dissolves in water?

   _____

   _____

   _____

Minerals · *Skills Lab*

Designing Experiments

Pyrite is sometimes called "fool's gold" because its color and appearance are similar to real gold. Design an experiment to determine if a sample that looks like gold is in fact real gold.

Minerals

How Minerals Form

Ability Levels Key
L1 Basic to Average
L2 For All Students
L3 Average to Advanced

🕐 *2 periods, 1 block*

Objectives
F.4.2.1 Explain how minerals form from magma and lava.
F.4.2.2 Explain how minerals form from water solutions.

Key Terms
• geode • crystallization • solution • vein

PRETEACH

Build Background Knowledge
Students are provided an analogy between how cotton candy is made and how crystals form.

 **Discover Activity** *How Does the Rate of Cooling Affect Crystals?* **L1**

Targeted Resources

❏ **All in One Teaching Resources**
    L2 Reading Strategy Transparency F37: Asking Questions
❏ 💿 **PresentationExpress™ CD-ROM**

INSTRUCT

Minerals From Magma and Lava
Explain that the size of crystals in minerals depends on the location of molten rock as it cools. Discuss these differences and hypothesize how fast volcanic glass cools.

Minerals From Solutions
Use Figure 10 to help explain how some minerals crystallize from hot water solutions underground.

Targeted Resources

❏ **All in One Teaching Resources**
    L2 Guided Reading, pp. 262–264
    L2 Transparency F38
❏ 📼 **Lab Activity Video/DVD**
    Skills Lab: *Finding the Density of Minerals*
❏ **PHSchool.com** Web Code: cfd-1042
❏ **PHSchool.com** Web Code: cfd-1040
❏ 💿 **Student Edition on Audio CD**

ASSESS

Section Assessment Questions
🔄 Have students use their completed graphic organizers with their questions and answers to answer the questions.

Reteach
Students list examples of minerals from magma or lava and minerals from solutions.

Targeted Resources

❏ **All in One Teaching Resources**
Section Summary, p. 261
L1 Review and Reinforce, p. 265
L3 Enrich, p. 266

Minerals • *Section Summary*

How Minerals Form

Key Concepts
- How do minerals form from magma and lava?
- How do minerals form from water solutions?

A **geode** is a rounded, hollow rock that is often lined with mineral crystals. It is formed in the way that all minerals generally are formed—through **crystallization,** the process by which atoms are arranged to form a material with a crystal structure.

One of the two ways minerals form is by crystallization of magma and lava. **Minerals form as hot magma cools inside the crust, or as lava hardens on the surface. When these liquids cool to a solid state, they form crystals.** The size of these crystals depends on several factors. The rate at which magma cools, the amount of gas magma contains, and the chemical composition of magma all affect crystal size. Slow cooling leads to the formation of large crystals. If the crystals remain undisturbed while cooling, they grow according to a regular pattern. Magma closer to the surface cools much faster than magma that hardens deep below ground. With rapid cooling, there is no time for magma to form large crystals. If magma erupts to the surface and becomes lava, the lava will also cool quickly and form minerals with small crystals.

Sometimes the elements and compounds that form minerals can be dissolved in water to form solutions. A **solution** is a mixture in which one substance is dissolved in another. **When elements and compounds that are dissolved in water leave a solution, crystallization occurs.**

Some minerals form when solutions evaporate. For example, deposits of the mineral halite, or table salt, formed over millions of years when ancient seas slowly evaporated. Other useful minerals that can form by evaporation include gypsum and calcite.

Some minerals form from hot water solutions. When a hot water solution heated by magma deep underground begins to cool, the elements and compounds leave the solution and crystallize as minerals. Pure metals that crystallize from hot water solutions underground often form veins. A **vein** is a narrow channel or slab of a mineral that is different from the surrounding rock.

Minerals

Minerals • *Guided Reading and Study*

How Minerals Form (pp. 124–127)

This section describes how minerals form and where minerals are found.

Use Target Reading Skills

As you preview the headings in this section, complete the graphic organizer with questions in the left column. As you read, fill in the answers in the second column.

Formation of Minerals

Question	Answer
How do minerals form from magma?	

Introduction (p. 124)

1. The process by which atoms are arranged to form a material with a

   crystal structure is referred to as _____.

2. In what two ways do minerals form?

   _____

   _____

   _____

Minerals From Magma and Lava (p. 125)

3. What affects the size of crystals formed from magma? _____

   _____

   _____

   _____

Minerals • *Guided Reading and Study*

4. Why does magma that cools deep below the surface have large crystals?

_____

_____

5. Is the following sentence true or false? Lava cools quickly and forms

minerals with small crystals. _____

Minerals From Solutions (pp. 125–127)

6. A mixture in which one substance dissolves in another is called a(n)

_____.

7. Is the following sentence true or false? Minerals can form when

solutions evaporate. _____

8. Circle the letter of each sentence that is true about halite deposits in the United States.

a. Deposits are found in the Midwest and Southwest.

b. Deposits are found along the Gulf Coast.

c. Deposits formed over the past thousand years.

d. Deposits formed when ancient seas evaporated.

9. How do minerals form from a hot water solution? _____

_____

_____

_____

_____

10. A narrow channel or slab of a mineral that is much different from the

surrounding rock is called a(n) _____.

11. How do veins form? _____

_____

_____

_____

Minerals · *Guided Reading and Study*

How Minerals Form *(continued)*

12. Complete the Venn diagram by labeling the circles with the type of minerals they represent.

a. _____   b. _____

Form from
melted materials

Form through
crystallization

Form from
dissolved materials

c. Use the Venn diagram to explain how the two main ways in which minerals can form are alike and how they are different. _____

_____

_____

Minerals ▪ *Review and Reinforce*

How Minerals Form

Understanding Main Ideas

Complete the flowchart below by filling in the blanks.

1. _____ heats water underground.

➡ 2. _____ and _____ dissolve in the hot

water to form solutions. ➡ These solutions follow cracks within the rock.

➡ Elements and compounds leave the solutions during cooling and

3. _____ as minerals. ➡ The minerals form a narrow

channel or slab in the rock called a(n) 4. _____.

Answer the following questions in the spaces provided.

5. In general, what are the two ways in which minerals form?

_____

_____

6. Describe conditions in which large and small crystals are likely to form.

_____

_____

_____

7. Describe how halite deposits form.

_____

Building Vocabulary

Fill in the blank to complete each statement.

8. A(n) _____ is a mixture in which one substance is
dissolved in another.

9. A(n) _____ is a rounded, hollow rock that is often lined
with mineral crystals.

10. The process by which atoms are arranged to form a material with a

crystal structure is called _____.

Name _____ Date _____ Class_____

Minerals ▪ *Enrich*

Diamond-Studded Pipes in the Crust

Diamonds are the hardest natural substance. Because of their brilliant luster, they are prized as precious gems. Diamonds are also very rare minerals. For thousands of years, they have been collected from stream beds and similar places. It was only in the late 1800s that the source of diamonds was discovered—long, narrow cracks in the crust called pipes. These are similar to volcanic pipes, except there is no volcano above. The first such pipe was discovered near Kimberley, South Africa, in 1867. The type of rock in the pipe was named kimberlite after the South African town. Since then, kimberlite pipes have been discovered in other areas, including Australia and Russia.

Geologists think that diamonds form in the asthenosphere, where high temperatures and intense pressures cause pure carbon to crystallize. Study the figures below to learn how diamonds become part of Earth's lithosphere.

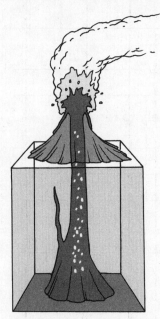

Under intense pressure, magma that contains diamonds quickly bursts up through the lithosphere. The magma cools to form a carrot-shaped pipe made of kimberlite. The only surface evidence of the kimberlite pipe is a small cone. Over time this cone wears away.

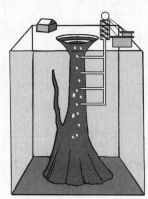

Miners dig directly down into the pipe, making an open pit. Then shafts are dug to mine diamonds deep underground.

Answer the following questions on a separate sheet of paper.

1. What are diamonds, and why are they highly valued?

2. Where and under what conditions do diamonds form?

3. What is a kimberlite pipe?

4. What is kimberlite, and how did it get its name?

5. Why do shafts need to be dug to mine diamonds underground?

Using Mineral Resources

 2 periods, 1 block

Objectives
F.4.3.1 Describe how minerals are used.
F.4.3.2 Explain how ores are processed to obtain metals.

Key Terms
• gemstone • ore • smelting • alloy

Local Standards

PRETEACH

Build Background Knowledge
Students name items they use every day that are made from minerals and recall that steel mills melt ore in furnaces.

 **Discover Activity** *How Are Minerals Processed Before They Are Used?* **L1**

Targeted Resources

❏ **All in One Teaching Resources**
  L2 Reading Strategy Transparency F39: Using Prior Knowledge
❏ **PresentationExpress™ CD-ROM**

INSTRUCT

The Uses of Minerals
Challenge students to name items that are not made from rock or minerals to help them understand the importance of minerals. Guide a discussion on how the use of minerals has affected the development of society.

Producing Metals From Minerals
Work with students as a class to create a concept map that shows how ore is prospected, mined, and processed. Given the fictional scenario of an iron shortage, guide them to apply their knowledge to develop a plan to increase iron supplies.

 Consumer Lab *A Mouthful of Minerals* **L2**

Targeted Resources

❏ **All in One Teaching Resources**
  L2 Guided Reading, pp. 269–272
  L2 Transparency F40
  L2 Lab: *A Mouthful of Minerals*, pp. 275–276
❏ **Lab Activity Video/DVD**
  Consumer Lab: *A Mouthful of Minerals*
❏ **www.SciLinks.org** Web Code: scn-1043
❏ **Discovery SCHOOL Video Field Trip**
❏ **Student Edition on Audio CD**

ASSESS

Section Assessment Questions
Have students use the graphic organizers that they completed using prior knowledge to answer the questions.

Reteach
Students make a table of minerals and their uses.

Targeted Resources

❏ **All in One Teaching Resources**
  Section Summary, p. 268
  L1 Review and Reinforce, p. 273
  L3 Enrich, p. 274

Minerals

Minerals • *Section Summary*

Using Mineral Resources

Key Concepts

- How are minerals used?

- How are ores processed to obtain metals?

Minerals are the source of gemstones, metals, and a variety of materials used to make many products. Usually, a **gemstone** is a hard, colorful mineral that has a brilliant or glassy luster. People value gemstones for their color, luster, and durability, and for the fact that they are rare. Once a gemstone is cut and polished, it is called a gem. Gems are used mainly for jewelry and decoration. They are also used for mechanical parts and for grinding and polishing.

Some minerals are the sources of metals such as aluminum, iron, copper, or silver. Metals are useful because they can be stretched into wire, flattened into sheets, and hammered or molded without breaking. Metal tools and machinery, the metal filament in a light bulb, aluminum foil, and the steel beams used to frame office buildings all began as minerals inside Earth's crust.

There are many other useful minerals besides metals and gems. People use materials from these minerals in foods, medicines, fertilizers, and building materials.

To produce metal from a mineral, a rock containing the mineral must be located through prospecting and mined, or removed from the ground. Then the rock must be processed to extract the metal. A rock that contains a metal or other useful mineral that can be mined and sold at a profit is called an **ore.** A prospector is anyone who searches, or prospects, for an ore deposit. Geologists prospect for ores by observing rocks on the land surface and by studying maps of rocks beneath the surface.

The geologists' map of an ore deposit helps miners decide how to remove the ore from the ground. There are three types of mines: strip mines, open pit mines, and shaft mines. In strip mining, earthmoving equipment scrapes away soil to expose ore. In open pit mining, miners use giant earthmoving equipment to dig a tremendous pit and remove ore deposits. For ore deposits that occur in veins, miners dig shaft mines. Shaft mines often have a network of tunnels that extend deep into the ground, following the veins of ores.

Ores must be processed before the metals they contain can be used. In the process of **smelting,** an ore is mixed with other substances and then melted to separate the useful metal from other elements the ore contains. After smelting, additional processing is needed to remove impurities from the metal. After the iron is purified, a small amount of carbon may be added to it. The result is steel, which is an **alloy,** a solid mixture of two or more elements, at least one of which is a metal.

Minerals • *Guided Reading and Study*

Using Mineral Resources (pp. 130–135)

This section describes the uses of minerals and how minerals are obtained.

Use Target Reading Skills

As you come to each head in the section, stop and write what you know about that topic. As you read the passage, write what you learn.

What You Know
I. The gems used in jewelry are minerals.
2.

What You Learned
I.
2.

The Uses of Minerals (p. 131)

1. Any hard, colorful mineral that has a brilliant or glassy luster is called

   a(n) _____.

2. A gemstone that has been cut and polished is called a(n)

   _____.

Minerals • *Guided Reading and Study*

Using Mineral Resources *(continued)*

3. Circle the letter of each choice that is a way gems are used.

    a. jewelry

    b. fuel

    c. mechanical parts

    d. grinding and polishing

4. List four examples of metals.

    a. _____

    b. _____

    c. _____

    d. _____

5. Why are metals useful? _____

_____

_____

_____

6. What are some uses of metals? _____

_____

_____

Match each mineral with the product in which it is found.

Mineral	**Product**
____ **7.** talc	**a.** cement
____ **8.** calcite	**b.** microscopes
____ **9.** quartz	**c.** watches
____ **10.** gypsum	**d.** powder

Producing Metals From Minerals *(pp. 132–135)*

11. A rock that contains a metal or economically useful mineral is called

    a(n) _____.

12. Is the following sentence true or false? Most metals occur in a pure form.

    _____

13. Much of the world's copper is contained in the mineral ore

    _____.

Minerals · *Guided Reading and Study*

14. Anyone who searches for an ore deposit is called a(n) _____.

15. What features do geologists look for when they prospect for ores?

_____

_____

_____

16. Is the following sentence true or false? The map of an ore deposit helps

miners decide how to mine the ore. _____

17. Complete the compare/contrast table to show the similarities and
differences among the different types of ore deposits and mines.

How Ores Are Mined	
Kind of Ore Deposit	**Type of Mine Used**
Starts near the surface and extends deep underground	a.
Occurs in veins	b.
Is exposed on the surface	c.

d. Use the table to explain how the ore deposits removed by shaft
mining and by strip mining are similar to the ore deposits removed
in open pit mining. _____

_____

_____

_____

_____

18. Describe strip mining. _____

_____

_____

19. Describe open pit mining. _____

_____

_____

20. Describe a shaft mine. _____

_____

_____

Minerals

Minerals • *Guided Reading and Study*

Using Mineral Resources *(continued)*

21. The process in which an ore is melted to separate the useful metal from other elements is _____.

22. Is the following sentence true or false? People first developed smelting in the 1800s. _____

23. A solid mixture of two or more metals is called a(n)

_____.

24. Fill in the flowchart with the following steps in the correct sequence: produce carbon dioxide and molten iron, pour off molten iron, mix with limestone and coal, place in blast furnace.

Smelting Iron Ore

a. _____

↓

b. _____

↓

c. _____

↓

d. _____

Minerals • *Review and Reinforce*

Using Mineral Resources

Understanding Main Ideas

Fill in the blanks in the table below.

Mineral(s)	Use(s)
1. _____	tools, machinery, light-bulb filaments, steel girders
2. _____	jewelry, decoration, mechanical parts, abrasives
3. _____	glass, electronic equipment
4. _____	wallboard, cement, stucco

Answer the following questions in the spaces provided.

5. What are the three types of mines?

_____

6. Describe the smelting of iron ore.

_____

_____

_____

7. Why are alloys useful? Describe an example.

_____

_____

Building Vocabulary

Fill in the blank to complete each statement.

8. A(n) _____ is a solid mixture of two or more metals.

9. A(n) _____ is a rock that contains a metal or economically useful mineral.

10. A process in which an ore is melted to separate the useful metal from other elements the ore contains is called _____.

Minerals

Minerals • *Enrich*

Alloys in Your Life

An alloy is a solid mixture of two or more metals. There are thousands of different alloys, and people use them for many different purposes. The table below lists some important alloys and their uses.

Some Common Alloys

Alloy	Composition	Properties	Representative Uses
Aluminum alloys	aluminum, copper, manganese, magnesium	Strength, lightness	Cans, house siding, machines
Brass	copper, zinc	Corrosion resistance	Instruments, castings
Bronze	copper, tin	Good for casting	Castings
Cupronickel	copper, nickel	Corrosion resistance	Coins
German silver	copper, zinc, nickel	Good looking, inexpensive	Candlesticks
Invar	iron, nickel	Barely expands or contracts	Measuring devices
Pewter	tin, copper, lead, antimony	Easy to work with	Utensils
Phospher bronze	copper, tin, zinc, phosphorus	Corrosion resistance	Machine parts
Solder	tin, lead	Low melting point	Melted to join metal surfaces
Carbon steel	iron, carbon	Hard, strong	Girders, tools
Stainless steel	iron, chromium, nickel	Hard, strong, rust resistance	Machines, utensils
Superalloys	nickel or cobalt with many other elements	Great strength and durability	Spacecraft

Answer the following questions on a separate sheet of paper.

1. Do all alloys contain only two metals? Give evidence for your answer.

2. What metals does a pewter cup contain?

3. What alloy would you use to join metal parts? Explain why.

4. What is the difference between brass and bronze?

5. Why are superalloys used for spacecraft?

Minerals • *Consumer Lab*

A Mouthful of Minerals

Problem

What effect do the minerals in toothpaste have on the toothpaste's ability to clean?

Materials

samples of 3 different types of toothpaste

worn-out toothbrushes

tap water

a ceramic tile stained on the unglazed side with a felt-tip marker or pen

Procedure

Review the safety guidelines in the front of your lab book.

1. Copy the data table into your notebook.

2. Your teacher will give you samples of toothpaste, a list of the mineral or minerals in each type of toothpaste, a toothbrush, and a ceramic tile.

3. In your data table, record the substances found in each toothpaste sample. Common minerals in toothpaste include mica, calcite, and quartz (silica). Toothpaste also may include compounds such as sodium bicarbonate (baking soda), sodium fluoride, aluminum or calcium phosphates, and titanium dioxide.

4. For each toothpaste sample, predict how effective you think it will be in removing the stain from the tile. Record your predictions in the data table.

DATA TABLE

Toothpaste	Minerals Present	Predictions	Observations
1			
2			
3			

5. Put a pea-sized amount of the first toothpaste onto a toothbrush. **CAUTION:** *Do not ingest any of the toothpaste.*

Minerals · *Consumer Lab*

A Mouthful of Minerals *(continued)*

6. Brush one of the stain marks on the tile 50 times. As you brush, try to use the same amount of force for each stroke.

7. Using tap water, rinse the tile to remove all of the paste. Then rinse the toothpaste out of the toothbrush.

8. Repeat Steps 5–7 for the other toothpaste samples, using a different stain mark for each test. Be sure to brush with the same amount of force and for the same number of times.

9. Compare how well the different toothpastes cleaned the stains. Record your observations in the data table.

Analyze and Conclude

Respond to the following items on a separate sheet of paper.

1. **Classifying** Which mineral or minerals were found in all of the toothpastes tested? Did any toothpaste contain minerals not found in the other toothpastes?

2. **Observing** Which toothpaste was most effective in removing stains from the tile?

3. **Interpreting Data** Were your predictions about which toothpaste would be most effective correct?

4. **Interpreting Data** Does the toothpaste that was most effective in cleaning the tile differ in mineral content from the other toothpastes that were tested?

5. **Controlling Variables** What was the independent variable in this experiment? What was the dependent variable? Why did you use the same amount of toothpaste, force, and number of brushstrokes in each trial?

6. **Drawing Conclusions** How do the minerals in toothpaste affect the toothpaste's cleaning ability? Explain.

7. **Developing Hypotheses** Your teeth have the same composition as apatite, which has a hardness of 5 on the Mohs scale. What would be the advantages and disadvantages of using a toothpaste containing a mineral that is harder than apatite? Softer than apatite? Explain.

8. **Communicating** Write a lab report for this experiment. In your report, describe your predictions, your procedure, how you controlled variables, and whether or not your results supported your predictions.

Design Your Own Experiment

Some brands of toothpaste claim that they whiten teeth. Design an experiment to test the effectiveness of different kinds of whitening toothpaste. Make a data table to organize your findings. *Obtain your teacher's permission before carrying out your investigation.*

Key Terms

Use the clues to help you unscramble the key terms from the chapter. Then put the numbered letters in order to find the answer to the riddle.

Clues   **Key Terms**

1. It's how it looks when it breaks.   tarfceur $\underset{1}{—}$ — — — — — —

2. It contains two or more metals.   ylaol   — $\underset{2}{—}$ — — —

3. It could be shiny or pearly.   rutels   — $\underset{3}{—}$ — — —

4. It was never alive.   rincanoig   — — $\underset{4}{—}$ — — — — — —

5. It's the color of the powder.   rsaekt   — — $\underset{5}{—}$ — — —

6. It includes melting.   temsilgn   — — $\underset{6}{—}$ — — — —

7. It has a repeating pattern.   ratlycs   — — — $\underset{7}{—}$ — —

8. It contains two or more elements.   pucnoodm $\underset{8}{—}$ — — — — — —

9. It's valued because it's beautiful and rare. nsgoteem   — $\underset{9}{—}$ — — — — —

10. It's a mixture.   situnloo   — — — — — — $\underset{10}{—}$

11. It's how it splits.   elagveac $\underset{11}{—}$ — — — — — —

12. It's composed of a single kind of atom.   teemlen   — — $\underset{12}{—}$ — — —

Riddle: Why do some minerals glow?

Answer: $\overline{}\ \overline{}\ \overline{}\ \overline{}\ \overline{}\ \overline{}\ \overline{}\ \overline{}\ \overline{}\ \overline{}\ \overline{}\ \overline{}$
   1   2   3   4   5   6   7   8   9 10 11 12

Minerals · *Connecting Concepts*

Connecting Concepts

Develop a concept map that uses the key concepts and key terms from this chapter. Keep in mind the big idea of this chapter: Minerals, formed by magma or by elements or compounds in hot solutions, share five characteristics that make them valuable resources. The concept map shown is one way to organize how the information in this chapter is related. You may use an extra sheet of paper.

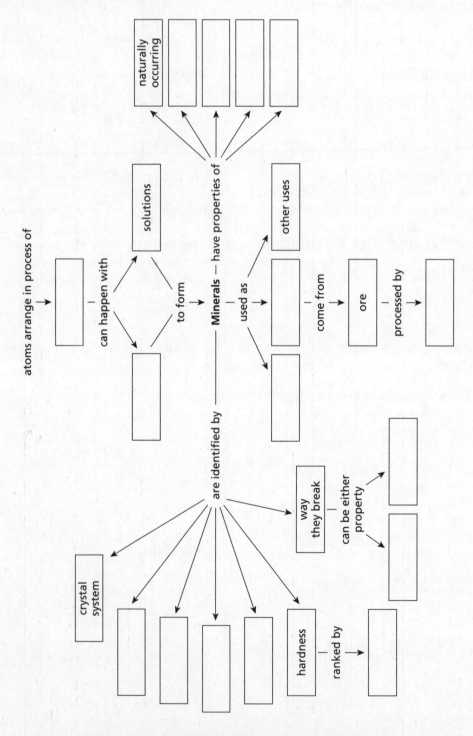

How Tessellating!

Key Concept

Repeating patterns, or tessellations, of atoms that have no gaps or overlaps form crystals.

Skills Focus

observing, classifying, making models, forming operational definitions

Time

50 minutes

Materials

index cards

tape

scissors

plain white paper

colored pencils

ruler

Advance Preparation

Gather several small mirrors for More to Explore. Mirrors should be unframed and have edges that aren't sharp.

Teaching Tips

- Be sure that students don't choose final patterns that are too simple. Encourage students to use rectangles and triangles only until they understand how to tessellate patterns.

- When students tape smaller peices of paper together to make a shape, the tape should not extend over the edge of the pieces and affect the tessellation by causeing overlap of the patterns.

- Have more index cards available for studdents if they need them.

- Tessellation models are not complete models of three-dimensional crystal shapes. After the activity, have students use identical three-dimensional shapes to model actual crystal structure. Another option is to show students pieces of rock salt, which are cubic crystals. Carefully break the rock salt into smaller pieces of salt with a hand lens and observe that the salt crystals remain cubic.

Minerals · *Laboratory Investigation*

How Tessellating!

Pre-Lab Discussion

A floor covered with tiles may be made of repeated squares. A honeycomb is made of repeated hexagons. Crystal shapes within a mineral have definite repeating patterns, too. A pattern tessellates if it repeats and covers a plane (such as a sheet of paper, a floor, or a wall) with no gaps or overlaps. See Figure 1. In this investigation, you will model crystal shapes by creating patterns that tessellate.

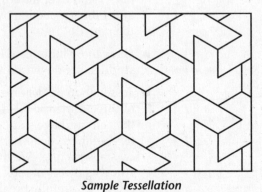

Figure 1

Sample Tessellation

1. Think about what makes up a mineral. Why isn't coal a mineral?

   _____

   _____

2. How many sides does a hexagonal figure have?

   _____

   _____

Problem

What patterns tessellate?

Materials *(per group)*

- index cards
- tape
- scissors
- plain white paper
- colored pencils
- ruler

Name _____ Date _____ Class_____

Minerals · *Laboratory Investigation*

Safety ✂ *Review the safety guidelines in Appendix A of your textbook.*
Use caution in handling sharp scissors.

Procedure

1. Use a ruler and scissors to carefully cut simple geometric shapes with straight edges from an index card. Begin with squares, rectangles, or hexagons. The simpler the shape, the easier it will be to get it to tessellate.

2. Tape the pieces of the card together to form an interesting new shape that you think will tessellate. Remember, if you make your shape very complicated, you will have trouble getting it to repeat.

3. Trace your new shape repeatedly onto a piece of paper. Does the shape tessellate? Sketch it in the appropriate space in the Observations section below. If it doesn't tessellate, try taping the pieces in a different arrangement or make a different pattern. Sketch shapes that do not tessellate in the appropriate space below.

4. Once you get a shape to tessellate, cover the entire area in the Observations section on the next page with your design.

5. Look for other patterns that tessellate in your design. Can you find any? Use colored pencils to outline several different shapes that tessellate.

Observations

Patterns That Tessellate	Patterns That Don't Tessellate

Minerals · *Laboratory Investigation*

How Tessellating! *(continued)*

Tessellation	Sample Tessellation

Analyze and Conclude

1. Did your first pattern tessellate? With what basic geometric shape did you begin?

   _____

2. Could you use a circle or an oval to tessellate? Give a reason for your answer.

   _____

   _____

3. A mineral has a definite crystal shape, as shown in your textbook. Which crystal shapes tessellate? Are any of the shapes the same as the ones that tessellated for you?

   _____

   _____

Minerals ▪ *Laboratory Investigation*

Critical Thinking and Applications

1. How is your tessellating pattern like a crystal's shape?

   _____

   _____

   _____

2. List examples of tessellating patterns in your everyday life.

   _____

   _____

3. How does your model of tessellating patterns differ from actual crystal shapes?

   _____

   _____

More to Explore

The crystals found within all minerals form tessellating patterns. Almost all of these patterns have another interesting property—symmetry. A pattern has symmetry if it looks exactly the same on either side of a center line through the pattern.

New Problem How can you determine whether your pattern has symmetry?

Possible Materials Use your tessellating pattern from the previous activity. Think of how you could use a mirror to find out if your pattern tessellates.

Safety Use caution in handling any sharp items or items that could break.

Procedure Write a procedure you would follow to answer the question. Have the teacher approve your procedure before you carry out the investigation.

Observations Make a drawing of your shape that shows how the pattern does or does not have symmetry.

Analyze and Conclude

1. Does your shape have symmetry? How do you know?

   _____

2. What are some examples of symmetry in nature?

   _____

   _____

Minerals

Identifying a Mystery Mineral

Students are presented with the problem of identifying a mystery mineral sample. To solve this problem, they must apply their knowledge of mineral properties and the tests used for each property. Once the properties of the mineral are determined, students can then identify the mineral using the table in *Appendix B, Common Minerals.*

Expected Outcome

Students should be able to identify the mineral sample through observation and some simple tests. Through observation, they can determine the color and luster of the sample. With the materials provided for a scratch test, they can roughly determine the sample's hardness. With the streak plate, they can observe the color of the sample's streak. By hefting the sample, students can make a relative determination of the sample's density. Through observation of the minerals exterior, students can make a judgment about whether the sample has cleavage or fracture. Once these properties have been determined, students can identify the sample using *Appendix B.*

Content Assessed

This activity assesses students' knowledge of mineral properties and the tests used to identify minerals.

Skills Assessed

observing, applying concepts, drawing conclusions

Materials

Mineral samples should be ones that appear in the table in *Appendix B, Common Minerals.*

Mystery mineral samples might include pyrite, galena, olivine, hornblende, feldspar, quartz, talc, hematite, or others on the table. Assign mineral samples to students arbitrarily.

The back of a ceramic tile makes a good streak plate.

Any heavy piece of glass will do for the scratch test. For safety reasons, a baby-food jar is useful because it doesn't break easily.

A steel knife can be used in place of the metal nail file.

Advance Preparation

Gather enough materials for each student a day in advance.

Time

20 minutes

Safety

Caution students that they will be working with a metal nail file that can cause a cut or abrasion if mishandled. Caution them that they will be using glass jars that are breakable. Instruct them to wear safety goggles and to handle the jars with care. Tell students that if glass does break, they should notify you immediately and not touch the broken pieces.

Monitoring the Task

Review each student's list of tests they can do to identify the sample.

Suggest that students make a list of properties used to identify a mineral and then try to figure out how to determine each property in the sample.

Identifying a Mystery Mineral

In assessing students' performance, use the following rubric.

	4	3	2	1
Mineral Identification	The student correctly identifies the mystery mineral using evidence of six properties, including hardness, color, streak, luster, density (heft), and cleavage/fracture.	The student correctly identifies the mystery mineral using evidence of four to five properties.	The student correctly identifies the mystery mineral using evidence of two to three properties.	The student incorrectly identifies the mystery mineral using evidence of one or two properties.
			The student correctly identifies the mystery mineral or misidentifies the mineral despite using evidence of three to five properties.	
Concept Understanding	The student demonstrates a mastery of the concepts related to the characteristics of a mineral and the properties used for mineral identification.	The student demonstrates an adequate understanding of the concepts related to the characteristics of a mineral and the properties used for mineral identification.	The student demonstrates some understanding of the concepts related to the characteristics of a mineral and the properties used for mineral identification.	The student demonstrates a weak understanding of the concepts related to the characteristics of a mineral and the properties used for mineral identification.

Minerals • *Performance Assessment*

Identifying a Mystery Mineral

Problem

How can you identify a mineral sample from its properties?

Suggested Materials

mystery mineral sample
streak plate
metal nail file
penny
glass baby-food jar
scrap piece of metal
Mohs hardness scale
Appendix B

Devise a Plan

1. Study the materials and think of a way you could use them to identify the mystery mineral sample.

2. Make a list of the tests you can make to identify the mystery mineral.

3. Keep a record of the results of all tests you carry out.

Analyze and Conclude

Respond to the following items on a separate sheet of paper.

1. What are the characteristics that a substance needs to have to be considered a mineral?

2. What characteristic of minerals gives each mineral its own specific properties?

3. What tests did you carry out to identify the mineral sample? Give a reason why you carried out each test.

4. Which property or properties could you not test for? Why?

5. Identify the mystery mineral, and give as many reasons as possible for your identification.

Minerals

Multiple Choice

Write the letter of the correct answer on the line at the left.

_____ 1. Friedrich Mohs invented a system
   a. to smelt two kinds of iron ore.
   b. to use explosives to find mineral deposits underground.
   c. to find minerals near the mid-ocean ridge.
   d. to describe and compare hardness of minerals.

_____ 2. What is a narrow channel or slab of a mineral that is sharply different from the surrounding rock?
   a. fracture   b. vein
   c. crystal   d. ore

_____ 3. The purpose of heating iron ore to a very high temperature in a blast furnace is
   a. to add hematite to the final product.
   b. to eliminate one kind of iron from the iron ore.
   c. to heat the iron so that it separates from other elements in the ore.
   d. to cool down the hot furnace.

_____ 4. Hard, colorful minerals that have a brilliant or glassy luster are
   a. crystals   b. ores
   c. metals   d. gemstones

_____ 5. Steel is an example of a useful
   a. ore.   b. gemstone.
   c. alloy.   d. crystal.

_____ 6. A mineral that splits apart easily along flat surfaces has the property called
   a. cleavage.   b. crystal shape.
   c. fracture.   d. hardness.

_____ 7. Color alone cannot be used to identify a mineral because
   a. only a few minerals always have their own characteristic color.
   b. luster usually hides a mineral's true color.
   c. the color of most minerals is hidden by veins.
   d. color and streak are never the same color.

_____ 8. Earthy, shiny, waxy, metallic, and pearly are terms used to describe a mineral's
   a. streak.   b. luster.
   c. color.   d. density.

Minelals ▪ *Chapter Test*

     9. The size of a mineral's crystals depends on which of the following?
       a. the mineral's crystal group
       b. the solution from which the mineral formed
       c. the smelting process in which the magma formed
       d. the rate of cooling of the magma or solution from which the mineral formed

     10. Which of the following is NOT one of the six types of crystal shapes?
       a. cubic   **b.** tetragonal
       c. triclinic   **d.** metallic

Completion

Fill in the line to complete each statement.

11. In a process called _____, an ore is melted to separate the useful metal from other elements in the ore.

12. The property of _____ is the mass of the mineral sample per unit volume.

13. A(n) _____ mine is used when ore deposits occur in veins.

14. Table salt is made from deposits of the mineral _____.

15. A rock that contains a metal or economically useful mineral is called a(n) _____.

True or False

If the statement is true, write true. *If it is false, change the underlined word or words to make the statement true.*

     16. A <u>miner</u> is anyone who searches for an ore deposit.

     17. Minerals form when a hot water solution cools and the minerals <u>crystallize</u>.

     18. The mineral <u>silver</u> is used in the making of glass.

     19. A substance is <u>organic</u> if it did not arise from materials that were once part of a living thing.

     20. The vast majority of minerals are <u>compounds</u>.

Minerals · *Chapter Test*

Using Science Skills: Interpreting Data

Use the table below to answer questions 21–23. Write your answers in the spaces provided.

Mineral	Hardness	Density	Luster	Streak	Color
Pyrite	6–6.5	5.0	Metallic	Greenish, brownish black	Yellow
Gold	2.5–3	19.3	Metallic	Yellow	Yellow
Silver	2.5–3	10.0–11.0	Metallic	Silver to light grey	Silver

21. Could you tell samples of these minerals apart just by using a scratch test? Why or why not?

_____

_____

22. One of these minerals is known as "fool's gold." Identify that mineral, and use evidence from the table to explain why the name fits.

_____

_____

23. What tests could you do to make sure a mineral sample was gold instead of "fool's gold"?

_____

_____

Essay

Answer each of the following in the spaces provided.

24. What characteristics does a piece of quartz have that can be used to classify it as a mineral?

_____

_____

25. In what two general ways do minerals form? Give an example of a mineral that forms in each way.

_____

_____

Minerals

Name _____ Date _____ Class_____

Minerals · *Chapter Test*

Using Science Skills

Use the figure below to answer questions 26 and 27. Write your answers in the spaces provided.

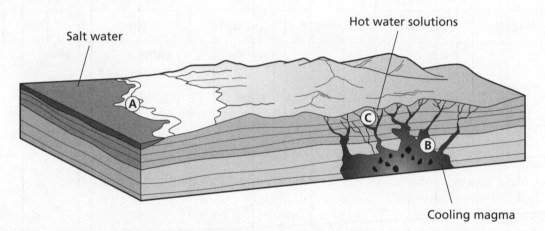

Salt water

Hot water solutions

Cooling magma

26. Interpreting Diagrams How do minerals form at B?

_____

_____

_____

_____

_____

27. Comparing and Contrasting Compare how minerals form at A with how minerals form at C.

_____

_____

_____

Essay

Answer each of the following on a separate sheet of paper.

28. Prospectors have discovered a halite deposit near the Great Salt Lake in Utah. Describe how that deposit might have formed.

29. Explain what slag is and how it forms.

30. When feldspar breaks apart, it splits easily at right angles. When quartz breaks apart, it produces curved, shell-like surfaces. What properties are being tested here? Is the way a mineral splits or breaks apart enough to enable you to identify it? Why or why not?

Properties of Minerals
Guided Reading and Study

Use Target Reading Skills

Properties of Minerals

I. What Is a Mineral?
    A. Naturally Occurring
    B. Inorganic
    C. *Solid*
    D. *Crystal Structure*
    E. *Definite Chemical Composition*
II. Identifying Minerals
    A. Color
    B. *Streak*
    C. *Luster*
    D. Density
    E. *Hardness*
    F. *Crystal Systems*
    G. *Cleavage and Fracture*
    H. Special Properties

1. naturally occurring.
2. **a.** Inorganic **b.** Solid **c.** Crystal Structure **d.** Definite Chemical Composition **e.** Possible answer: A mineral is naturally occurring, inorganic, and solid. It has a crystal structure and a definite chemical composition.
3. inorganic
4. solid
5. crystal
6. true
7. false
8. compound
9. in a pure form and as part of a compound
10. copper, silver, and gold
11. false
12. true
13. Different minerals may have the same color.
14. streak
15. luster
16. true
17. c, d
18. a scale that ranks ten minerals from softest to hardest
19. talc; diamond
20. false
21. true
22. into six groups based on the number and angle of the crystal faces
23. a
24. c
25. b

Properties of Minerals
Review and Reinforce

1. Hardness
2. Streak
3. Density
4. Crystal structure
5. A mineral must be a naturally occurring, inorganic solid with a crystal structure and a definite chemical composition.
6. Each mineral has its own properties because each mineral has a definite chemical composition.
7. c
8. f
9. a
10. d
11. g
12. e
13. b

Skills Lab

Finding the Density of Minerals

For answers, see Teacher's Edition.

How Minerals Form
Guided Reading and Study

Use Target Reading Skills This is one possible way to complete the graphic organizer. Accept all logical answers.

Formation of Minerals

Question	Answer
How do minerals form from magma?	They form when magma cools and crystals grow.
How do minerals form from solution?	They form when solutions evaporate or cool and harden, forming crystals.

1. crystallization
2. by crystallization of magma and lava or by crystallization of materials dissolved in water
3. the rate at which the magma cools, the amount of gas the magma contains, and the chemical composition of the magma
4. It cools slowly over many thousands of years; slow cooling leads to the formation of large crystals.
5. true
6. solution
7. true
8. a, b, d
9. When water is heated to a high temperature, elements and compounds that form a mineral dissolve in the hot water. When the water solution begins to cool, the elements and compounds leave the solution and crystallize, forming minerals.
10. vein
11. Solutions of hot water and metals often flow through cracks within the rock. Then the metals crystallize into veins.
12. **a.** Minerals From Magma and Lava **b.** Minerals From Solutions **c.** Possible answer: Formation of minerals is different because the materials that form minerals can be melted or dissolved. It is the same because both types form through crystallization.

How Minerals Form
Review and Reinforce

1. Magma
2. Elements; compounds
3. crystallize
4. vein
5. In general, minerals can form in two ways: by crystallization of magma and lava and through crystallization of materials dissolved in water.
6. Large crystals are likely to form when magma cools slowly, such as deep underground. Small crystals are likely to form when magma cools rapidly, as when magma cools near the surface or when lava cools. Ocean water seeps down through cracks in the crust, where magma heats it to a high temperature. The hot water dissolves minerals from the crust and rushes upward. The hot solution billows out of vents, or "chimneys." When the solution hits the cold sea, minerals crystallize and settle to the ocean floor.
7. Halite deposits form when seawater slowly evaporates.
8. solution
9. geode
10. crystallization

How Minerals Form
Enrich

1. Diamonds are a mineral composed of pure carbon. They are highly valued for their hardness, brilliant luster, and rarity.
2. Diamonds form in the asthenosphere, where high temperatures and intense pressures cause carbon to crystallize.
3. A kimberlite pipe is a long, carrot-shaped crack in the crust with no volcano above it.
4. Kimberlite is a type of rock that contains diamonds and forms when magma cools in a pipe; Kimberlite was named after Kimberley, South Africa, where it was first discovered.
5. Shafts are dug beside the pipe to get to the kimberlite containing diamonds deep underground.

Using Mineral Resources
Guided Reading and Study

Use Target Reading Skills This is one possible way to complete the graphic organizer. Accept all logical answers.

What You Know
1. The gems used in jewelry are minerals.
2. Metals come from Earth.

What You Learned
1. Minerals are also the source of metals and other useful materials, like quartz and gypsum.
2. Most metals come from ores, which must be mined and smelted before the metals can be used.

1. gemstone
2. gem
3. a, c, d
4. **a.** aluminum **b.** iron **c.** copper **d.** silver
5. They can be stretched into wire, flattened into sheets, and hammered or molded without breaking.
6. metal tools and machinery, the metal filament in a light bulb, aluminum foil, and steel beams used to frame office buildings
7. d
8. b
9. c
10. a
11. ore
12. false
13. chalcopyrite
14. prospector
15. They observe rocks on the land surface and study maps of rocks beneath the surface. They map the location, size, and shape of an ore deposit by using the echoes of seismic waves.
16. true
17. **a.** Open Pit **b.** Shaft **c.** Strip **d.** Possible answer: The ore deposits removed in shaft mining occur in veins, similar to the deposits that extend deep underground in open pit mining. The ore deposits removed in strip mining are exposed on the surface, similar to the deposits that start near the surface in open pit mining.
18. Earthmoving equipment scrapes away soil to expose ore.
19. Miners use giant earthmoving equipment to dig a tremendous pit and remove ore deposits.
20. It has a network of tunnels that extend deep into the ground, following the veins of ore.
21. smelting
22. false
23. alloy
24. **a.** mix with limestone and coal **b.** place in blast furnace **c.** produce carbon dioxide and molten iron **d.** pour off molten iron

Using Mineral Resources
Review and Reinforce

1. Metals
2. Gemstones
3. Quartz
4. Gypsum
5. Strip mines, open-pit mines, shaft mines
6. Answers may vary. A typical answer should mention: (1) iron ore is crushed and mixed with limestone and coke; (2) the mixture is placed in a blast furnace; (3) chemical changes in the furnace produce molten iron and carbon dioxide; (4) iron and slag are produced and poured from the furnace.
7. Alloys are useful because they have special properties. An example is stainless steel, which is an alloy of iron, chromium, and nickel. The special property of stainless steel that is useful is that it doesn't rust.
8. alloy
9. ore
10. smelting

Using Mineral Resources
Enrich

1. No, alloys can contain two or more metals. For example, aluminum alloys contain aluminum, copper, manganese, and magnesium.
2. A pewter cup contains tin, copper, lead, and antimony.
3. Solder can be used to join metal parts because it has a low melting point.
4. Brass is an alloy of copper and zinc, while bronze is an alloy of copper and tin.
5. Superalloys have great strength and durability.

Consumer Lab
A Mouthful of Minerals

For answers, see Teacher's Edition.

Key Terms

1. fracture
2. alloy
3. luster
4. inorganic
5. streak
6. smelting
7. crystal
8. compound
9. gemstone
10. solution
11. cleavage
12. element
Hidden message: fluorescence

Connecting Concepts

Minerals, formed by magma or by elements or compounds in hot solutions, share five characteristics that make them valuable resources.

This concept map is only one way to represent the main ideas and relationships in this chapter. Accept other logical answers from students.

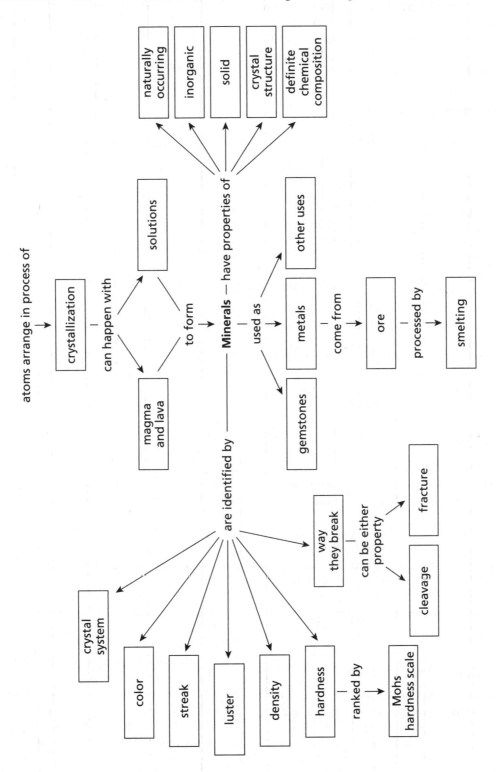

Laboratory Investigation

How Tessellating!
Pre-Lab Discussion

1. Coal is naturally occurring and a solid, but it is not inorganic because it is made from plant matter. There are several types of coal, so it does not have a definite composition. Students may not be aware that coal has no crystal shape.
2. Six

Analyze and Conclude

1. Answers will vary. Students might begin with rectangles and diamonds.
2. Circles and ovals won't tessellate. To tessellate, sides must line up. Because circles and ovals have an infinite number of sides, they can't tessellate.
3. Any of the six crystal shapes will tessellate. Many of the shapes will likely be the ones that tessellated for students.

Critical Thinking and Applications

1. The pattern repeats without overlaps or gaps. The atoms forming the crystal shape add on in a pattern without overlaps or gaps.
2. Answers will vary. Examples might include title on a floor or bricks on a building.
3. Answers will vary. Sample answer: The patterns are two-dimensional and the crystal shapes are three-dimensional.

More to Explore

Analyze and Conclude

1. Most likely the shape will have symmetry because it looks the same on either side of a center line.
2. Students may say mineral crystals and bodies of most animals. [*Note:* Symmetry can be checked with a mirror in the center of the pattern. If the mirror image of the pattern makes it look complete, the pattern has symmetry. Caution students to handle mirrors carefully and to report any breakage to you instead of trying to clean it up.]

Performance Assessment

1. A substance needs to be a naturally occurring, inorganic solid with a crystal structure and a definite chemical composition.

2. A mineral's definite chemical composition gives each mineral its own specific properties.
3. Answers will vary. Students could have observed the sample for color, luster, and cleavage/fracture, done a scratch test for hardness, a streak test for streak, and a heft test for density.
4. Students probably had no way of testing for crystal structure or any special properties.
5. Identification will vary, depending on the sample. Students could cite color, luster, cleavage/fracture, streak, and density in confirming an identification.

Chapter Test

1. d
2. b
3. c
4. d
5. c
6. a
7. a
8. b
9. d
10. d
11. smelting
12. density
13. shaft
14. halite
15. ore
16. prospector
17. true
18. quartz
19. inorganic
20. true
21. You could not tell them apart with just a scratch test because silver and gold have the same hardness.
22. Pyrite is known as "fool's gold" because it has the same color and luster as gold.
23. You could do a streak test or determine and compare densities.
24. Quartz occurs naturally, is inorganic, is a solid, has a crystal structure, and has a definite chemical composition.
25. In general, minerals form through crystallization of melted materials and through crystallization of materials dissolved in water. An example of the former is silver; an example of the latter is halite, gypsum, or calcite.
26. Minerals form at B as magma slowly cools and hardens, forming large crystals.

27. At A, minerals form as salt water evaporates along the shore of a lake or sea that is drying up. At C, minerals form as metals dissolved in hot water solutions come out of solution and crystallize, forming veins.

28. The halite deposit might have formed through the evaporation of salt water from the Great Salt Lake.

29. Slag is a combination of impurities in iron ore and limestone. It forms in a blast furnace once the iron in iron ore has melted and sunk to the bottom of the furnace.

30. The splitting of feldspar at right angles is evidence of the property of cleavage, which only some minerals have. The breaking of quartz into shell-like surfaces is evidence of fracture, a property of most minerals. Neither property alone is enough to enable you to identify a mineral, because other minerals also have these properties, though fewer have the property of cleavage.

Rocks

Lab zone Chapter Project **Collecting Rocks**

The following steps will walk you through the Chapter Project. Use the hints and detailed directions as you guide your students through planning, collecting, and presenting their rock collections and reflecting on their work.

Chapter Project Overview

In the Chapter Project, students will collect rocks in the field, describe and classify each rock, create a rock collection, and present the collection to the class.

To introduce the project, show students a professional rock collection. Talk with students about how they could make a display like it.

Invite students to brainstorm a list of places in the neighborhood and community where they could hunt safely and legally for different kinds of rocks. Such places might include city or state parks, roadcuts, stream beds, and various other areas near where they live.

Distribute Chapter Project Overview. Review the project's rules. You may also want to hand out the Chapter Project Scoring Rubric, so students will understand what is expected of them.

You may wish to divide the class into pairs or small groups. The advantages of using groups include fewer materials needed and more collaboration among students of differing abilities. In addition, rock collection at this age should never be done alone. Some students may have adults to accompany them on outings, but others will need a student partner or group. The advantage of individual rock collections is that each student will gain a better understanding of the various kinds of rocks.

Set a deadline for the project presentation and some interim dates at the end of Sections 1, 3, 4, and 6. Have each student copy the dates in his or her Project Time Line.

Materials and Preparation

For the collection phase of the project, each student will need a heavy bag to carry the rock samples collected. A canvas bag is traditional for this purpose, but an old book backpack will work as well. Each student should also carry resealable plastic sandwich bags in which to place individual rock samples, with an identification number or note. Advise students to wear gloves when rock collecting.

For classification and identification, each student will need a hand lens and materials such as a penny and a nail file to do a scratch test. To test for the presence of calcite, students will need to use an acid, such as in the Discover activity at the beginning of Section 4. However, have students use vinegar instead of hydrochloric acid, unless they are under your supervision. In addition, it might be helpful for students to break up rock samples they bring to class, a process that would require a hammer and goggles.

Rock and mineral field guides are necessary for identification of the rock samples. In addition, many such books have sections on how to recognize the three major groups of rocks. Most public libraries have field guides in their stacks, often in the 540s or 550s. Up-to-date copyrights are not important. Since students won't need these books in the field, keep them in a reference section in the classroom so students can consult the books as they classify and try to identify their rock samples.

To create the display, each student will need an egg carton or some other kind of box divided into compartments. Some students might make their own display cases with cardboard or wood. The rock samples can be placed on cotton pads at the bottom of each compartment. The samples themselves can be labeled with numbers using white typewriter correcting fluid and an indelible marker. To make an information card for each rock in the collection, students will need 3 × 5 index cards.

Rocks

Keep Students on Track— Section 1

Review each student's or group's list of places where they might hunt rocks and make suggestions. Encourage students to begin their collecting, but caution them to never go alone on these hunts. Remind students to obtain permission if they collect on private property.

Distribute Chapter Project Worksheet 1 and Chapter Project Worksheet 2. After students have read the worksheets, ask if they have any questions.

Make sure each student or group has the materials needed to collect rocks. Remind students that they must keep good records of where they find each rock, and this means that they should bag each rock as it is picked up. Without such care, they will not be able to complete an information card for each rock.

Keep Students on Track— Section 3

As students begin to collect rocks, set up an area in the classroom for them to examine and test the rocks. They may want to do a scratch test or check for density or the presence of calcite.

Because many of the rocks will be dirty or weathered, it may be desirable for students to break up rock samples into smaller pieces. Demonstrate how to do this by putting a rock into a bag or under a newspaper and then striking the rock with a hammer, through the bag or paper. Although the bag or paper should eliminate flying pieces of rock, caution students to wear goggles just in case.

Keep Students on Track— Section 4

Advise students to complete information cards using 3 × 5 index cards. Worksheet 2 provides support for this process.

At this point, rock and mineral field guides are extremely useful in classifying the rocks into the three major groups, as well as in identifying individual rocks.

Keep Students on Track— Section 6

Students should have classified and tried to identify most of the rocks they collected. Help students or groups begin to create their displays, providing materials or making suggestions when appropriate.

Chapter Project Wrap Up

Examine each student's or group's rock collection before presentation. Have students "talk you through" what they will say, and make suggestions about logical sequence or any missing information.

Provide class time for the presentations. Allow each student or group to present the rock collection, with an emphasis on the rocks they found, how and where the rocks were collected, and how they classified and identified the rocks. Encourage other students to ask questions about the rocks in the collection.

After all presentations have been made, discuss with students which collections are best, both in the rocks included and how they are displayed.

Encourage students to evaluate how effective they were in hunting for rocks and how well they created the display. Since most students probably were not able to classify or identify some of the rocks they found, they should have experience to draw from in describing the difficulty in such identification.

Extension

Have interested students create a large rock collection display by using the best rock samples from the collections of all students or groups. This larger collection could be placed in the school hall or some other public area, where students from other classes and grades can examine the rocks. Along with the collection, students can prepare explanatory material about the specific kinds of rocks, the three major groups of rocks, and the rock cycle.

Rocks • *Chapter Project*

Lab zone Chapter Project **Collecting Rocks**

All rocks are the same, right? Many people think that is true, but they couldn't be more wrong. There are many different kinds of rocks, and each has a story to tell about where and how it formed. If you look closely at rocks, you'll find there are striking differences between them, just as there are differences between various kinds of trees or birds. In this project, you will get to hunt for rocks at several locations in your community and create a display of the rocks you collect.

Project Rules

- Brainstorm a list of places in your neighborhood or community where you can safely and legally collect rocks. You should be prepared to discuss your list with your teacher at the Check Your Progress at the end of Section 1.

- Prepare to collect rocks by gathering the materials you will need. These include a strong bag, such as an old backpack. You'll also need resealable plastic sandwich bags to bag individual rock samples, and paper and a pencil. A rock collector needs to wear gloves, too.

- Collect rock samples at neighborhood locations or other places agreed upon by you and your teacher. Be sure to get permission before collecting on private property. Keep a good record as you collect. Worksheet 1 will help you in this task.

- Bring your rock samples to class, where you can examine them closely and perform tests to help you classify and identify them.

- Classify each rock as sedimentary, igneous, or metamorphic. Worksheet 2 will help you in this task.

- Identify each rock sample using a field guide to rocks and minerals. Your teacher may provide such books, but you might also see if a family member or friend will let you borrow one.

- Create a display of your rock collection that shows off your best rock samples and your best efforts at classification and identification. Use an index card to make an information card for each rock in your display. On this card include as much information about the rock as you can.

- Prepare a presentation to the class of your rock collection. As part of your presentation, describe each rock, including where you found it and how you classified and identified it.

Project Hints

The best places to hunt for rocks are places where many rocks are exposed. These include dry stream beds, roadcuts, and farm fields. Such places can be dangerous, though. Never go rock hunting without someone with you, such as an adult family member or a classmate. Be careful when collecting in places where loose rocks might fall.

For many places, you need to get permission to collect rocks. This is true

Rocks • *Chapter Project*   **Overview**

for national and state parks and private property. Go to the authorities and explain your project. If permission is denied, find other locations.

When you go rock collecting, you should wear heavy shoes as well as long pants. Be prepared to hunt for rocks in places you might not normally walk.

Sometimes rock samples are too big to display easily or are dirty or dull. Breaking apart such rocks provides smaller samples and cleaner surfaces. Your teacher will show you how to break apart rocks safely. Do this at school in a place designated for that purpose. And always wear goggles.

Examine each rock with a hand lens. Notice its texture. Do a scratch test. Note its color. Try to identify the minerals in it. Determine the rock's density or heft. In other words, do everything you can to correctly classify and identify the rocks you collect.

As you create your rock display, think of how you've seen other sorts of collections displayed. Display each rock in a separate compartment, with numbers on the rocks or labels nearby. Your information card can be part of the display, or you could make special labels. The figure shows two rock collections and might give you some ideas.

As you prepare your presentation, think of what you want to say and the order in which you want to present the information. You may want to make notes on index cards to help you remember what you want to say.

Project Time Line

Task	Due Date
1. Plan where you'll collect rocks and review the plan with your teacher	_____
2. Gather materials needed for rock collecting	_____
3. Collect rocks at several locations	_____
4. Classify rocks into major groups	_____
5. Identify rocks using field guides	_____
6. Create rock collection display	_____
7. Present rock collection to class	_____

Rocks · *Chapter Project*

A Record for Each Rock

You will need to make a record card for each rock that you collect. To help you in this task, make copies of this sheet so that you have one for each rock. Either fill out the sheet as you collect rocks or use your field notes to fill out the sheet later.

Rock number _____

Date found _____

Location where found _____

Description of location, including rocks near this rock _____

_____

_____

_____

_____

Description of rock _____

_____

_____

_____

_____

_____

Classification (igneous, sedimentary, or metamorphic) _____

Reasons for classification _____

_____

_____

_____

_____

Identification of rock (specific kind of rock) _____

Reasons for identification _____

_____

_____

_____

_____

Source used for identification _____

_____

Rocks · *Chapter Project*   **Worksheet 2**

Classifying Rocks into Major Groups

Classifying rocks into the three major groups is not always easy—for some rocks it can be difficult for anyone but a geologist. But for many rocks, you can determine their classification if you know the important characteristics of each major group. Study the characteristics below for each major group of rocks. Then examine the rocks you collect and use these characteristics to help you classify the rocks.

Characteristics of Igneous Rocks

- Igneous rocks often contain grains that can be seen with the unaided eye. See Figure 1.

- Some igneous rocks have no visible grain and appear glassy. See Figure 2.

- Igneous rocks may be found in many different colors and often show different-colored grains that are not in bands.

Magnified section

Crystals
Figure 1

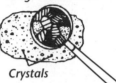

Figure 2

Characteristics of Sedimentary Rocks

- Clastic sedimentary rocks are made up of fragments of other rocks and look very much like rocks or particles cemented together. Some sedimentary rocks have a range of grain sizes, while others consist mainly of one grain size. See Figure 3.

- Organic sedimentary rocks are made up of plant and animal products or remains. Such rocks may contain fossils. See Figure 4.

- Sedimentary rocks often have distinct parallel layers. See Figure 5.

- Many sedimentary rocks appear dull or earthy.

Figure 3

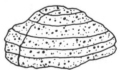

Figure 4

Characteristics of Metamorphic Rocks

- Metamorphic rocks often look like igneous rocks except that they are foliated, showing bands of different mineral grains. See Figure 6.

- Metamorphic rocks may show signs of bending or distortion. See Figure 7.

- The grains in metamorphic rocks generally appear to be flattened.

Figure 5

Figure 6

Figure 7

Rocks

Rocks • *Chapter Project* **Scoring Rubric**

Lab zone™ Chapter Project Collecting Rocks

In evaluating how well you complete the Chapter Project, your teacher will judge your work in the following categories. In each, a score of 4 is the best rating.

	4	3	2	1
Collecting Rocks	Collects 12–15 rock samples and accurately describes each rock and the location where it was found.	Collects 10–12 rock samples and accurately describes most of the rocks and the locations where they were found.	Collects 8–10 rock samples and describes most of the rocks and the locations where they were found.	Collects fewer than 8 rock samples and describes only a few of the rocks and the locations where they were found.
Creating a Rock Collection	Makes a correct classification of all the rock samples, creates a logical and attractive display, and correctly identifies over half of the rocks.	Makes a correct classification of most of the rock samples, creates an attractive display, and correctly identifies approximately half of the rocks.	Makes a correct classification of about half of the rock samples, creates an attractive but somewhat unorganized display, and correctly identifies fewer than half of the rocks.	Makes a correct classification of a few of the rock samples, attempts rather unsuccessfully to create a display, and correctly identifies only 1 or 2 of the rocks.
Presenting the Rock Collection	Makes a thorough and interesting presentation that includes a clear and thoughtful description of each rock in the collection.	Makes a thorough presentation that includes a thoughtful description of each rock in the collection.	Makes a somewhat unorganized presentation that includes a description of most of the rocks in the collection.	Presentation is poorly prepared and includes an effective description of only a few of the rocks in the collection.
Working Cooperatively (optional)	Takes a lead in collecting the rocks, creating the display, and presenting the collection.	Participates in all aspects of collecting the rocks, creating the display, and presenting the collection.	Participates in most aspects of collecting the rocks, creating the display, and presenting the collection.	Participates minimally in collecting the rocks, creating the display, and presenting the collection.

Classifying Rocks

⏱ *1 period, 1/2 block*

Rocks

Objectives

F.5.1.1 List the characteristics used to identify rocks.
F.5.1.2 Identify and describe the three major groups of rocks.

Key Terms

• granite • rock-forming mineral • basalt • grains
• texture • igneous rock • sedimentary rock
• metamorphic rock

Local Standards

PRETEACH

Build Background Knowledge
Students share their knowledge of rocks and rock types. Display samples or pictures of rocks with which most students will be familiar.

 **Discover Activity** *How Do Rocks Compare?* **L1**

Targeted Resources

❏ **All in One Teaching Resources**
  L2 Reading Strategy Transparency F42: Asking Questions
❏ ⊙ **PresentationExpress™ CD-ROM**

INSTRUCT

Mineral Composition and Color
Explain that rocks are mixtures of minerals and other materials and show students how to connect a rock's color to the types of minerals that may be present.

Texture
Ask students to suggest adjectives to describe the size, shape, and arrangement of grains in rocks.

How Rocks Form
Ask leading questions to help students connect rock formation to locations that provide the conditions necessary for the different types of rocks to form.

Targeted Resources

❏ **All in One Teaching Resources**
  L2 Guided Reading, pp. 309–312
❏ **PHSchool.com** Web Code: cfd-1051
❏ ⊙ **Student Edition on Audio CD**

ASSESS

Section Assessment Questions
↻ Have students use their completed graphic organizers with their questions and answers to answer the questions.

Reteach
Students classify rocks based on their description and how they were formed.

Targeted Resources

❏ **All in One Teaching Resources**
  Section Summary, p. 308
  L1 Review and Reinforce, p. 313
  L3 Enrich, p. 314

Rocks • *Section Summary*

Classifying Rocks

Key Concepts

- What characteristics do geologists use to identify rocks?
- What are the three main groups of rocks?

The rock of Earth's crust forms mountains, hills, valleys, beaches, and the ocean floor. **When studying a rock sample, geologists observe the rock's mineral composition, color, and texture.**

Rocks are made of mixtures of minerals and other materials, although some rocks may contain only a single mineral. The 20 minerals that make up most of the rocks of Earth's crust are known as **rock-forming minerals.** A rock's color provides clues to the rock's mineral composition. **Granite** is generally a light-colored rock that has high silica content. **Basalt** is a dark-colored rock that is low in silica. Geologists also observe the shape and color of crystals in a rock to identify its minerals. They may perform other tests, such as testing the surface of a rock with acid, to determine the presence of certain compounds.

Color alone does not provide enough information to identify a rock. A rock's **texture,** the look and feel of the rock's surface, is very useful in identifying a rock. Most rocks are made up of **grains,** particles of minerals or other rocks. Grains give the rock its texture. Geologists use a number of terms to describe a rock's texture based on the size, shape, and pattern of the rock's grains. Often, the grains in a rock are large and easy to see. These are said to be coarse-grained. In other rocks, the grains are so small that they can be seen only with a microscope. These are said to be fine-grained. Some rocks have no visible grain even when they are examined under a microscope. Rock grains vary widely in shape. Some look like tiny particles of sand, while others look like small seeds or exploding stars. In some rocks, the grain shapes result from the shapes of the crystals that form the rock. In other rocks, the grain shapes result from fragments of other rock.

The grains in a rock often form patterns. Some grains lie in flat layers. Other grains form swirling patterns. Some rocks have grains of different colors in bands, while in others the grains occur randomly throughout.

Geologists classify rocks into three major groups: igneous rock, sedimentary rock, and metamorphic rock. These terms refer to how the rocks in each group formed. **Igneous rock** forms from the cooling of molten rock. **Sedimentary rock** forms when particles of other rocks or the remains of plants and animals are cemented together. **Metamorphic rock** forms when an existing rock is changed by heat, pressure, or chemical reactions.

Rocks · *Guided Reading and Study*

Classifying Rocks (pp. 144–147)

This section explains how geologists classify rocks.

Use Target Reading Skills

As you preview the headings in this section, complete the graphic organizer with questions in the left column. Then as you read, fill in the answers in the second column.

Question	Answer
What does a rock's color tell about the rock?	

Introduction (p. 144)

1. Earth's crust is made of _____.

2. Circle the letter of each characteristic that geologists use to classify rocks.

   a. texture

   b. mineral composition

   c. hardness

   d. color

Mineral Composition and Color (p. 145)

3. What are rocks made of? _____

   _____

   _____

4. Circle the letter of each mineral that is found in granite.

   a. quartz

   b. feldspar

   c. mica

   d. hornblende

Rocks · *Guided Reading and Study*

Classifying Rocks *(continued)*

Texture *(p. 146)*

5. Is the following sentence true or false? Most rocks can be identified by color alone. _____

6. The look and feel of a rock's surface is its _____.

7. Particles of minerals and other rocks that make up a rock are called _____.

8. Is the following sentence true or false? A rock's grains give the rock its texture. _____

9. Circle the letter of each sentence that is true about the grain size in rock.

   a. An example of a coarse-grained rock is diorite.

   b. An example of a fine-grained rock is slate.

   c. Grains in fine-grained rock are easy to see.

   d. Grains in coarse-grained rock are microscopic.

10. Complete the concept map showing the characteristics of rock texture.

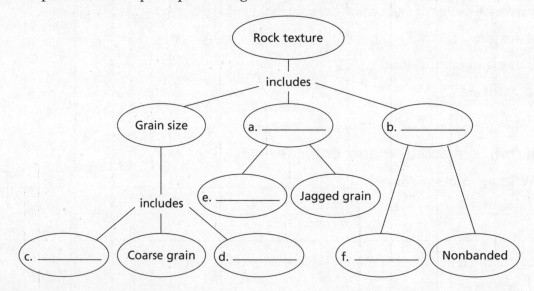

g. Is the following sentence true or false? *Coarse grain* is a term that describes a rock's grain pattern. _____

Rocks ▪ *Guided Reading and Study*

11. Circle the letter of the choice that determines the grain shape of a rock such as granite.

   a. Shape of the rock's crystals   **b.** Size of the rock's crystals

   c. Shape of fragments of other rock   **d.** Coarseness of the rock's grains

12. Circle the letter of the choice that determines the grain shape of a rock such as conglomerate.

   a. Fineness of the rock's grains   **b.** Size of the rock's grains

   c. Shape of the rock's crystals   **d.** Shape of fragments of other rock

13. Circle the letter of the description of the grain pattern of gneiss.

   a. It looks like different colors in bands.

   b. It looks like a stack of pancakes.

   c. It looks like waves.

   d. It looks like rows of squares and rectangles.

14. Circle the letter of the sentence that is true about rocks with no visible grain.

   a. Some rocks without crystal grains cooled very quickly.

   b. Some rocks have no visible grain even under a microscope.

   c. Rocks without crystal grains look rough and coarse.

   d. An example of a rock with a glassy texture is slate.

How Rocks Form (p. 147)

15. How do geologists classify a rock? _____

   _____

   _____

16. List the three major groups of rock.

   a. _____

   b. _____

   c. _____

Rocks • *Guided Reading and Study*

Classifying Rocks *(continued)*

17. Complete the compare/contrast table to show the similarities and differences among the types of rocks and how they form.

How Rocks Form	
Type of Rock	**How It Forms**
a.	Molten rock cools.
b.	Particles are pressed and cemented.
c.	Existing rock is changed.

    d. What do the three major types of rocks have in common? _____

_____

    e. How are they different? _____

_____

18. The type of rock that forms from magma or lava is _____ rock.

19. The type of rock that forms in layers is _____ rock.

20. Is the following sentence true or false? Most metamorphic rocks form close to the surface. _____

Rocks ▪ *Review and Reinforce*

Classifying Rocks

Understanding Main Ideas
Fill in the blanks in the table below.

Grain Property	Description	Texture
Size	Large, easy to see	**1.** _____
Size	**2.** _____	Fine-grained
Shape	Mineral crystals	Crystalline
3. _____	Rock fragments	Rounded or jagged
4. _____	Layered or random grains	Banded or nonbanded

Answer the following questions on a separate sheet of paper.

5. What characteristics do geologists look for when observing a rock sample?

6. Name the three major groups of rocks and describe how each forms.

7. Give two examples of how a rock's color provides clues to the rock's mineral composition.

Building Vocabulary
Fill in the blank to complete each statement.

8. The look and feel of a rock's surface is its _____.

9. The particles of minerals or other rocks that make up a rock are called

_____.

10. The 20 minerals that make up most of the rocks of Earth's crust are

known as _____.

Rocks · *Enrich*

A Crust Full of Rocks

The three major groups of rocks make up Earth's crust. But these groups of rocks are not found in equal amounts. The circle graph in the center below shows each group's percentage of the crust. The three circle graphs that surround the central one show the percentage of rocks that make up each group. You'll learn about many of these rocks as you read the rest of the chapter. Study the circle graphs below, and then answer the questions that follow.

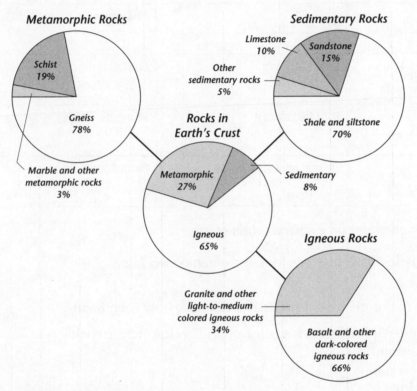

Answer the following questions on a separate sheet of paper.

1. Which rock group makes up most of Earth's crust, and what is its percentage?

2. How do rocks in that rock group form?

3. What kind of rocks make up most of the igneous rocks? From your knowledge of Earth's crust, where would you most likely find such rocks?

4. Which rock group makes up the least part of Earth's crust, and what is its percentage?

5. How do rocks in that rock group form?

6. What kind of rock makes up the greatest part of metamorphic rocks, and what is its percentage?

7. How do metamorphic rocks form?

Igneous Rocks

 *1 period, 1/2 block*

Rocks

Objectives

F.5.2.1 Identify the characteristics used to classify igneous rocks.

F.5.2.2 Describe ways in which igneous rocks are used.

Key Terms

• extrusive rock • intrusive rock

Local Standards

PRETEACH

Build Background Knowledge

Students answer questions that help them recall their knowledge about molten material and where it rises.

Discover Activity *How Do Igneous Rocks Form?* **L1**

Targeted Resources

❑ **All in One Teaching Resources**
   L2 Reading Strategy Transparency F43: Identifying Main Ideas

❑ **PresentationExpress™ CD-ROM**

INSTRUCT

Classifying Igneous Rocks

Discuss classification criteria used to describe the origin, texture, and mineral composition of igneous rocks.

Uses of Igneous Rocks

Igneous rocks are used for their properties and beauty. Help students to connect the properties of obsidian, granite, and other igneous rocks to their uses.

Targeted Resources

❑ **All in One Teaching Resources**
   L2 Guided Reading, pp. 317–320
   L2 Transparency F44

❑ **www.SciLinks.org** Web Code: scn-1052

❑ **Discovery SCHOOL Video Field Trip**

❑ **Student Edition on Audio CD**

ASSESS

Section Assessment Questions

Have students use their completed graphic organizers with main ideas to answer the questions.

Reteach

Students create a table to show how some common igneous rocks are classified.

Targeted Resources

❑ **All in One Teaching Resources**
   Section Summary, p. 316
   L1 Review and Reinforce, p. 321
   L3 Enrich, p. 322

Rocks • *Section Summary*

Igneous Rocks

Key Concepts

■ What characteristics are used to classify igneous rocks?

■ How are igneous rocks used?

Igneous rock is any rock that forms from magma or lava. The name "igneous" comes from the Latin word *ignis,* meaning "fire." **Igneous rocks are classified according to their origin, texture, and mineral composition.**

Extrusive rock is igneous rock formed from lava that erupted onto Earth's surface. Basalt is the most common extrusive rock. Igneous rock that formed when magma hardened beneath Earth's surface is called **intrusive rock.** Granite is the most abundant intrusive rock in continental crust.

The texture of an igneous rock depends on the size and shape of its mineral crystals. The only exceptions to this rule are the different types of volcanic glass—igneous rock that lacks a crystal structure. Igneous rocks may be similar in mineral composition and yet have very different textures. Rapidly cooling lava forms fine-grained igneous rocks with small crystals. Slowly-cooling magma forms coarse-grained rock with large crystals. Intrusive rocks have larger crystals than extrusive rocks. Extrusive rocks have a fine-grained or glassy texture. Basalt, for example, is an extrusive rock whose crystals are too small to be seen without a microscope.

The silica content of magma and lava can vary. Lava that is low in silica usually forms dark-colored rocks, such as basalt. Magma that is high in silica usually forms light-colored rock, such as granite. Granite, however, comes in many shades and colors, from nearly black to light gray, red, and pink. The mineral composition of granite determines its color.

Many igneous rocks are hard, dense, and durable. **People throughout history have used igneous rock for tools and building materials.** Granite has a long history as a building material. Ancient Egyptians used granite for statues. In the United States in the 1800s and early 1900s, granite was widely used to build bridges and public buildings and for paving streets with cobblestones. Granite is still used in decorative stonework, curbstones, and floors. Basalt is crushed to make gravel that is used in construction.

The rough surface of pumice makes it a good abrasive for cleaning and polishing. Obsidian was used by ancient native Americans to make sharp tools. Perlite, formed from the heating of obsidian, is often mixed with soil for starting vegetable seeds.

Rocks · *Guided Reading and Study*

Igneous Rocks (pp. 148–151)

This section describes the characteristics and uses of igneous rocks.

Use Target Reading Skills

As you read about igneous rocks, fill in the detail boxes that explain the main idea in the graphic organizer below.

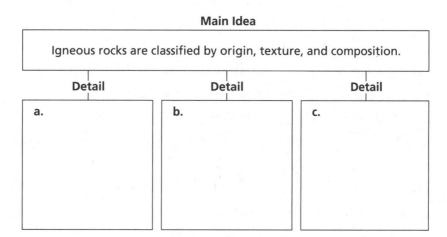

Main Idea

Igneous rocks are classified by origin, texture, and composition.

Detail	**Detail**	**Detail**
a.	b.	c.

Classifying Igneous Rocks (pp. 148–150)

1. Circle the letter of the definition of igneous rock.

   a. Rock that forms from minerals

   b. Rock that contains iron

   c. Rock that forms from magma or lava

   d. Rock that contains crystals

Name _____ Date _____ Class _____

Igneous Rocks *(continued)*

2. Complete the Venn diagram by labeling each circle with the type of rock it represents.

a. _____   b. _____

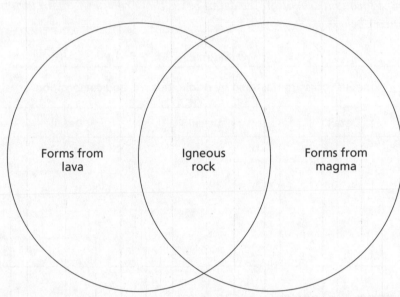

Forms from lava   Igneous rock   Forms from magma

    c. Use the Venn diagram to explain how the types of rocks shown are alike and different. _____

_____

3. Is the following sentence true or false? Extrusive rock forms beneath Earth's surface. _____

4. Circle the letter of each sentence that is true about basalt.

    a. It forms oceanic crust.

    b. It is the most common intrusive rock.

    c. It forms from lava.

    d. It forms beneath Earth's surface.

5. Circle the letter of each sentence that is true about granite.

    a. It is the most abundant intrusive rock in continental crust.

    b. It forms the core of many mountain ranges.

    c. It forms from magma.

    d. It forms on top of the crust.

6. The texture of an igneous rock depends on the size and shape of its

_____.

Rocks • *Guided Reading and Study*

7. Is the following sentence true or false? Igneous rocks with similar mineral compositions always have the same textures.

_____

Match the type of texture of igneous rocks with how rocks of that texture form.

Type of Texture

_____ 8. fine-grained

_____ 9. coarse-grained

_____ 10. porphyry rock

How Rocks of That Texture Form

a. Magma cools in two stages.

b. Lava cools rapidly.

c. Magma cools slowly.

11. Is the following sentence true or false? Intrusive rocks have smaller crystals than extrusive rocks. _____

12. A rock with large crystals surrounded by small crystals is called _____.

13. What type of texture do extrusive rocks such as basalt have?

_____

_____

14. What is obsidian? _____

_____

15. Describe the texture of obsidian. _____

_____

16. Circle the letter of each sentence that is true about the silica composition of igneous rocks.

   a. Igneous rocks low in silica are usually dark-colored.

   b. An example of an igneous rock low in silica is granite.

   c. Igneous rocks high in silica are usually light-colored.

   d. An example of an igneous rock high in silica is basalt.

17. Describe the different minerals that determine the color of granite.

_____

_____

18. How do geologists determine the mineral composition of granite?

_____

_____

Rocks · *Guided Reading and Study*

Igneous Rocks (continued)

Uses of Igneous Rocks (p. 151)

19. Why have people throughout history used igneous rocks for tools and building materials? _____

_____

20. Describe three ways granite has been used throughout history.

a. _____

b. _____

c. _____

21. Complete the table that shows the ways igneous rocks are used.

How Some Igneous Rocks Are Used	
Type of Igneous Rock	**Way It Is Used**
Basalt	Gravel for construction
a.	Cleaning and polishing
b.	Soil mixes

c. Use the information in the table to draw a conclusion about the uses of igneous rocks. You may use more than one sentence.

_____

_____

_____

_____

Rocks • *Review and Reinforce*

Igneous Rocks

Understanding Main Ideas

Fill in the blanks in the table below.

Origin of Igneous Rock	Resulting Texture
Slow cooling of magma far beneath Earth's surface	1. _____
Extremely rapid cooling of lava in which no crystals form	2. _____
Rapid cooling of lava in which tiny crystals form	3. _____

Answer the following questions on a separate sheet of paper.

4. What is the most common extrusive rock? Where is it found?

5. What is the most common intrusive rock? Where is it found?

6. Explain how the silica content of molten material affects the color of igneous rocks.

7. What qualities of igneous rocks have long made them useful for tools and building materials?

8. Describe one use each for the igneous rocks granite, basalt, and pumice.

Building Vocabulary

Fill in the blank to complete each statement.

9. Igneous rock formed from lava that erupted onto Earth's surface is called

   _____ rock.

10. Igneous rock formed from magma below Earth's surface is called

    _____ rock.

Rocks · *Enrich*

The Same but Different

Can two different rocks with different names have the same mineral composition? The answer is yes. There are six major kinds of igneous rocks: granite, diorite, gabbro, rhyolite, andesite, and basalt. Geologists usually group these six kinds of igneous rocks in pairs, because each pair generally contains the same minerals. Study the table below to see which igneous rocks are the same but different.

Common Igneous Rocks

Intrusive rocks (Coarse-grained)	Granite	Diorite	Gabbro
Extrusive rocks (Fine-grained)	Rhyolite	Andesite	Basalt
Minerals	Quartz, Feldspar, Muscovite, Amphibole	Amphibole, Feldspar, Pyroxene	Feldspar, Pyroxene, Olivine, Amphibole
Color	Light colored	Medium gray or green	Dark gray to black
→ → → → → → → Silica content of rock decreases → → → → → → → →			
→ → → → → → → Rock color becomes darker → → → → → → → →			

Answer the following questions on a separate sheet of paper.

1. Which of the six major kinds of rock are intrusive and which are extrusive?

2. Compare granite with rhyolite. How are they similar? How are they different?

3. Compare the mineral composition of diorite with the mineral composition of andesite.

4. In what way is gabbro different from basalt? What can you infer from this about how these two kinds of igneous rocks form?

5. How is granite like gabbro?

6. Which rock has more silica in it, granite or basalt?

7. Is a rock with more silica in it likely to be lighter or darker than a rock with less silica in it?

Sedimentary Rocks

🕐 *1 period, 1/2 block*

Rocks

Objectives

F.5.3.1 Describe how sedimentary rocks form.
F.5.3.2 List and describe the three major types of sedimentary rocks.
F5.3.3 Explain how sedimentary rocks are used.

Key Terms

• sediment • erosion • deposition • compaction
• cementation • clastic rock • organic rock
• chemical rock

PRETEACH

Build Background Knowledge
Students recall a beach they have walked on and infer what causes sand to harden into sandstone. If they need help, stack books on top of one another to illustrate.

 *How Does Pressure Affect Particles of Rock?* **L1**

Local Standards

Targeted Resources

❑ **All in One Teaching Resources**
   L2 Reading Strategy Transparency F45: Outlining

❑ 💿 **PresentationExpress™ CD-ROM**

INSTRUCT

From Sediment to Rock
Guide students to discuss types of sediment and how they form and help them to apply their knowledge to a piece of sandstone.

Types of Sedimentary Rock
Discuss the formation of the three major groups of sedimentary rocks. Help students to name the types of rock that might form in various environments.

Uses of Sedimentary Rocks
Challenge students to identify common uses of sedimentary rock and to identify sedimentary rock resources in your state.

Targeted Resources

❑ **All in One Teaching Resources**
   L2 Guided Reading, pp. 325–329
   L2 Transparency F46
❑ **www.SciLinks.org** Web Code: scn-1053
❑ 💿 **Student Edition on Audio CD**

ASSESS

Section Assessment Questions
🔄 Have students use their completed outlines to answer the questions.

Reteach
Students gather photographs that illustrate examples of erosion and deposition.

Targeted Resources

❑ **All in One Teaching Resources**
Section Summary, p. 324
   L1 Review and Reinforce, p. 330
   L3 Enrich, p. 331

Rocks · *Section Summary*

Sedimentary Rocks

Key Concepts

- How do sedimentary rocks form?

- What are the three major types of sedimentary rocks?

- How are sedimentary rocks used?

Sediment is small, solid pieces of material that come from rocks or living things. **Most sedimentary rocks are formed through a series of processes: erosion, deposition, compaction, and cementation.**
  Erosion occurs when running water, wind, or ice loosen and carry away fragments of rock. Eventually, the moving water, wind, or ice slows and deposits the sediment in layers. **Deposition** is the process by which sediment settles out of the water or wind carrying it. The process that presses sediments together is **compaction.** Over millions of years, thick layers of sediment build up. These heavy layers press down on the layers beneath them. While compaction is taking place, the minerals in the rock slowly dissolve in the water. **Cementation** is the process in which dissolved minerals crystallize and glue particles of sediment together.
  There are three major groups of sedimentary rocks: clastic rocks, organic rocks, and chemical rocks. Most sedimentary rocks are made up of broken pieces of other rocks. A **clastic rock** is a sedimentary rock that forms when rock fragments are squeezed together. Clastic rocks are grouped by the size of the rock fragments, or particles, of which they are made. Common clastic rocks include shale, sandstone, conglomerate, and breccia.
  Organic rock forms where the remains of plants and animals are deposited in thick layers. Two important organic sedimentary rocks are coal and limestone. Coal forms from the remains of swamp plants buried in water. Over millions of years, they slowly change into coal. Limestone forms in the ocean, where many living things, such as coral, clams, and oysters, have hard shells or skeletons made of calcite. As they die, their shells pile up in layers on the ocean floor. Over millions of years, compaction and cementation change the sediment to limestone.
  Chemical rock forms when minerals that are dissolved in a solution crystallize. Limestone can form when calcite that is dissolved in lakes, seas, or underground water comes out of solution and forms crystals. Chemical rocks can also form from mineral deposits left when seas or lakes evaporate.
  People have used sedimentary rocks through history for many different purposes, including building materials and tools. Sandstone and limestone have been used as building materials because they are soft enough to be cut easily into blocks or slabs. Limestone is used in making cement.

Sedimentary Rocks (pp. 152–156)

This section describes how sedimentary rocks form and how they are classified and used.

Use Target Reading Skills

As you read about sedimentary rocks, use the headings to complete the outline below.

Sedimentary Rocks

I. From Sediment to Rocks

   A. Erosion

   B. _____

   C. _____

   D. Cementation

II. Types of Sedimentary Rock

   A. _____

   B. Organic Rocks

   C. _____

   D. _____

III. _____

From Sediment to Rock (pp. 152–153)

1. What remains of living things may sediment include? _____

_____

_____

2. Small, solid pieces of material that come from rocks or living things are

called _____.

3. Is the following sentence true or false? Sedimentary rocks form from

particles deposited by water and wind. _____

Sedimentary Rocks (continued)

4. List three forces that can carry sediment.

   a. _____

   b. _____

   c. _____

Match the process with its description.

Process

____ **5.** erosion

____ **6.** deposition

____ **7.** compaction

____ **8.** cementation

Description

a. Dissolved minerals glue sediments together.

b. Sediments are pressed together in layers.

c. Water or wind loosen and carry away fragments of rock.

d. Sediments settle out of water or wind.

9. What happens to rock fragments and other materials carried by water?

   _____

   _____

10. The process in which thick layers of sediment press down on the layers beneath them is called _____.

11. Complete the flowchart to show how sediment is turned into sedimentary rock and what happens to it at each step.

Sedimentary Rock Formation

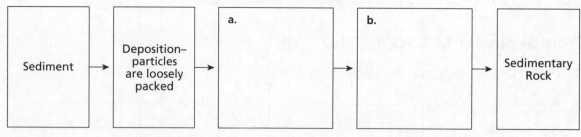

   c. Describe what happens to sediment as it is changed to sedimentary rock. _____

   _____

12. Is the following sentence true or false? It takes millions of years for sedimentary rock to form. _____

Rocks · *Guided Reading and Study*

Types of Sedimentary Rock (pp. 154–155)

13. How do geologists classify sedimentary rock? _____

_____

14. List the three major groups of sedimentary rock.

    a. _____

    b. _____

    c. _____

15. Is the following sentence true or false? The same process forms all types of sedimentary rock. _____

16. Is the following sentence true or false? Clastic rocks form when rock fragments are squeezed together. _____

17. How are clastic rocks classified? _____

_____

_____

18. Complete the table to show the different materials from which clastic rock forms.

How Clastic Rock Forms	
Type of Clastic Rock	**Material From Which It Forms**
a.	Tiny particles of clay
b.	Small particles of sand
c.	Different-sized rock fragments

    d. How are the types of clastic rocks shown in the table similar and different? _____

_____

19. The type of rocks that form where the remains of plants and animals are deposited in thick layers is called _____ rock.

Rocks • *Guided Reading and Study*

Sedimentary Rocks *(continued)*

20. List two important organic rocks.

a. _____

b. _____

21. Organic rock that forms from the remains of swamp plants buried in water is _____ .

22. How does organic limestone form? _____

_____

_____

_____

_____

_____

23. Circle the letter of each sentence that describes a way that chemical rocks can form.

a. Minerals that are dissolved in a solution crystallize.

b. Sediments of plants and animals form oil and other chemicals in rock.

c. Mineral deposits form when seas or lakes evaporate.

d. Tiny particles of clay are cemented together with chemicals.

24. Is the following sentence true or false? Some limestone is considered to be a chemical rock. _____

25. Rock salt crystallizes from the mineral _____ .

Rocks ▪ *Guided Reading and Study*

Uses of Sedimentary Rocks (p. 156)

26. Why have sandstone and limestone been used as building materials for thousands of years? _____

_____

_____

27. Is the following sentence true or false? The White House in Washington, D.C., is built of limestone. _____

28. What are some ways that builders today use sandstone and limestone?

_____

_____

_____

29. Is the following sentence true or false? Limestone is used for making cement. _____

Sedimentary Rocks

Understanding Main Ideas

The flowchart below shows a sequence of processes that form sedimentary rock. Put the processes into the correct sequence by writing their letters in the correct order in the blank.

a. Compaction ➡ **b.** Erosion ➡ **c.** Cementation ➡ **d.** Deposition

1. _____

Classify each of the following sedimentary rocks by writing Clastic, Organic, or Chemical in the blank beside it.

_____ **2.** Sandstone _____ **6.** Coal

_____ **3.** Limestone made from shells _____ **7.** Breccia

_____ **4.** Conglomerate _____ **8.** Rock salt

_____ **5.** Limestone made from precipitated calcite _____ **9.** Shale

Building Vocabulary

Match each term with its definition by writing the letter of the correct definition on the line beside the term.

_____ **10.** erosion

_____ **11.** clastic rock

_____ **12.** sediment

_____ **13.** cementation

_____ **14.** organic rock

_____ **15.** compaction

_____ **16.** chemical rock

_____ **17.** deposition

a. small, solid pieces of material from rocks or living things

b. the process that presses sediments together

c. sedimentary rock that forms from remains of plants and animals

d. the process in which running water, wind, or ice loosen and carry away rock fragments

e. the process in which dissolved minerals crystallize and glue sediments together

f. sedimentary rock that forms when rock fragments are squeezed together

g. the process by which sediment settles out of wind or water

h. sedimentary rock that forms when minerals dissolved in a solution crystallize

Name _____ Date _____ Class _____

The Formation of Coal

Coal is an organic sedimentary rock. One of its properties is that it burns. Coal provides energy for industries and for the production of electricity.

Much of the country's best coal is found in Pennsylvania, Ohio, West Virginia, Kentucky, Tennessee, and Alabama. The formation of this large coalfield began about 300 million years ago during a time geologists call the Carboniferous Period. During that period, vast tropical swamp forests covered much of North America. When these ancient trees died, they fell into the swamp water, which was low in oxygen. Instead of rotting—as they would in an oxygen-rich environment—the dead vegetation piled up. The sequence of pictures below tells the rest of the story of how this plant matter became coal.

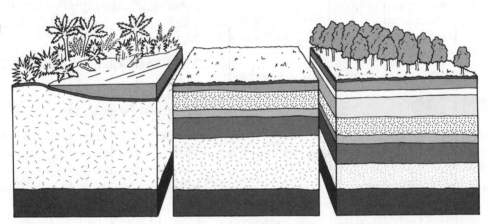

Dead plant matter built up on the bottom of a vast swamp during the Carboniferous Period.

Layers of sediment were deposited. The weight of the sediment compacted the plant matter into a substance called peat.

More and more sediment was deposited on top of the peat. Over millions of years, the weight of overlying sediment compressed the peat into coal.

Answer the following questions on a separate sheet of paper.

1. What is coal?

2. When did the coal deposits of the eastern United States begin to form? What were environmental conditions like at that time?

3. What is peat?

4. What process caused the peat to become coal?

5. A type of coal called anthracite is classified by geologists as a metamorphic rock. It is much harder than sedimentary coal. Describe how you think anthracite forms.

Rocks From Reefs

🕐 *1 period, 1/2 block*

Objectives

F.5.4.1 Describe the formation of coral reefs.
F.5.4.2 Explain how limestone deposits from coral reefs provide information about Earth's history.

Key Terms
• coral reef

PRETEACH

Local Standards

Build Background Knowledge
Students share their knowledge of coral reefs. They answer questions about where reefs occur and how to describe reef structure.

 Discover Activity *How Does a Rock React to Acid?* **L1**

Targeted Resources

❏ **All in One** Teaching Resources
  L2 Reading Strategy Transparency F47: Outlining

❏ 💿 **PresentationExpress™ CD-ROM**

INSTRUCT

Coral Reefs
Use leading questions to develop an understanding of how reefs form and why they are important.

Limestone From Coral Reefs
Demonstrate how limestone deposits that began as coral reefs provide evidence of how plate motions have changed Earth's surface. Open a discussion of the conditions under which ancient coral reefs formed.

Targeted Resources

❏ **All in One** Teaching Resources
  L2 Guided Reading, pp. 334–336
❏ **PHSchool.com** Web Code: cfd-1054
❏ 💿 **Student Edition on Audio CD**

ASSESS

Section Assessment Questions
🔄 Have students use their completed graphic organizers with their paragraphs using prior knowledge to answer the questions.

Reteach
Students discuss the structure of a coral animal.

Targeted Resources

❏ **All in One** Teaching Resources
Section Summary, p. 333
  L1 Review and Reinforce, p. 337
  L3 Enrich, p. 338

Rocks · *Section Summary*

Rocks From Reefs

Key Concepts

- How do coral reefs form?
- What evidence do limestone deposits from coral reefs provide about Earth's history?

Coral animals are tiny relatives of jellyfish that live together in vast numbers. They produce skeletons that grow together to form a structure called a **coral reef.**

Tiny algae grow within the body of each coral animal. The algae provide substances that the coral animals need to live. Like plants, algae need sunlight. For this reason, almost all growth in a coral reef occurs within 40 meters of the water's surface.

Coral animals absorb the element calcium from the ocean water. The calcium is then combined with carbon and oxygen to form calcite. **When coral animals die, their skeletons remain. More corals build on top of them, gradually forming a coral reef.**

Coral reefs form only in the warm, shallow water of tropical oceans. Reefs are most abundant around islands and along the eastern coasts of continents. In the United States, only the coasts of southern Florida and Hawaii have coral reefs. Over thousands of years, reefs may grow to hundreds of kilometers long and hundreds of meters thick.

A coral reef is really organic limestone. **Limestone deposits that began as coral reefs provide evidence of how plate motions have changed Earth's surface. These deposits also provide evidence of past environments.** Limestone has been forming in Earth's oceans for more than 400 million years. The limestone formed when shallow seas covered the low-lying parts of the continents. The limestone was exposed when the seas retreated. Plate motions have slowly moved these deposits far from the tropical oceans where they formed.

Deposits of organic limestone help geologists understand past environments. Where geologists find fossils of an ancient coral reef, they know that the reef formed in an area with a warm climate and shallow ocean water.

Rocks · *Guided Reading and Study*

Rocks From Reefs (pp. 157–159)

This section explains how coral reefs form and how coral reefs can become limestone deposits.

Use Target Reading Skills

As you preview the section headings, write what you know about the topic in the box "What You Know." As you read the section, complete the "What You Learned" box.

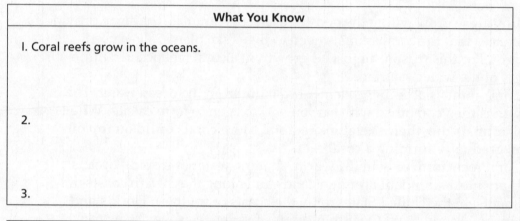

What You Know
1. Coral reefs grow in the oceans.
2.
3.

What You Learned
1.
2.
3.

Coral Reefs (p. 158)

1. Circle the letter of each sentence that is true about living coral.

   a. It is a tiny plant.

   b. It is related to jellyfish.

   c. It lives in deep oceans.

   d. It eats microscopic creatures.

2. Skeletons of living coral grow together to form a structure called a(n)

   _____ .

Rocks • *Guided Reading and Study*

3. Is the following sentence true or false? Almost all growth in a coral reef occurs close to the water's surface. _____

4. Coral animals absorb the element _____ from ocean water.

5. The protective outer shells of coral animals are formed from

   _____.

6. Circle the letter of each sentence that is true about coral reefs.

   a. They form only in cool water.

   b. They form only in tropical oceans.

   c. They form their skeletons by absorbing calcium.

   d. They form only in deep water.

7. Where are coral reefs most abundant? _____

   _____

   _____

   _____

8. In the United States, where are the only living coral reefs found? _____

   _____

   _____

9. Circle the letter of each sentence that is true about the growth of coral reefs.

   a. Coral reefs may grow to be hundreds of kilometers long.

   b. Coral reefs may grow to be hundreds of kilometers thick.

   c. Coral reefs usually grow inward away from the open ocean.

   d. Coral reefs may grow for thousands of years.

Rocks

Rocks • *Guided Reading and Study*

Rocks From Reefs *(continued)*

Limestone From Coral Reefs (p. 159)

10. How do limestone deposits formed from reefs provide evidence of how plate motions have changed Earth's surface? _____

_____

_____

_____

_____

11. Where in the United States are ancient coral reefs preserved in rock? _____

_____

_____

Rocks · *Review and Reinforce*

Rocks From Reefs

Understanding Main Ideas
Fill in the blanks in the flowchart below.

Coral animals absorb the element **1.** _____ from ocean

water. ➡ Corals change the element into calcite to form protective

2. _____. ➡ When corals die, new **3.** _____

build on top of the dead corals' shells, creating a structure. ➡ Over

thousands of years, **4.** _____ grow outward toward
the ocean.

Answer the following questions in the spaces provided.

5. What conditions are present in the water just south of Florida that explain
why coral reefs can be found there?

_____

6. Explain why almost all growth in a coral reef occurs within 40 meters of
the water's surface.

_____

_____

7. What explains how limestone that began as coral can be found on continents?

_____

_____

_____

_____

8. How do geologists know that shallow seas once covered the central part
of North America?

_____

_____

_____

Building Vocabulary
Fill in the blank to complete the statement.

9. A structure formed when the skeletons of coral animals grow together is

a(n) _____.

Name _____ Date _____ Class _____

Changing From One Reef to Another

In the South Pacific and Indian oceans, there are many atolls. These circular islands usually form a ring around a central lagoon, a shallow body of water cut off from the ocean. How do these atolls form? The nineteenth-century English biologist Charles Darwin was the first to propose that atolls began as fringing reefs around a volcanic island. Few scientists believed his theory at first. But modern scientists have drilled through the reefs of atolls and discovered that underneath are hundreds of meters of volcanic rock. Examine the series of pictures below to see how an atoll forms.

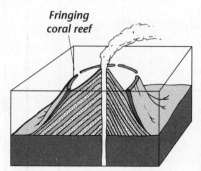
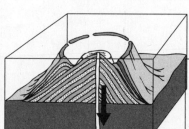
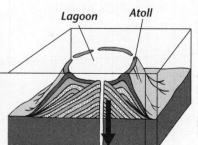

A reef grows around the base of a volcanic island. When volcanic activity ends, rain and waves begin to wear away the part of the volcanic island that is above sea level.

The volcanic island also begins to sink as the ocean floor beneath it sinks. This is the result of the fact that oceanic crust cools, becomes more dense, and sinks during sea-floor spreading. The coral reef continues to grow upward as the island sinks.

The volcanic island finally sinks underwater. Above water is a reef ring, or atoll. The shallow water above the old volcano forms a lagoon.

Answer the following questions on a separate sheet of paper.

1. What is an atoll?

2. How does an atoll originally form?

3. Why does a volcanic island sink?

4. What happens to the fringing reef as the island sinks?

5. What is at the center of an atoll?

Metamorphic Rocks

🕐 *2 periods, 1 block*

Rocks

Objectives

F.5.5.1 Describe the conditions under which metamorphic rocks form.

F.5.5.2 Identify the ways in which geologists classify metamorphic rocks.

F.5.5.3 Explain how metamorphic rocks are used.

Key Terms
• foliated

Local Standards

PRETEACH

Build Background Knowledge
Students recall forces that can change rocks by answering questions about plate boundaries and plate collisions.

 *How Do Grain Patterns Compare?* **L1**

Targeted Resources

❏ **All in One** Teaching Resources
  L2 Reading Strategy Transparency F48: Previewing Visuals

❏ ◉ **PresentationExpress™ CD-ROM**

INSTRUCT

Types of Metamorphic Rocks
Review with students the difference between foliated and nonfoliated rocks and how these characteristics form. Help students apply their knowledge to a given example.

Uses of Metamorphic Rock
Describe the properties of marble and slate that make them useful in statues and buildings. Guide a discussion of these properties and help students apply their knowledge to other uses.

 Mystery Rocks **L2**

Targeted Resources

❏ **All in One** Teaching Resources
  L2 Guided Reading, pp. 341–343
  L2 Transparency F49
  L2 Lab: *Mystery Rocks*, p. 346–348

❏ 📼 **Lab Activity Video/DVD**
  Skills Lab: *Mystery Rocks*

❏ **www.SciLinks.org** Web Code: cfa-1055

❏ ◉ **Student Edition on Audio CD**

ASSESS

Section Assessment Questions
🔁 Have students use the questions and answers they prepared by previewing visuals to answer the questions.

Reteach
Students discuss places where metamorphic rocks might form.

Targeted Resources

❏ **All in One** Teaching Resources
  Section Summary, p. 340
  L1 Review and Reinforce, p. 344
  L3 Enrich, p. 345

Rocks • *Section Summary*

Metamorphic Rocks

Key Concepts

- Under what conditions do metamorphic rocks form?

- How do geologists classify metamorphic rocks?

- How are metamorphic rocks used?

Every metamorphic rock is a rock that has changed its form. In fact, the word *metamorphic* comes from the Greek words meta, meaning "change," and morphos, meaning "form." **Heat and pressure deep beneath Earth's surface can change any rock into metamorphic rock.** When rock changes into metamorphic rock, its appearance, texture, crystal structure, and mineral content change. Metamorphic rock can form out of igneous, sedimentary, or other metamorphic rock.

Collisions between Earth's plates can push rocks down toward the heat of the mantle. Magma rising through the crust can also provide heat to produce metamorphic rocks. Rock buried deep in the crust is under pressure hundreds or thousands of times greater than at Earth's surface, and that pressure can change rock into metamorphic rock.

When metamorphic rock is forming, high temperatures can change the size and shape of grains in the rock. Tremendous pressure can also squeeze rock so tightly that the mineral grains may line up in flat, parallel layers. **Geologists classify metamorphic rocks according to the arrangement of the grains that make up the rocks.** Metamorphic rocks that have their grains arranged in parallel layers or bands are said to be foliated. **Foliated** rocks—including slate, schist, and gneiss—may split apart along these bands. One common foliated rock is slate, which is basically a denser, more compact version of shale.

Some metamorphic rocks are nonfoliated. The mineral grains in these rocks are arranged randomly. Nonfoliated metamorphic rocks—including marble and quartzite—do not split into layers. Quartzite forms out of sandstone. The weakly cemented quartz particles in the sandstone recrystallize to form quartzite, which is extremely hard.

Certain metamorphic rocks are important materials for building and sculpture. Marble and slate are two of the most useful metamorphic rocks. Marble can be cut into thin slabs, and it can be polished so that its surface is smooth and mirrorlike. These qualities have led architects and sculptors to use marble for many buildings and statues. For example, one of America's most famous sculptures is in the Lincoln Memorial in Washington, D.C.

Like marble, slate comes in a variety of colors, including gray, black, red, and purple. Slate, because it is foliated, splits easily into flat pieces that can be used for flooring, roofing, outdoor walkways, or chalkboards.

Metamorphic Rocks (pp. 160–162)

This section explains how metamorphic rocks form, how they are classified, and how they are used.

Use Target Reading Skills

Look at Figure 17 and write two questions you have about the visuals in the graphic organizer below. As you read about metamorphic rocks, write the answers to your questions.

Q. Why do the crystals in gneiss line up in bands?
A.
Q.
A.

Introduction (p. 160)

1. List the two forces that can change rocks into metamorphic rocks.

   a. _____

   b. _____

Metamorphic Rocks *(continued)*

2. Is the following sentence true or false? Metamorphic rocks form deep beneath Earth's surface. _____

3. How do rocks change when they become metamorphic rocks?

_____

_____

4. What kinds of rocks can be changed into metamorphic rocks?

_____

_____

5. Is the following sentence true or false? The deeper a rock is buried in the crust, the less pressure there is on that rock. _____

Types of Metamorphic Rocks (pp. 160–161)

6. Is the following sentence true or false? Geologists classify metamorphic rocks by the arrangement of grains making up the rocks.

_____

7. Metamorphic rocks with grains arranged in parallel layers or bands are said to be _____.

8. Circle the letter of each type of metamorphic rock that is foliated.

a. slate

b. quartzite

c. gneiss

d. marble

9. Metamorphic rocks with grains arranged randomly are said to be

_____.

10. List two examples of nonfoliated metamorphic rocks.

a. _____

b. _____

Rocks · *Guided Reading and Study*

11. Complete the flowchart to show the metamorphic rocks that are formed.

How Some Metamorphic Rocks Form

Heat/Pressure

| Granite | → | b. |

| Shale | → | c. |

| a. | → | Quartzite |

d. What does the flow chart show is happening to the rocks to the left?

_____

_____

Uses of Metamorphic Rock (p. 162)

12. Why is marble useful for buildings and statues? _____

_____

_____

13. What are some of the ways that slate is used? _____

_____

_____

Rocks • *Review and Reinforce*

Metamorphic Rocks

Understanding Main Ideas

Fill in the blanks in the flowchart below.

Collisions between Earth's plates push rock down toward the heat of Earth's **1.** _____. ➡ As the rock is buried deeper in the crust, **2.** _____ also increases on the rock. ➡ The rock is squeezed so tightly that the **3.** _____ of the rock change, creating metamorphic rock.

Answer the following questions in the spaces provided.

4. Describe a situation in which heat can change rock to metamorphic rock.

_____

_____

_____

5. What characteristic do geologists use to classify metamorphic rocks?

_____

_____

6. Describe how quartzite forms.

_____

_____

7. Explain what characteristics make marble a useful metamorphic rock.

_____

_____

_____

Building Vocabulary

Classify each of the following metamorphic rocks by writing either Foliated *or* Nonfoliated *in the blank beside it.*

_____ **8.** marble

_____ **9.** slate

_____ **10.** gneiss

Rocks • *Enrich*

The Metamorphic Rocks

Tremendous pressure and high temperatures can change any rock into metamorphic rock. This process often occurs near plate boundaries. There, pressure builds as one plate collides with another. In addition, hot magma flows upward into rock near these boundaries. Such intense conditions change one kind of rock into another, such as shale, a sedimentary rock, into slate, a metamorphic rock. But what happens if the pressure and temperature continue to increase after shale becomes slate? Look at Figure 1 below. Increasing pressure and temperature change the slate into schist, and the schist changes into gneiss.

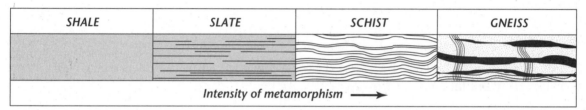

Figure 1

Gneiss and schist are the most common metamorphic rocks. Gneiss is a foliated rock usually composed of quartz and feldspar. Schist is also foliated, but its mineral composition varies. The terms gneiss and schist actually describe certain textures of metamorphic rock. That's why both shale and granite can change into gneiss, and both granite and basalt can change into schist. Figure 2 shows common metamorphic rocks to the right. The rocks on the left are igneous and sedimentary rocks. The arrows represent the pressure and temperatures that cause the formation of metamorphic rocks.

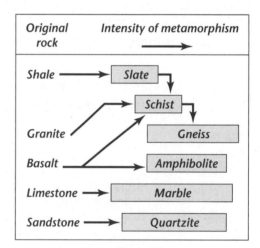

Figure 2

Answer the following questions on a separate sheet of paper.

1. What causes shale to change into slate?

2. What happens to the slate if these conditions increase?

3. What are gneiss and schist?

4. How do tremendous pressures and high temperatures affect limestone?

5. How does metamorphism affect basalt?

6. What rocks can change into schist?

7. How does increased metamorphism affect schist?

Rocks · *Skills Lab*

Mystery Rocks

Problem

What properties can be used to classify rocks?

Materials

1 "mystery rock"

2 unknown igneous rocks

2 unknown sedimentary rocks

2 unknown metamorphic rocks

hand lens

Procedure

1. For this activity, you will be given six rocks and one sample that is not a rock. They are labeled A through G.

2. Use the data table to record your observations.

3. Using the hand lens, examine each rock for clues showing that the rock formed from molten material. Record the rock's color and texture. Observe if there are any crystals or grains in the rock.

4. Use the hand lens to look for clues showing that the rock formed from particles of other rocks. Observe the texture of the rock to see if it has any tiny, well-rounded grains.

DATA TABLE

Sample	Color (dark, medium, light, or mixed colors)	Texture (fine, medium, or coarse-grained)	Foliated or Banded	Rock Group (igneous, metamorphic, sedimentary
A				
B				
C				
D				
E				
F				
G				

5. Use the hand lens to look for clues showing that the rock formed under heat and pressure. Observe if the rock has a flat layer of crystals or shows colored bands.

6. Record your observations in the data table.

Analyze and Conclude

Write your answers in the spaces provided.

1. **Inferring** Infer from your observations the group in which each rock belongs.

   _____

   _____

   _____

   _____

2. **Classifying** Which of the samples could be classified as igneous rocks? What physical properties do these rocks share with the other samples? How are they different?

   _____

   _____

   _____

   _____

3. **Classifying** Which of the samples could be classified as sedimentary rocks? How do you think these rocks formed? What are the physical properties of these rocks?

   _____

   _____

   _____

   _____

4. **Classifying** Which of the samples could be classified as metamorphic rocks? What are their physical properties?

   _____

   _____

   _____

   _____

Rocks · *Skills Lab*

Mystery Rocks *(continued)*

5. **Drawing Conclusions** Decide which sample is not a rock. How did you determine that the sample you chose is not a rock? What do you think the "mystery rock" is? Explain.

_____

_____

_____

_____

6. **Communicating** What physical property was most useful in classifying rocks? Which physical property was least useful? Explain your answer.

_____

_____

_____

More to Explore

Can you name each rock? Use a field guide to rocks and minerals to find the specific name of each rock sample.

The Rock Cycle

 *2 periods, 1 block*

Rocks

Objectives

F.5.6.1 Describe the rock cycle.
F.5.6.2 Explain the role of plate tectonics in the rock cycle.

Key Term
• rock cycle

Local Standards

PRETEACH

Build Background Knowledge
Students brainstorm a list of Earth processes that affect rock in Earth's crust and explain why rocks are not permanent.

Lab zone Discover Activity *Which Rock Came First?* **L1**

Targeted Resources

❑ **All in One Teaching Resources**
  L2 Reading Strategy Transparency F50: Sequencing
❑ ◉ **PresentationExpress™ CD-ROM**

INSTRUCT

A Cycle of Many Pathways
Review with students the meaning of *cycle* and discuss products and processes in the rock cycle. Help students apply their knowledge to real-world events and use the Active Art to connect products and processes to the various pathways in the rock cycle.

The Rock Cycle and Plate Tectonics
Help students develop an understanding of the rock cycle products and processes that occur at various plate tectonic settings.

Lab zone Design Your Own Lab *Testing Rock Flooring* **L2**

Targeted Resources

❑ **All in One Teaching Resources**
  L2 Guided Reading, pp. 351–352
  L2 Transparency F51
  L2 Lab: *Testing Rock Flooring*, pp. 355–356
❑ 📼 **Lab Activity Video/DVD**
  Design Your Own Lab: *Testing Rock Flooring*
❑ **PHSchool.com** Web Code: cfp-1056-6
❑ ◉ **Student Edition on Audio CD**

ASSESS

Section Assessment Questions
↻ Have students use their completed graphic organizers showing the sequence of steps in the rock cycle to answer the questions.

Reteach
Students work together to explain how a silicon atom in a sand grain could someday erupt from a volcano.

Targeted Resources

❑ **All in One Teaching Resources**
  Section Summary, p. 350
  L1 Review and Reinforce, p. 353
  L3 Enrich, p. 354

Rocks • *Section Summary*

The Rock Cycle

Key Concepts

- What is the rock cycle?
- What is the role of plate tectonics in the rock cycle?

Earth's rocks are not as unchanging as they seem. **Forces deep inside Earth and at the surface produce a slow cycle that builds, destroys, and changes the rocks in the crust.** The **rock cycle** is a series of processes on Earth's surface and in the crust and mantle that slowly change rocks from one kind to another.

One possible pathway through the rock cycle began with the formation of the igneous rock granite beneath the surface. The forces of mountain building slowly pushed the granite upward, forming a mountain. Slowly, water and wind wore away the granite. The resulting sand was carried by streams to the ocean. Over millions of years, layers of sediment piled up on the ocean floor and changed to sandstone, a sedimentary rock. Over time, the sandstone became deeply buried. Heat and pressure changed the sandstone to the metamorphic rock quartzite.

The changes of the rock cycle are closely related to plate tectonics. **Plate movements start the rock cycle by helping to form magma, the source of igneous rocks. Plate movements also cause faulting, folding, and other motions of the crust that help to form sedimentary and metamorphic rocks.**

Where oceanic plates move apart, magma formed from melted mantle rock moves upward and fills the gap with new igneous rock. A collision of continental plates may push rocks so deep that they melt and form magma. This magma slowly cools and hardens to form igneous rock.

Sedimentary rock is formed when mountains are worn away by erosion. The mountains were formed by the collision of continental plates that produced faults, folds, and uplift of the crust. Metamorphic rock forms from heat and pressure on rocks pushed down deep in the mantle by a collision between continental plates.

Rocks · *Guided Reading and Study*

The Rock Cycle (pp. 164–166)

This section describes the cycle that builds, destroys, and changes rocks in Earth's crust. The section also explains how this cycle is related to movements in Earth's crust.

Use Target Reading Skills

As you read about the rock cycle, fill in the cycle diagram below. Write each stage of the rock cycle in a separate circle.

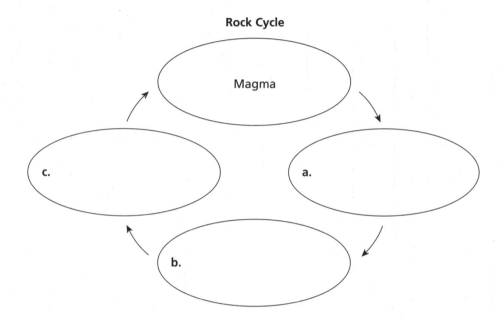

Rock Cycle

Introduction (p. 164)

1. What forces move rocks through the rock cycle?

   _____

   _____

The Rock Cycle *(continued)*

A Cycle of Many Pathways (pp. 164–165)

2. The series of processes that slowly change rocks from one kind to another is referred to as the _____.

3. Is the following sentence true or false? All rocks follow the same pathway through the rock cycle. _____

4. How could granite be changed into sandstone? _____

_____

_____

_____

The Rock Cycle and Plate Tectonics (p. 166)

5. How do plate movements drive the rock cycle? _____

_____

_____

_____

_____

Name _____ Date _____ Class _____

Rocks · *Review and Reinforce*

The Rock Cycle

Understanding Main Ideas

Use these terms to fill in the blanks in the figure below: metamorphic rock, sedimentary rock, magma and lava, igneous rock, sediment.

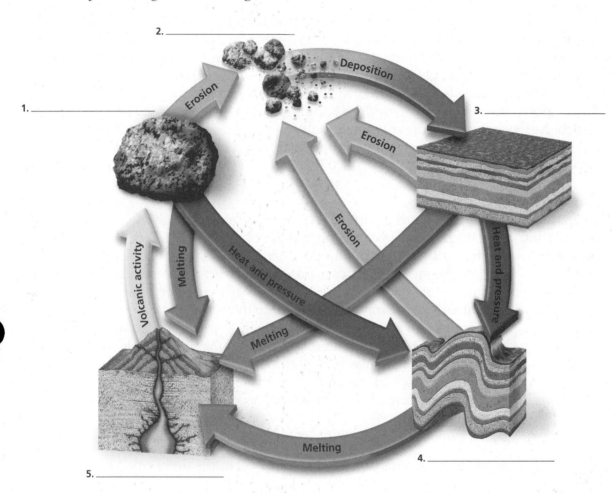

2. _____

1. _____

Erosion

Deposition

Erosion

3. _____

Erosion

Volcanic activity

Melting

Heat and pressure

Heat and pressure

Melting

Melting

4. _____

5. _____

Answer the following questions on a separate sheet of paper.

6. Describe how the granite of a mountain could change first into sandstone and then into quartzite.

7. Describe how a collision between continental plates can result in the formation of metamorphic rock.

Building Vocabulary

Using your own words, write a definition of the rock cycle on the lines below.

_____

_____

_____

Rocks • *Enrich*

Alternate Pathways

Rock can follow many different pathways through the rock cycle. Here are two examples.

Pathway 1

Between New Zealand and South America, at the bottom of the Pacific Ocean, molten material from the mantle erupts from the mid-ocean ridge. As the material comes into contact with the very cold ocean water, it cools quickly to become rock. Over time, this rock ever so slowly moves away from the mid-ocean ridge, as sea-floor spreading makes changes in the ocean floor. About 200 million years later, the rock is subducted at a deep-ocean trench. As the rock moves downward, it melts to become part of the mantle. Eventually, this melted material moves back up through the mid-ocean ridge to become rock again.

Pathway 2

Deep underground, a new rock forms as heat and pressure change its crystals and cause its grains to become foliated. Over millions of years, this rock is uplifted to become part of a mountain. Then, layers of rock above the foliated rock wear away, until it becomes exposed at the surface. Destructive forces wear it down, and its fragments are carried away by a river's swift-flowing water. Eventually, these fragments flow into the ocean. Ocean water carries the rock fragments away from the river, and they are deposited on a beach. Over time, more and more sediment is deposited there, until the fragments that came from the foliated rock become cemented into a new rock. Then more and more rock forms above this rock, until the heat and pressure change its crystals and cause its grains to become foliated.

Answer the following questions on a separate sheet of paper.

1. Which major group or groups of rocks are involved in the description of Pathway 1?

2. Make a flowchart that describes what occurs in Pathway 1.

3. Which major group or groups of rocks are involved in the description of Pathway 2?

4. Make a flowchart that describes what occurs in Pathway 2.

5. Write a description of another pathway through the rock cycle. In your description, tell how igneous rock changes to metamorphic rock, which then changes to sedimentary rock.

Rocks · *Design Your Own Lab*

Testing Rock Flooring

Problem

What kind of building stone makes the best flooring?

Skills Focus

designing experiments

forming operational definitions

drawing conclusions

Suggested Materials

- steel nail
- plastic dropper
- wire brush
- hand lens
- water
- samples of igneous, sedimentary, and metamorphic rock with flat surfaces
- materials that form stains, such as ink and paints
- greasy materials, such as butter and crayons

Procedure   *Review the safety guidelines in Appendix A.*

1. Brainstorm with your partner the qualities of good flooring. For example, good flooring should resist stains, scratches, and grease marks, and be safe to walk on when wet.

2. Predict what you think is the best building stone for a kitchen floor. Why?

3. Write the steps you plan to follow to answer the problem question. As you design your plan, consider the following factors:

   - What igneous, sedimentary, and metamorphic rocks will you test? (Pick at least one rock from each group.)
   - What materials or equipment will you need to acquire, and in what amounts?
   - What tests will you perform on the samples?
   - How will you control the variables in each test?
   - How will you measure each sample's resistance to staining, grease, and scratches?
   - How will you measure slipperiness?

Rocks • *Design Your Own Lab*

Testing Rock Flooring *(continued)*

4. Review your plan. Will it lead to an answer to the problem question?

5. Check your procedure and safety plan with your teacher.

6. Create a data table that includes a column in which you predict how each material will perform in each test.

Analyze and Conclude

Write your answers on a separate sheet of paper.

1. **Interpreting Data** Which material performed the best on each test? Which performed the worst on each test?

2. **Drawing Conclusions** Which material is best for the kitchen flooring? Which material would you least want to use?

3. **Drawing Conclusions** Do your answers support your initial prediction? Why or why not?

4. **Applying Concepts** The person installing the floor might want stone that is easy to cut to the correct size or shape. What other qualities would matter to the flooring installer?

5. **Communicating** Based on your results for flooring, what materials would you use for kitchen counters? How might the qualities needed for countertops differ from those for flooring?

Design an Experiment

Suppose you are trying to select flooring material for a laboratory where heavy equipment is frequently moved across the floor. Make a hypothesis predicting which type of stone flooring will be strongest. Then design an experiment to compare how well each type resists breakage.

Key Terms

Test your knowledge of rocks by using key terms from the chapter to solve the crossword puzzle.

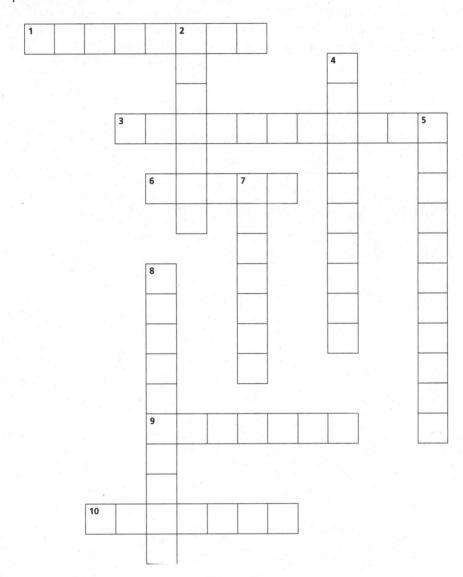

Clues across

1. Rocks with grains arranged in parallel layers

3. Rock formed by heat or pressure

6. Particle that gives rock texture

9. Sedimentary rock formed under pressure

10. Movement of fragments of rock

Clues down

2. Look and feel of a rock's surface

4. Process in which sediment is deposited in layers

5. Process of gluing sediments

7. Rock formed from molten rock

8. Process of pressing sediments

Connecting Concepts

Develop a concept map that uses the key concepts and key terms from this chapter. Keep in mind the big idea of this chapter: Rocks are classified into three main categories and undergo changes through a process called the rock cycle. The concept map shown is one way to organize how the information in this chapter is related. You may use an extra sheet of paper.

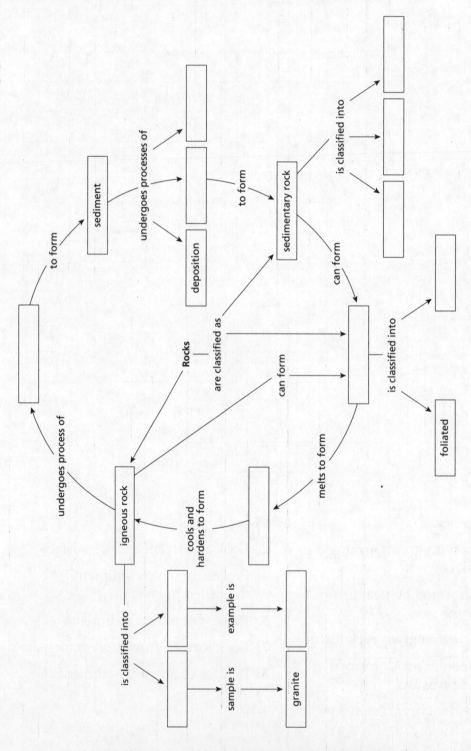

Making Models of Sedimentary Rocks

Key Concept

Sedimentary rocks are typically formed by particles undergoing erosion, deposition, compaction, and cementation. The three types of sedimentary rocks are clastic, organic, and chemical, based on what materials they contain and how they were formed.

Skills Focus

observing, inferring, making models, designing experiments

Time

40 minutes for planning and making rocks (break after Step 4); after "rocks" dry, 40 minutes for determining properties

Possible Materials

sand

soil

gravel

fossils

plaster of Paris

powdered chalk

salt

pans

spoons

water

paper towels

streak plate

materials of known hardness

newspapers

Alternative Materials

The list of materials is a suggestion. Similar materials can be used. You might suggest students use a water hose to test resistance to weathering in Step 5. Some of the minerals found in actual sedimentary rocks are comercially available. Don't let students use materials that are toxic, corrosive, or caustic, such as Portland cement. Plastic fossil models can be substituted for real fossils.

Advance Preparation

Collect, or have students bring from home, materials that can be used to form the rocks. Have plenty of newspaper on hand for students to work on.

Teaching Tips

- To speed drying, have students use paper towels to blot excess water out of newly made rocks.

- Review mechanical weathering and how it differs from chemical weathering.

- Students can explore chemical weathering in More to Explore.

Rocks · *Laboratory Investigation*

Making Models of Sedimentary Rocks *(continued)*

Pre-Lab Discussion

Layers of rock that formed at the bottom of ancient seas in some cases now lie exposed, thousands of meters above sea level. The processes that formed this rock lasted millions of years. So did the Earth movements that exposed the rock, pushing and tilting it into high mountains. To study such slow natural processes, scientists and engineers use models in their laboratories to imitate, or simulate, the real thing. They try to give their models the look and feel of actual rock.

The three types of rock—igneous, metamorphic, and sedimentary—are all formed in different ways. In this investigation, you will create models of sedimentary rocks and explore their properties.

1. How do sedimentary rocks differ from other rocks?

_____

_____

2. What four steps occur during the formation of a clastic sedimentary rock?

_____

_____

Problem

How is sedimentary rock formed, and what are its properties?

Possible Materials *(per group)*

sand
soil
gravel
fossils
plaster of Paris
powdered chalk
salt
pans
spoons
water
paper towels
streak plate
materials of known hardness
newspapers

Rocks ▪ *Laboratory Investigation*

Making Models of Sedimentary Rocks

Safety 🦺 🧤 🥽 *Review the safety guidelines in Appendix A of your textbook.* Wear safety goggles and lab aprons. Wash hands frequently during this activity.

Procedure

1. Starting with the list of materials, brainstorm with other students how to create models of sedimentary rocks. You may also be able to collect natural materials outside of your school or near your home. You do not have to use all of the listed the materials. You may want to use other materials as well.

2. **CAUTION:** *Put on your safety goggles and lab apron.* Start to experiment with materials to create your model rocks. How will you form layers? How could your model imitate the pressures that cement particles and fragments into rock? Will the rock layers have fossils?

3. Start to record your rock-making procedures on a separate sheet of paper. Your plans should include all classes of sedimentary rock: clastic, organic, and chemical. What materials can you use to model clastic rock? How will you model layered formations? How can you simulate different-size particles for a conglomerate? How might you model an organic rock? A chemical rock?

4. After the teacher approves your procedure, create your rock models. If your models are not coming out the way you want, modify your procedures. Sketch your rock models in Observations. Set the models aside to dry. Wash your hands when you've finished.

5. When your model rocks are completely dry, explore their properties. Observe and record in the Data Table color, texture, overall hardness, pattern, and resistance to weathering. Resistance to weathering is determined by whether the rock remains intact or crumbles when tested. What type of test could show whether your rock is weak or strong? What other properties should you evaluate? Have the teacher approve any test before you conduct it.

6. Compare models with several classmates. For each model rock, state what type of sedimentary rock it represents, how it was made, and its properties.

Rocks • *Laboratory Investigation*

Making Models of Sedimentary Rocks *(continued)*

Observations

Sketches of Sedimentary Rock Models		
Clastic	**Organic**	**Chemical**

Properties of Model Rocks			
	Type of Sedimentary Rock		
Property	**Clastic**	**Organic**	**Chemical**
Color			
Textrue			
Hardness			
Pattern			
Resistance to Weathering			

Rocks · *Laboratory Investigation*

Making Models of Sedimentary Rocks

Analyze and Conclude

1. What determines the properties of your model rocks?

   _____

   _____

2. Why might you choose to have fossils in your rock models?

   _____

   _____

3. How does compaction during the model-making process change the strength of the model rock?

   _____

   _____

Critical Thinking and Applications

1. Compare and contrast the different types of sedimentary rocks.

   _____

   _____

   _____

   _____

   _____

2. Would the actual rocks that your models represent be good materials to use to build bridges or buildings? Why or why not?

   _____

   _____

   _____

3. What properties of your rocks make them useful or limit their usefulness?

   _____

   _____

More to Explore

You have seen how sedimentary rocks differ in their resistance to physical weathering. How resistant are they to chemical weathering? Write a procedure you would follow to answer this question. Use actual sedimentary rocks and vinegar. Have the teacher approve your procedure before you carry out the investigation. Wear safety goggles and laboratory aprons while carrying out your procedure.

Making a Model of the Rock Cycle

Students are presented with the problem of creating a model of the rock cycle using the materials given. To solve this problem, students will have to apply the concepts they have learned about the major groups of rocks and how those rocks fit into the rock cycle.

Expected Outcome

Students should be able to classify the three unlabeled rock samples as igneous, sedimentary, and metamorphic. Once classification is accomplished, they can tape the rocks to the cardboard and use the marker to label the rocks and write the names of processes between them. The final product should be a model of the rock cycle that looks much like *The Rock Cycle* figure in their text.

Content Assessed

This activity assesses students' knowledge of characteristics of each major group of rocks, how each of those rocks forms, and how those groups fit into the rock cycle.

Skills Assessed

observing, classifying, making models

Materials

Provide each student with three unlabeled rock samples, one from each major group of rocks. Classification of these rock samples should be obvious to someone who has learned the material in the chapter. Therefore, the best choices might be granite (igneous), sandstone (sedimentary), and gneiss (metamorphic). The metamorphic rock should be foliated, so that students can easily observe that characteristic.

Provide each student with a piece of cardboard. This could be the side of a box that has been cut apart. The cardboard should be strong enough to hold the taped rock samples in place.

Two or three rolls of masking or duct tape should be sufficient for the whole class.

Students will need markers to label their rock cycle models.

Advance Preparation

Obtain enough rock samples for each student. These samples can be quite small, as long as they are large enough for students to be able to observe such characteristics as grain size and foliation.

Cut cardboard boxes into pieces about 30 cm × 30 cm with a utility knife or heavy scissors.

Obtain masking or duct tape and markers.

Time

20 minutes

Monitoring the Task

Advise students that they can tape the rock samples to the cardboard by making a loop of tape that they can stick to the cardboard and the back of the rock.

Allow students to pass rolls of tape around the classroom during the activity.

Advise students that the more labels they write, the clearer their models will be.

Making a Model of the Rock Cycle

In assessing students' performance, use the following rubric.

	4	3	2	1
Making a Model of the Rock Cycle	The student correctly classifies igneous, sedimentary, and metamorphic rock samples and makes a neat and accurately labeled model of the rock cycle.	The student correctly classifies igneous, sedimentary, and metamorphic rock samples and makes a neat and mostly accurate model of the rock cycle.	The student correctly classifies one of the rock samples and makes a model of the rock cycle that has several minor errors.	The student incorrectly identifies the rock samples and makes a model of the rock cycle that is mostly inaccurate.
Concept Understanding	The student demonstrates a mastery of the concepts related to the major groups of rocks, how they form, and how they fit into the rock cycle.	The student demonstrates an adequate understanding of the concepts related to the major groups of rocks, how they form, and how they fit into the rock cycle.	The student demonstrates some confusion about the concepts related to the major groups of rocks, how they form, and how they fit into the rock cycle.	The student demonstrates a weak understanding of the concepts related to the major groups of rocks, how they form, and how they fit into the rock cycle.

Rocks ▪ *Performance Assessment*

Making a Model of the Rock Cycle

Problem

How can you make a model of the rock cycle?

Suggested Materials

- igneous rock sample
- sedimentary rock sample
- metamorphic rock sample
- hand lens
- tape
- cardboard
- marker

Devise a Plan

1. Study the materials and think of a way they could be used to make a model of the rock cycle.

2. Classify the rock samples as igneous, sedimentary, or metamorphic.

3. Use the classified rocks in your model.

Analyze and Conclude

On a separate sheet of paper, respond to the items that follow.

1. Explain why you classified one rock sample as igneous, and describe how that rock might have formed.

2. Explain why you classified one rock sample as sedimentary, and describe how that rock might have formed.

3. Explain why you classified one rock sample as metamorphic, and describe how that rock might have formed.

4. What forces drive the rock cycle?

5. Where does the rock cycle begin and end? Give reasons for your answer.

Rocks

Multiple Choice

Write the letter of the correct answer on the line at the left.

_____ 1. Most metamorphic rock forms
   a. deep underground.
   b. on Earth's surface.
   c. when solutions evaporate.
   d. when minerals in magma crystallize.

_____ 2. A rock called a porphyry
   a. lacks a crystal structure.
   b. began as coral in an ancient sea.
   c. has large crystals surrounded by smaller crystals.
   d. splits easily along its parallel bands.

_____ 3. Which of the following is NOT a sedimentary rock?
   a. granite   **b.** conglomerate
   c. sandstone   **d.** limestone

_____ 4. The minerals that make up most of Earth's crust are called
   a. sediments   **b.** rock-forming minerals
   c. organic rocks   **d.** foliated rocks

_____ 5. A rock's texture is the
   a. look and feel of the rock.
   b. shape of the rock's crystals.
   c. thinness of a rock's crust.
   d. silica content of the rock.

_____ 6. Erosion and deposition play roles in the formation of what kind of rock?
   a. metamorphic rock   **b.** foliated rock
   c. sedimentary rock   **d.** igneous rock

_____ 7. Slate is basically a denser, more compact version of
   a. granite.   **b.** shale.
   c. marble.   **d.** sandstone.

_____ 8. Which of the following is an igneous rock?
   a. marble   **b.** basalt
   c. gneiss   **d.** limestone

Rocks · *Chapter Test*

____ 9. The names of the three major groups of rocks refer to
   a. where the rocks formed.
   b. the size and shape of the rocks' grains.
   c. when the rocks formed.
   d. how the rocks formed.

____ 10. What kind of rocks form when minerals that are dissolved in a
   solution crystallize on Earth's surface?
   a. chemical rocks   b. igneous rocks
   c. organic rocks   d. clastic rocks

Completion

Fill in the line to complete each statement.

11. Metamorphic rocks that have their grains arranged in parallel bands are
    said to be _____.

12. The process in which dissolved materials crystallize and glue particles of
    sediment together is called _____.

13. The series of processes that change rock from one type to another is
    called the _____.

14. Igneous rocks may be similar in mineral composition and yet have
    different _____.

15. A sedimentary rock that forms when rock fragments are squeezed
    together is called a(n) _____ rock.

True or False

If the statement is true, write true. *If it is false, change the underlined word or words to make the statement true.*

____ 16. The process that presses sediments together is called <u>deposition</u>.

____ 17. Basalt is the most common <u>intrusive rock</u>.

____ 18. <u>Sandstone</u> that began as coral can be found on continents.

____ 19. <u>Plate</u> movements help to drive the rock cycle.

____ 20. Coal is a type of <u>organic rock</u>.

Using Science Skills: Interpreting Diagrams

Use the diagram below to answer Questions 21–23. Write your answers in the spaces provided.

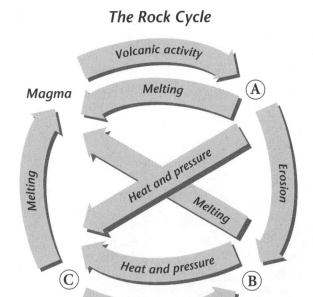

The Rock Cycle

21. The letters in the circles stand for the three major groups of rocks. Identify those groups.

_____

22. Describe how Rock Group C could change into Rock Group B.

_____

_____

_____

_____

23. Explain how plate movements are related to this cycle.

_____

_____

Rocks · *Chapter Test*

Essay

Answer each of the following on a separate sheet of paper.

24. What characteristics do geologists use to identify rocks?

25. Which would have larger crystals, an igneous rock formed from magma that cooled deep below the surface or an igneous rock that cooled from lava on the surface? Explain why.

Using Science Skills

Use the figure below to answer Questions 26 and 27. Write your answers on a separate sheet of paper.

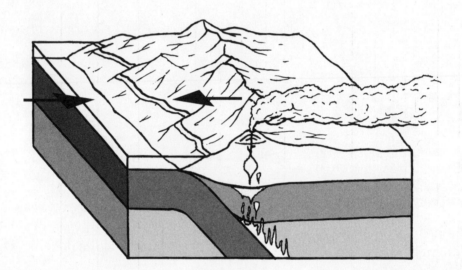

26. Interpreting Diagrams Explain how the process shown in the figure could produce metamorphic rock.

27. Inferring How could the process shown in the figure eventually result in the formation of sedimentary rock?

Essay

Answer each of the following on a separate sheet of paper.

28. Describe granite using the three characteristics geologists use to classify igneous rocks.

29. On the walls of the Grand Canyon, you can see many layers of sandstone, one on top of another. Describe how one of those layers might have formed.

30. What would happen to a coral reef if a disease suddenly killed most of the algae in the reef? Explain your answer.

Classifying Rocks
Guided Reading and Study

Use Target Reading Skills This is one possible way to complete the graphic organizer. Accept all logical answers.

Question	Answer
What does a rock's color tell you about the rock?	It can provide clues about the rock's mineral and chemical composition.
How do geologists describe a rock's texture?	Geologists use terms based on the size, shape, and patterns of the grains.

1. rock.
2. a, b, d.
3. mixtures of minerals and other materials.
4. a, b, c, d
5. false
6. texture
7. grains
8. true
9. a, b
10. a. Grain shape **b.** Grain pattern **c.** Fine grain **d.** No visible grain **e.** Rounded grain **f.** Banded **g.** false
11. a
12. a
13. a
14. a
15. according to its origin
16. a. igneous **b.** sedimentary **c.** metamorphic
17. a. Igneous **b.** sedimentary **c.** Metamorphic **d.** The three groups are alike because they are all rock, which means they are mixtures of minerals and other materials. **e.** They are different in the ways they are formed.
18. igneous
19. sedimentary
20. false

Classifying Rocks
Review and Reinforce

1. Coarse-grained
2. Very small
3. Shape
4. Pattern
5. The rock's color, texture, and mineral composition.

6. Igneous rock forms from the cooling of molten magma or lava. Sedimentary rock forms when particles of other rocks are pressed and cemented together. Metamorphic rock forms when an existing rock is changed by heat, pressure, or chemical reactions.
7. Granite is light-colored and has a high silica content. Gabbro is dark and has low silica content.
8. texture
9. grains
10. rock-forming minerals

Classifying Rocks
Enrich

1. Igneous rock makes up 65 percent of Earth's crust.
2. Igneous rocks form from cooling magma below the surface or lava at the surface.
3. Basalt and other dark-colored rocks make up most of the igneous rocks. They are probably found in oceanic crust.
4. Sedimentary rocks make up only 8 percent of Earth's crust.
5. Sedimentary rocks form when particles of other rocks or the remains of plants and animals are pressed and cemented together.
6. Gneiss makes up 78 percent of metamorphic rocks.
7. Metamorphic rocks form when an existing rock is changed by heat, pressure, or chemical reactions.

Igneous Rocks
Guided Reading and Study

Use Target Reading Skills This is one possible way to complete the graphic organizer. Accept all logical answers. **a.** Extrusive—forms on Earth's surface when lava cools; Intrusive—forms when magma cools beneath Earth's surface. **b.** Depends on the size and shape of a rock's mineral crystals. **c.** Light-colored—usually form from lava or magma that has high amounts of silica; Dark-colored—form from lava or magma that has less silica.
1. c
2. a. Extrusive rock **b.** Intrusive rock **c.** The two types of rocks are different because they form in different ways. The two types are alike because they are both igneous rock.
3. false
4. a, c

5. a, b, c
6. crystals
7. false
8. b
9. c
10. a
11. false
12. porphyry
13. Fine-grained or glassy texture
14. An extrusive rock that cooled very rapidly without forming crystals
15. It has the smooth, shiny texture of a thick piece of glass.
16. a, c
17. Granite that is rich in reddish feldspar is a speckled pink. Hornblende and dark mica give the color of light gray with dark specks. Quartz crystals add light gray or smoky specks.
18. They make very thin slices of granite and study each type of crystal in the rock under a microscope.
19. Igneous rocks are hard, dense, and durable.
20. a. Egyptians used granite for statues. **b.** The Incas of Peru fitted together great blocks of granite and other igneous rocks to build a fortress near their capital city. **c.** In the United States during the 1800s and early 1900s, granite was widely used to build bridges and public buildings and for paving streets with cobblestones.
21. a. Pumice **b.** Basalt **c.** Possible answer: Different types of igneous rocks have characteristics that make them suitable for specific uses. Igneous rocks are used in a wide variety of ways.

Igneous Rocks
Review and Reinforce

1. Coarse-grained
2. Smooth and shiny with no visible grain
3. Fine-grained
4. basalt; the ocean's crust, shield volcanoes, and lava plateau
5. granite; mountain ranges
6. Lava that is low in silica usually forms dark-colored rocks; magma that is high in silica usually forms light-colored rocks.
7. Igneous rocks are hard, dense, and durable.
8. Answers may vary. A typical answer might mention granite as a building material, basalt as a construction gravel, and pumice as an abrasive in polishes.
9. extrusive
10. intrusive

Igneous Rocks
Enrich

1. Granite, diorite, and gabbro are intrusive; rhyolite, andesite, and basalt are extrusive.
2. They are similar in mineral composition and color. They are different in texture; granite is coarse-grained and rhyolite is fine-grained.
3. Both rocks contain amphibole, feldspar, and pyroxene.
4. Gabbro is coarse-grained, while basalt is fine-grained. Gabbro forms underground from magma, while basalt forms on the surface from lava.
5. Granite is like gabbro in texture.
6. Granite has more silica than basalt.
7. A rock with more silica is likely to be lighter.

Sedimentary Rocks
Guided Reading and Study

Use Target Reading Skills

Sedimentary Rocks
I. From Sediment to Rocks
    A. Erosion
    B. *Deposition*
    C. *Compaction*
    D. Cementation
II. Types of Sedimentary Rock
    A. *Clastic Rocks*
    B. Organic Rocks
    C. *Chemical Rocks*
III. *Uses of Sedimentary Rocks*

1. shells, bones leaves, and stems
2. sediment
3. true
4 a. running water **b.** wind **c.** ice
5. c
6. d
7. b
8. a
9. They sink to the bottom of a lake or ocean.
10. compaction
11. a. Compaction—particles are squeezed together **b.** Cementation—particles are glued together **c.** The particles in the sediment are being exposed to greater pressure at each step.
12. true
13. according to the type of sediments that make up the rock
14. a. clastic **b.** organic **c.** chemical
15. false
16. true

17. They are grouped by the size of the rock fragments, or particles of which they are made.

18. **a.** Shale **b.** Sandstone **c.** Conglomerate **d.** Possible answer: They are similar in that they are formed from other rocks. They are different in that the particles of rocks from which they are made have different sizes.

19. organic

20. **a.** coal; **b.** limestone

21. coal

22. Coral, clams, oysters, and other living things in the ocean that have hard shells or skeletons made of calcite die. Their shells pile up on the ocean floor in layers. Over millions of years, compaction and cementation change the sediment to limestone.

23. a, c

24. true

25. halite

26. Both types of stone are soft enough to be cut easily into blocks or slabs.

27. false

28. for decorating or for covering the outside walls of buildings

29. true

Sedimentary Rocks
Review and Reinforce

1. b, d, a, c
2. Clastic
3. Organic
4. Clastic
5. Chemical
6. Organic
7. Clastic
8. Chemical
9. Clastic
10. d
11. f
12. a
13. e
14. c
15. b
16. h
17. g

Sedimentary Rocks
Enrich

1. Coal is an organic sedimentary rock that forms from the remains of swamp plants buried in water.

2. They began to form about 300 million years ago, during the Carboniferous Period. During that period, vast tropical swamp forests covered much of North America.

3. Peat is compacted plant matter.

4. The weight of the overlying sediment caused peat to become coal.

5. Metamorphic rock forms when an existing rock is changed by heat, pressure, or chemical reactions. Therefore, heat and pressure probably increase until the sedimentary coal is changed into anthracite.

Rocks From Reefs
Guided Reading and Study

Use Target Reading Skills This is one possible way to complete the graphic organizer. Accept all logical answers.

What You Know
1. Coral reefs grow in the oceans.
2. Florida has coral reefs.
3. Oceans used to be where there is now dry land.

What You Learned
1. Coral animals cannot live below 40 meters.
2. In the United States, only the coasts of Florida and Hawaii have coral reefs.
3. Some limestone deposits on land formed from ancient reefs.

1. b, d
2. coral reef
3. true
4. calcium
5. calcite
6. b, c
7. around islands and along the eastern coasts of continents
8. near the coasts of southern Florida and Hawaii
9. a, d
10. During the time that limestone from coral reefs has been forming in the oceans, plate motions have moved the deposits far from the warm, tropical oceans where they formed.
11. Wisconsin, Illinois, Indiana, Texas, New Mexico, and many other places.

Rocks From Reefs
Review and Reinforce

1. calcium
2. skeletons
3. corals
4. coral reefs
5. The water is warm and shallow.
6. Below that depth, not enough sunlight penetrates the water for the algae in corals to grow.
7. The limestone formed from coral reefs that developed in shallow seas that covered parts of the continents millions of years ago. When the seas later retreated, the limestone was exposed.
8. Where geologists find fossils of an ancient coral reef, they know that the reef formed in an area with a warm climate and shallow ocean water. In the United States, reefs that formed millions of years ago are exposed in Wisconsin, Illinois, Indiana, Texas, New Mexico, and many other places.
9. coral reef

Rocks From Reefs
Enrich

1. An atoll is a ring-shaped coral reef found far from land.
2. An atoll originally forms as a fringing reef around a volcanic island.
3. A volcanic island sinks because the oceanic crust beneath it sinks during sea-floor spreading.
4. The coral reef grows upward by growing on top of the old part of the reef.
5. A lagoon is at the center of a coral atoll.

Metamorphic Rocks
Guided Reading and Study

Use Target Reading Skills This is one possible way to complete the graphic organizer. Accept all logical answers.

Metamorphic Rocks

Q. Why do the crystals in gneiss line up in bands?	
A. Gneiss is a type of metamorphic rock that is foliated—the crystals are flattened to form parallel layers.	
Q. How does quartzite form from sandstone?	
A. High temperature and pressure on the mineral in sandstone cause the recrystallized grains to form quartzite.	

1. **a.** heat; **b.** pressure
2. true
3. in appearance, texture, crystal structure, and mineral content
4. igneous, sedimentary, and other metamorphic rock
5. false
6. true
7. foliated
8. a, c
9. nonfoliated
10. **a.** marble; **b.** quartzite
11. **a.** Sandstone **b.** Gneiss **c.** Slate **d.** The rocks have been changed into different rocks by heat and pressure.
12. Marble can be cut into thin slabs or carved into many shapes, and it is easy to polish.
13. Slate splits easily into flat pieces that can be used for flooring, roofing, outdoor walkways, and chalkboards, and as trim for stone buildings.

Metamorphic Rocks
Review and Reinforce

1. mantle
2. pressure
3. mineral crystals
4. Pockets of magma rising through Earth's crust can provide heat that can produce metamorphic rocks.
5. Geologists classify metamorphic rocks according to the arrangement of the grains that make up the rocks.
6. Quartzite forms when weakly cemented quartz particles in sandstone recrystallize because of heat and pressure deep beneath the surface.
7. Marble has a fine, even grain; it can be cut into thin slabs; and it can be easily polished.
8. Nonfoliated
9. Foliated
10. Foliated

Metamorphic Rocks
Enrich

1. Tremendous pressure and high temperatures
2. The slate first changes into schist and then changes into gneiss.
3. Gneiss and schist are foliated metamorphic rocks.
4. Limestone changes into marble.
5. Basalt changes into amphibole or schist.
6. Slate, granite, and basalt can change into schist.
7. Schist changes into gneiss.

Skills Lab
Mystery Rocks

For answers, see Teacher's Edition.

The Rock Cycle
Guided Reading and Study

Use Target Reading Skills a. Igneous Rock **b.** Sedimentary Rock **c.** Metamorphic Rock (Order may vary.)
1. forces deep inside Earth and at the surface
2. rock cycle
3. false
4. Water and wind wear away the granite. The granite particles become sand and are carried by streams to the ocean. Over time, layers of sandy sediment pile up on the ocean floor. The sediment changes to sandstone.

5. They help to form magma, the source of igneous rocks. Plate movements also cause faulting, folding, and other motions of the crust that help to form sedimentary and metamorphic rocks.

The Rock Cycle
Review and Reinforce

1. Igneous rock
2. Sediment
3. Sedimentary rock
4. Metamorphic rock
5. Magma and lava
6. Water and weather wear away the granite of the mountain, and sand grains from the granite are deposited on the ocean floor, where compaction and cementation change them to sandstone. If the sandstone is pushed deeper into the crust, heat and pressure change it into quartzite.
7. A collision between continental plates can push rocks down deep into the mantle, where heat and pressure could change the rocks to metamorphic rock.
8. Answers will vary. *Sample answer:* The rock cycle is the slow changing of rocks from one kind to another by the forces that build, destroy, and change rock.

The Rock Cycle
Enrich

1. Only igneous rocks are involved in that pathway.

2. Students' flowcharts should show igneous rock forming at the mid-ocean ridge, moving across the ocean floor, being subducted at a deep-ocean trench, melting into mantle material, and becoming igneous rock again.

3. Metamorphic rock changes into sedimentary rock, which changes into metamorphic rock again.

4. Students' flowcharts should show the formation of metamorphic rock, the erosion of that rock, the formation of sedimentary rock, and the change to metamorphic rock.

5. Answers will vary. Students should describe the processes that form the three major groups of rocks.

Design Your Own Lab
Testing Rock Flooring

For answers, see Teacher's Edition.

Use Key Terms

Across
1. foliated
3. metamorphic
6. grain
9. clastic
10. erosion

Down
2. texture
4. deposition
5. cementation
7. igneous
8. compaction

Connecting Concepts

Rocks are classified into three main categories and undergo changes through a process called the rock cycle. This concept map is only one way to represent the main ideas and relationships in this chapter. Accept other logical answers from students.

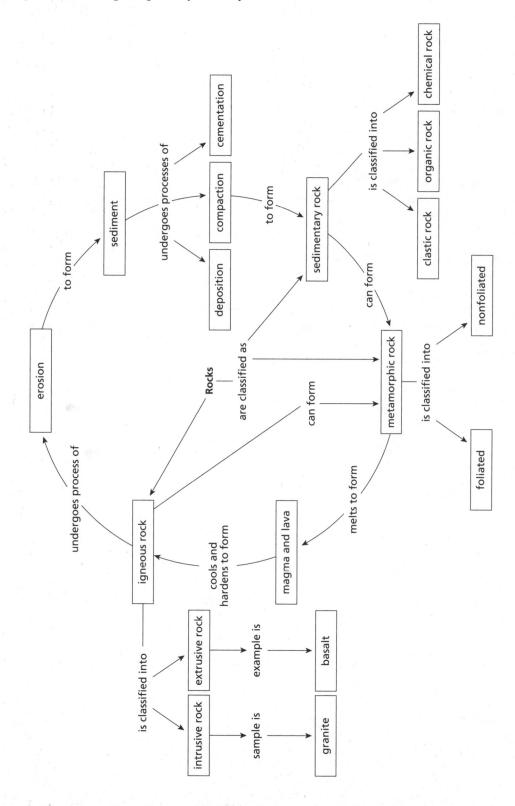

Laboratory Investigation

Making Models of Sedimentary Rocks

Pre-Lab Discussion

1. Sedimentary rocks are formed from particles deposited by wind or water.
2. Erosion, deposition, compaction, and cementation

Observations

Clastic Sketches of clastic rocks should show the individual ingredients, such as gravel and sand. **Organic** If fossils are used, they should be in the organic rocks. **Chemical** Chemical rocks should look uniform. Students will probably make chemical rocks out of concentrated salt water, allowing the water to evaporate.

Data Table

Properties of Model Rocks			
	Types of Sedimentary Rock		
Property	**Clastic**	**Organic**	**Chemical**
Color	dark	white	colorless
Texture	rough	some-what smooth	smooth
Hardness	rela-tively soft	relatively soft	relatively hard
Pattern	irregular	some-what irregular	crystal struc-ture
Resistance to Weathering	easily broken	easily broken	resistant
Students may test other properties			

Analyze and Conclude

1. The properties are determined by the composition of the rocks.
2. Organic rocks are made from previously living organisms. Fossils could be found in this type of rock.
3. Compaction increases strength.

Critical Thinking and Applications

1. All types are formed from particles by erosion, deposition, compaction, and cementation. They differ in composition. Clastic rocks are made of broken pieces of other rocks. Organic rocks are formed from previously living materials. Chemical rocks are formed from mineral solutions.
2. Many sedimentary rocks are useful building materials. They are soft enough to be easily cut and hard enough to be relatively weather resistant as building materials.
3. Answers may include that soft rocks have limited uses because they weather easily.

More to Explore

Most sedimentary rocks will react with the vinegar, indicating that they would be attacked by chemical weathering. Many chemical sedimentary rocks, such as salt, will not react with the acid. Encourage students to notice local buildings, tombstones, or statues that are made of sedimentary rock and have been affected by chemical weathering.

Performance Assessment

1. Answers may vary. A typical answer will mention the coarse grains of granite. Igneous rock forms as molten material cools.

2. Answers may vary. A typical answer will mention the cemented particles of sand in sandstone. Sedimentary rock forms when particles of other rocks or the remains of plants and animals are compacted and cemented together.

3. Answers may vary. A typical answer will mention the foliation of the gneiss. Metamorphic rock forms when an existing rock is changed by heat, pressure, or chemical reactions.

4. Earth's constructive and destructive forces drive rocks through the rock cycle.

5. Answers may vary. Some students may argue that the cycle has no beginning or end, while others may suggest that the formation of igneous rock must be considered the beginning.

Chapter Test

1. a
2. c
3. a
4. b
5. a
6. c
7. b
8. b
9. d
10. a
11. foliated
12. cementation
13. rock cycle
14. textures
15. clastic
16. compaction
17. extrusive rock
18. Limestone
19. true
20. true
21. A. Igneous rock **B.** Sedimentary rock **C.** Metamorphic rock
22. Metamorphic rock could be exposed at the surface and worn away. Erosion would carry particles of that rock to another place, where the particles would be deposited. Compaction and cementation could then change the sediment into sedimentary rock.

23. Plate movements start the rock cycle by helping to form magma, the source of igneous rocks.

24. Geologists observe a rock's color and texture and determine its mineral composition.

25. An igneous rock formed from magma that cooled below the surface would have larger crystals because it had cooled slowly.

26. The collision of plates produces high pressures that cause the formation of metamorphic rocks. Rock is also heated as it is pushed down toward the mantle or folded as a result of plate movements. The hot molten material from the mantle that rises through the crust near such plate boundaries can also cause the formation of metamorphic rocks.

27. Answers may vary. A typical answer should describe the uplift that occurs as a result of plate collisions and how uplift results in the exposure of igneous and metamorphic rock at the surface, where they could be worn away. Their sediments could eventually become sedimentary rock.

28. Granite is a coarse-grained igneous rock that is generally light-colored. Its mineral composition includes quartz and feldspar.

29. Answers may vary. A typical answer will describe the processes that form sedimentary rock, including erosion and deposition, compaction, and cementation.

30. The coral animals would die, because they are dependent on the algae for the food produced by photosynthesis, and the reef would stop growing.

Color Transparency Planner

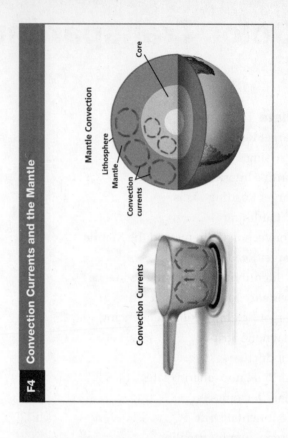

Earth's Layers

Outer core
2,266 km thick

Inner core
1,216 km thick

Mantle
2,867 km thick

Crust
5–70 km thick

Lithosphere and Asthenosphere

Lithosphere

Asthenosphere

Oceanic crust

Continental crust

Upper mantle

Depth (km)
0
100
200
300
350

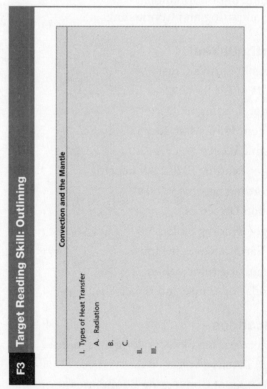

Mantle Convection

Core

Lithosphere

Mantle

Convection
currents

Convection Currents

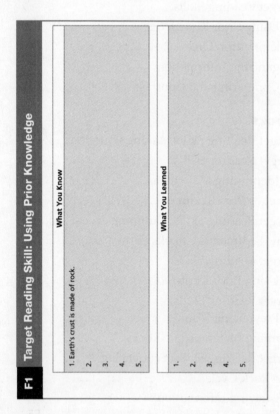

What You Know

1. Earth's crust is made of rock.

2.

3.

4.

5.

What You Learned

1.

2.

3.

4.

5.

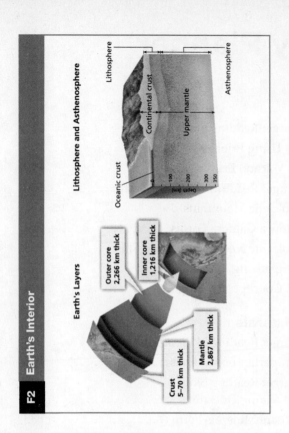

Convection and the Mantle

I. Types of Heat Transfer

A. Radiation

B.

C.

II.

III.

F6 Evidence for Continental Drift

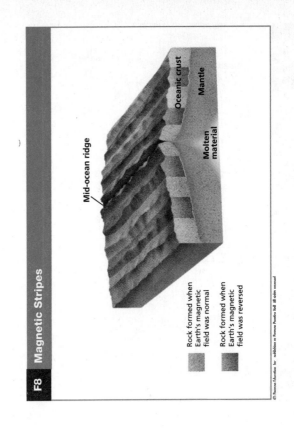

Key

Folded mountains	Glossopteris fossils
Coal beds	Lystrosaurus fossils
Glacial deposits	Mesosaurus fossils

F8 Magnetic Stripes

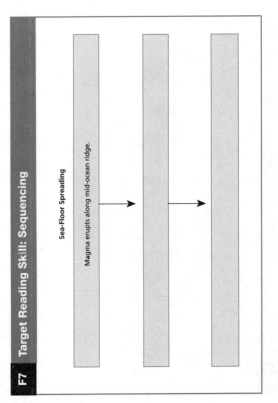

Rock formed when Earth's magnetic field was normal

Rock formed when Earth's magnetic field was reversed

F5 Target Reading Skill: Identifying Supporting Evidence

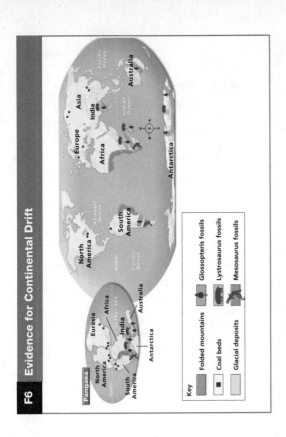

Evidence

Shape of continents

a.

b.

Hypothesis

Earth's continents have moved.

F7 Target Reading Skill: Sequencing

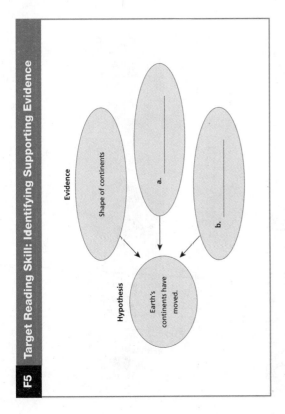

Sea-Floor Spreading

Magma erupts along mid-ocean ridge.

Transparencies

F9 Subduction

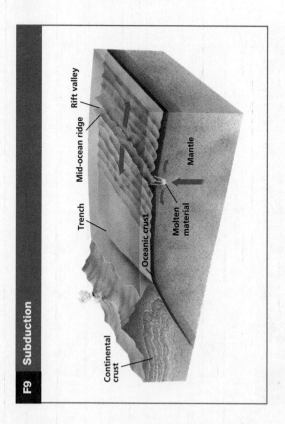

F10 Earth's Lithospheric Plates

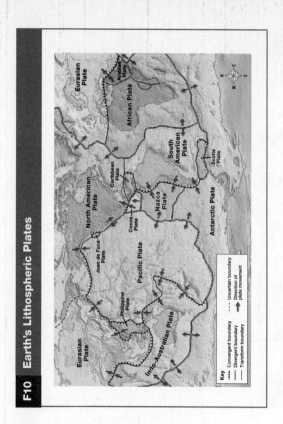

F11 Plate Tectonics

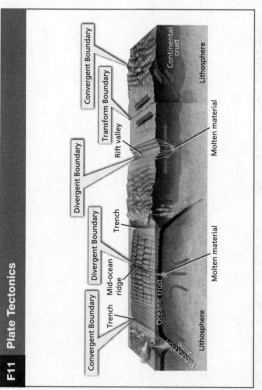

F12 Continental Drift

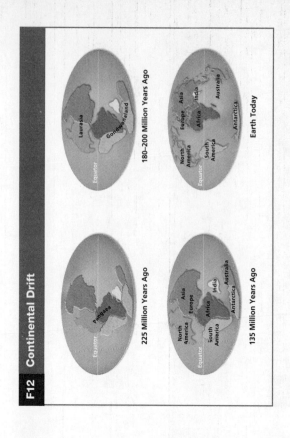

F14 Stress in Earth's Crust

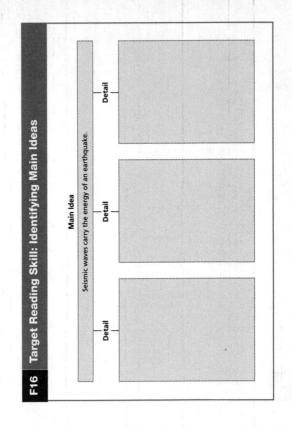

Before stress

Compression

Tension

Shearing

F16 Target Reading Skill: Identifying Main Ideas

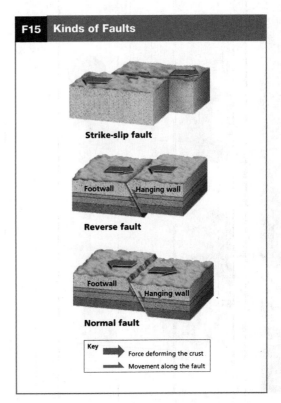

Main Idea

Seismic waves carry the energy of an earthquake.

Detail

Detail

Detail

F13 Organizing Information: Comparing and Contrasting

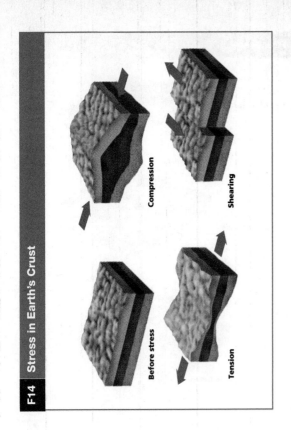

Types of Plate Boundaries

Type of Boundary	Type of Motion	Effect on Crust	Feature(s) Formed
a. _____ boundary	Plates slide past each other	b. _____	c. _____
d. _____ boundary	e. _____	Subduction or mountain building	f. _____
g. _____ boundary	h. _____	i. _____	Mid-ocean ridge, ocean floor

F15 Kinds of Faults

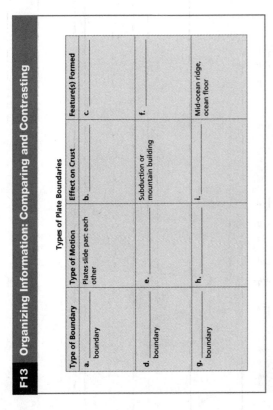

Strike-slip fault

Footwall   Hanging wall

Reverse fault

Footwall

Hanging wall

Normal fault

Key

➡ Force deforming the crust

→ Movement along the fault

Transparencies

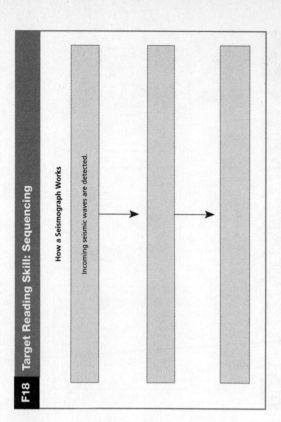

How a Seismograph Works

Incoming seismic waves are detected.

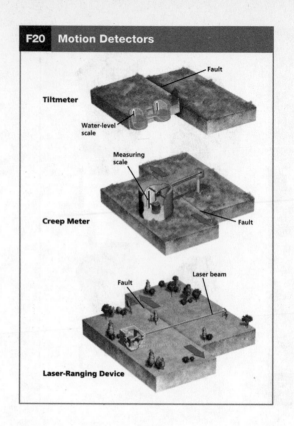

F20 Motion Detectors

Tiltmeter

Fault

Water-level scale

Creep Meter

Measuring scale

Fault

Laser-Ranging Device

Fault

Laser beam

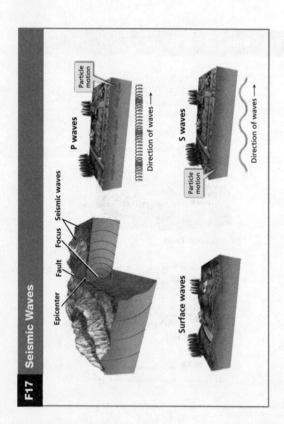

F17 Seismic Waves

Epicenter

Fault

Focus

Seismic waves

P waves

Particle motion

Direction of waves →

S waves

Particle motion

Direction of waves →

Surface waves

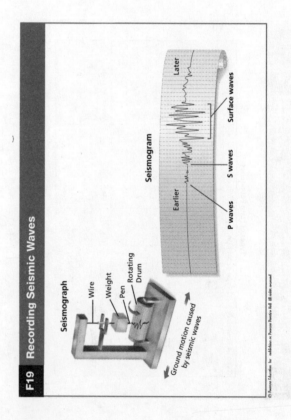

F19 Recording Seismic Waves

Seismograph

Wire

Weight

Pen

Rotating Drum

Ground motion caused by seismic waves

Seismogram

Earlier

Later

P waves

S waves

Surface waves

F22 An Earthquake-Safe House

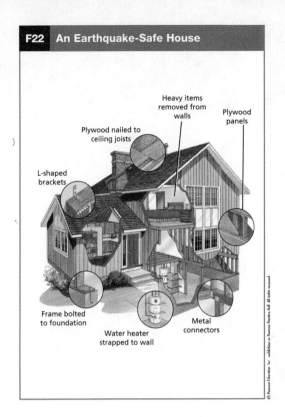

Plywood nailed to
ceiling joists

Heavy items
removed from
walls

Plywood
panels

L-shaped
brackets

Frame bolted
to foundation

Water heater
strapped to wall

Metal
connectors

Volcanoes and Plate Tectonics

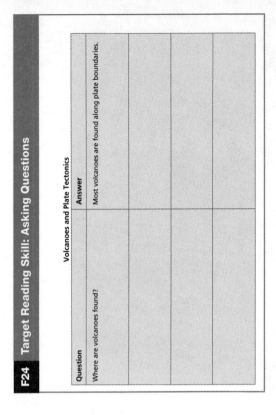

Question	Answer
Where are volcanoes found?	Most volcanoes are found along plate boundaries.

Earthquake Safety

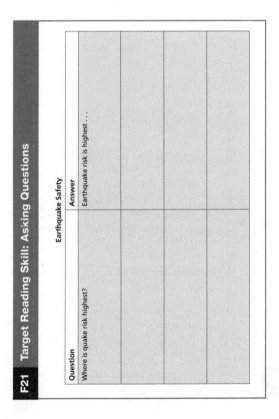

Question	Answer
Where is quake risk highest?	Earthquake risk is highest . . .

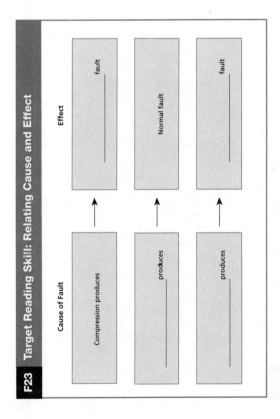

Cause of Fault   **Effect**

Compression produces → _____ fault

_____ produces → Normal fault

_____ produces → _____ fault

F25 Earth's Active Volcanoes

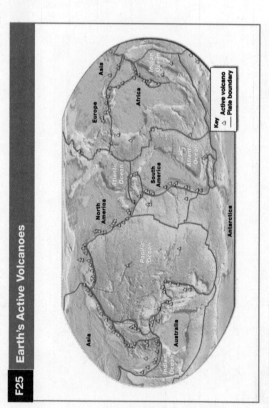

F26 Volcanoes at Converging Boundaries

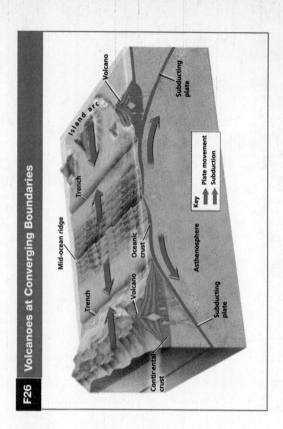

F27 Target Reading Skill: Identifying Main Ideas

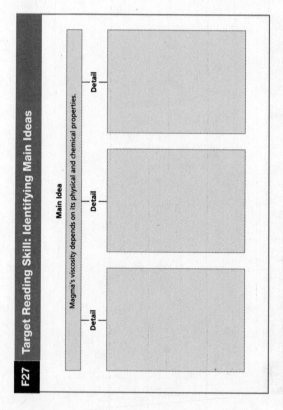

Main Idea

Magma's viscosity depends on its physical and chemical properties.

Detail

Detail

Detail

F28 Target Reading Skill: Using Prior Knowledge

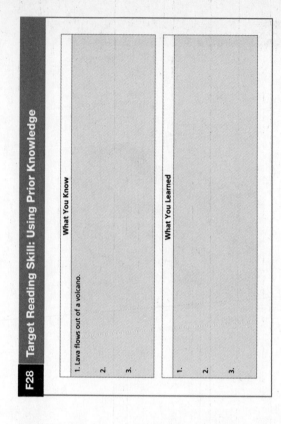

What You Know

1. Lava flows out of a volcano.

2.

3.

What You Learned

1.

2.

3.

Volcanic Landforms

I. Landforms From Lava and Ash

  A. Shield Volcanoes

  B.

  C.

  D.

  E.

  F.

II. Landforms From Magma

  A.

  B.

  C.

  D.

III.

  A.

  B.

  C.

Crater Lake

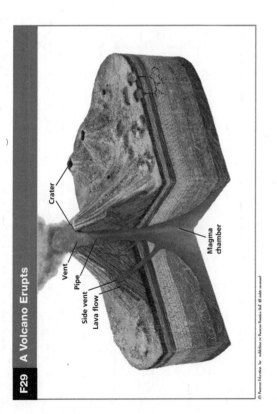

Crater

Vent

Pipe

Side vent

Lava flow

Magma chamber

© Pearson Education, Inc. publishing as Pearson Prentice Hall. All rights reserved.

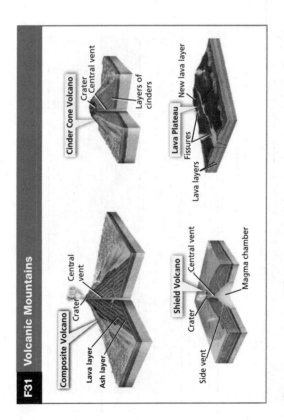

Cinder Cone Volcano

Crater

Central vent

Layers of cinders

Lava Plateau

New lava layer

Fissures

Lava layers

Composite Volcano

Central vent

Crater

Lava layer

Ash layer

Shield Volcano

Central vent

Crater

Magma chamber

Side vent

Transparencies

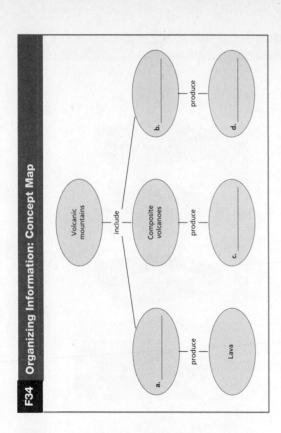

Volcanic mountains — include — Composite volcanoes

produce — a.

produce — Lava

b. ___ — produce — d. ___

Composite volcanoes — produce — c. ___

Magnetite
Crystal System: Cubic

Quartz
Crystal System: Hexagonal

Rutile
Crystal System: Tetragonal

Sulfur
Crystal System: Orthorhombic

Azurite
Crystal System: Monoclinic

Microcline Feldspar
Crystal System: Triclinic

Volcanic neck

Dike

Sill

Properties of Minerals

I. What Is a Mineral?

   A. Naturally Occurring

   B.

   C.

   D.

   E.

II. Identifying Minerals

   A.

   B.

   C.

   D.

   E.

   F.

   G.

   H.

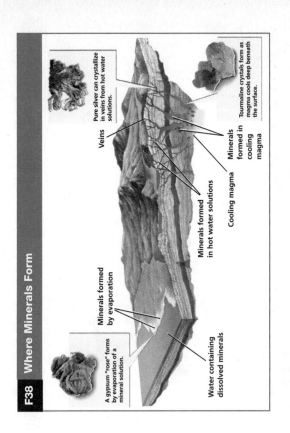

F38 Where Minerals Form

Pure silver can crystallize in veins from hot water solutions.

Tourmaline crystals form as magma cools deep beneath the surface.

Veins

Minerals formed in cooling magma

Cooling magma

Minerals formed in hot water solutions

Minerals formed by evaporation

A gypsum "rose" forms by evaporation of a mineral solution.

Water containing dissolved minerals

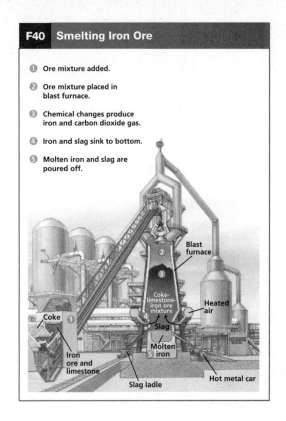

F40 Smelting Iron Ore

1. Ore mixture added.

2. Ore mixture placed in blast furnace.

3. Chemical changes produce iron and carbon dioxide gas.

4. Iron and slag sink to bottom.

5. Molten iron and slag are poured off.

Blast furnace

Coke-limestone-iron ore mixture

Heated air

Coke

Slag

Molten iron

Iron ore and limestone

Slag ladle

Hot metal car

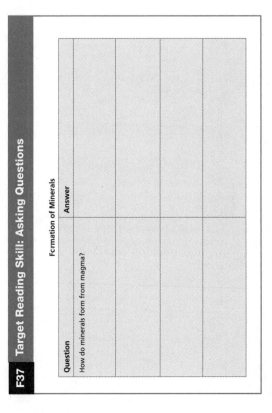

F37 Target Reading Skill: Asking Questions

Formation of Minerals

Question	Answer
How do minerals form from magma?	

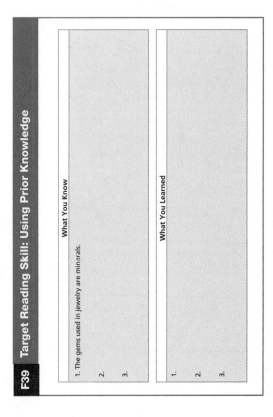

F39 Target Reading Skill: Using Prior Knowledge

What You Know

1. The gems used in jewelry are minerals.
2.
3.

What You Learned

1.
2.
3.

F41 **Organizing Information: Comparing and Contrasting**

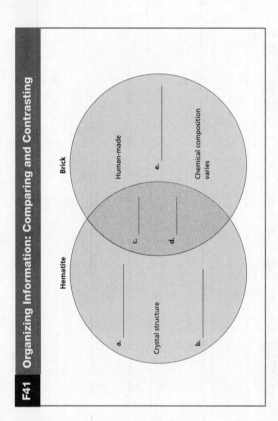

Hematite

Brick

Human-made

a. ___

Crystal structure

b. ___

c. ___

d. ___

e. ___

Chemical composition varies

F42 **Target Reading Skill: Asking Questions**

Classifying Rocks

Question	Answer
What does a rock's color tell about the rock?	

F43 **Target Reading Skill: Identifying Main Ideas**

Main Idea

Igneous rocks are classified by origin, texture, and composition.

Detail	Detail	Detail

F44 **Igneous Rock Textures**

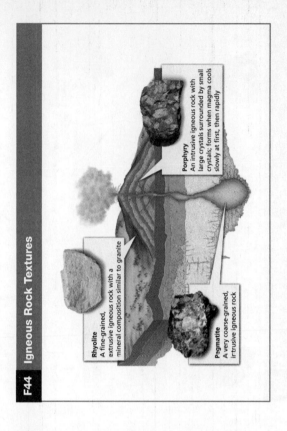

Rhyolite
A fine-grained, extrusive igneous rock with a mineral composition similar to granite

Porphyry
An intrusive igneous rock with large crystals surrounded by small crystals; forms when magma cools slowly at first, then rapidly

Pegmatite
A very coarse-grained, intrusive igneous rock

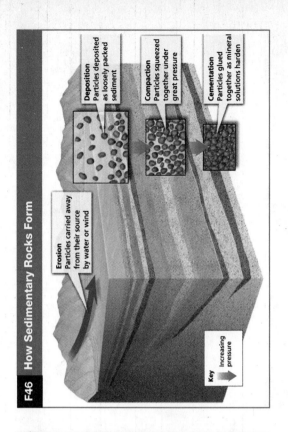

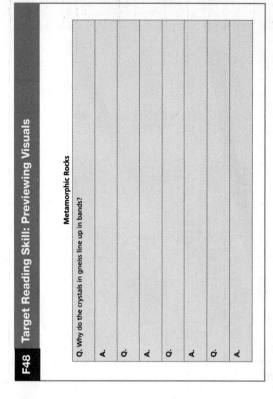

F46 How Sedimentary Rocks Form

Erosion Particles carried away from their source by water or wind

Deposition Particles deposited as loosely packed sediment

Compaction Particles squeezed together under great pressure

Cementation Particles glued together as mineral solutions harden

Key Increasing pressure

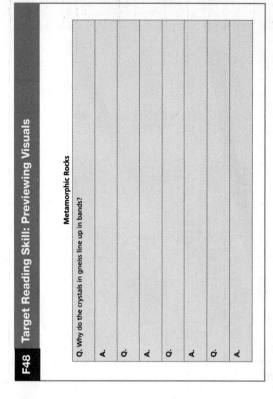

F48 Target Reading Skill: Previewing Visuals

Metamorphic Rocks

Q. Why do the crystals in gneiss line up in bands?

A.

Q.

A.

Q.

A.

Q.

A.

F45 Target Reading Skill: Outlining

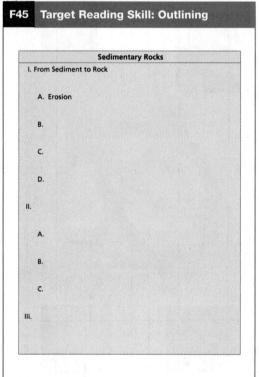

Sedimentary Rocks

I. From Sediment to Rock

   A. Erosion

   B.

   C.

   D.

II.

   A.

   B.

   C.

III.

F47 Target Reading Skill: Using Prior Knowledge

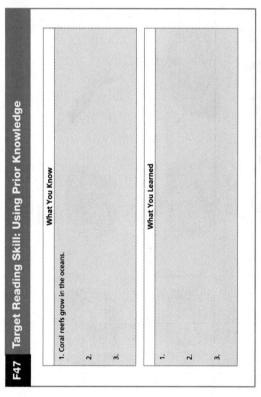

What You Know

1. Coral reefs grow in the oceans.

2.

3.

What You Learned

1.

2.

3.

Transparencies

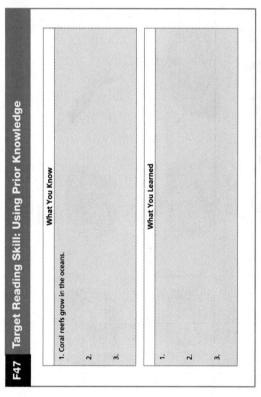

F49 Forming Metamorphic Rocks

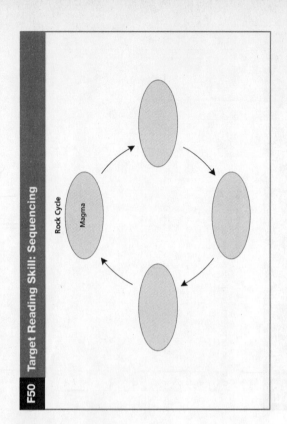

F50 Target Reading Skill: Sequencing

F51 The Rock Cycle

F52 Organizing Information: Concept Mapping

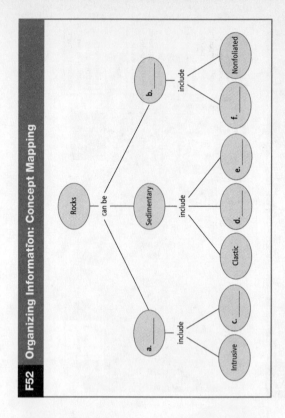